THE TECHNICAL WRITER

The Technical Writer

AN AID TO
THE PRESENTATION AND PRODUCTION
OF TECHNICAL LITERATURE

◻

J. W. GODFREY & G. PARR

F.R.S.A., formerly Editor
Technical Instructions, B.B.C.

M.I.E.E., Director
Chapman & Hall Ltd.

REPRINTED WITH REVISIONS

1960

NEW YORK : JOHN WILEY & SONS INC

808.066
G-583

Set in 10 point Times Roman (L.D.), Series 327, on 12 point
and printed in Great Britain by Butler & Tanner Ltd., Frome

To

Reginald O. Kapp

(*Professor Emeritus in the University of London*)

who first organized in Britain the study of the Presentation of Technical Information as a necessary part of a scientific education.

PREFACE

IN all branches of science and technology there is an urgent need to provide workers with new information as rapidly as developments take place. Unfortunately, those engaged in design or research rarely have the time and not always the ability to record progress in a way that will be understood by their colleagues in industry; thus there is a demand for skilled technical writers who can interpret research and design reports so that they will be easily understood by those concerned in their application.

In some organizations this technical writer forms part of a team engaged in the production of technical literature—in smaller firms the engineer or designer may be his own writing and production department. Whether as an individual or as a member of a team, a technical writer will have his task made easier and produce better work if he has a knowledge of the whole process of presenting and producing the information that he is setting down. Good writing not only demands accuracy and clarity but also the ability to select illustrations, present data, and display the material in the most attractive way to the reader.

This book was undertaken to give the writer of technical literature that insight into the technique of presentation and production. Many books on the art of technical writing have appeared during the past ten years or so, particularly from America; the majority have been mainly concerned with the putting down of information in an orderly way and in logical sequence—some have been preoccupied with grammar and composition. This approach is fundamental and sometimes necessary, but in this book the authors have assumed that the would-be writer is grounded in the principles of composition and requires mainly to avoid common pitfalls and put a polish on his work.

On the other hand, few writers know what happens to a manuscript when it leaves their hands, even though the finished work may go only to another department. One of the points that has been stressed in this book is that the responsibility of the writer for his work should not cease up to the time when the final publication is laid on his desk. Familiarity with the processes through

7

which a manuscript passes will ensure that the finished product is as efficiently and neatly presented as is economically possible.

Throughout this book there is a bias towards examples drawn from electrical and electronic engineering practice because this is the authors' home ground, but the principles of good writing apply to all branches of science. In modern engineering mechanical and electrical technologies are interdependent, and nearly all allied sciences make use of electronic circuits—hence the attention given to circuit diagrams.

In the chapters describing equipment used in the production of technical publications the authors have given examples that are reasonably up-to-date and readily available. There are obviously many other products of equal merit, and new devices are constantly becoming available; the mention of a particular product therefore does not imply any special preference.

Since the book was planned, the City & Guilds of London Institute has published a syllabus of lectures on Technical Authorship which constitutes a four-year course with a qualifying examination.* It will be found that this book forms a concise introduction to the Intermediate part of the syllabus on this subject.

ACKNOWLEDGEMENTS

The authors are grateful to many colleagues who have provided examples for criticism, information, and comments on the draft. In particular they acknowledge the help of the following individuals and firms:

Mr. S. W. Amos (B.B.C.)
Mr. Charles Batey (Oxford University Press)
Mr. G. E. Brown (Page Bros. Ltd.)
Mr. E. W. Hamilton (Chapman & Hall Ltd.)
Mr. G. J. Huber (J. J. Huber Ltd.)
The Imperial Typewriter Co. Ltd.
Vari-Typer Distributors Ltd.
Addressograph-Multigraph Ltd.
Lawes, Rabjohns Ltd.

Prof. R. O. Kapp (Kennedy & Donkin Ltd.)
Mr. J. Kennedy (Kynoch Press)
Mr. E. L. E. Pawley (B.B.C.)
Mr. Alan Steele (Butler & Tanner Ltd.)

Holmes & Co. Ltd.
Hall, Harding Ltd.
Hunter-Penrose Ltd.
British Brehmer Ltd.

* *Technical Authorship* (No. 229). Obtainable from the C. & G. Institute, 76 Portland Place, London, W.1.

E.M.I. Sales & Service Ltd.　　　The Monotype Corporation
Virtue & Co. Ltd.　　　　　　　Linotype & Machinery Ltd.
The British Standards Institution　Vactric Ltd.
Copeland-Chatterson Ltd.　　　　Lascelles & Co. Ltd.

One of the authors (J. W. G.) acknowledges his indebtedness to the Chief Engineer of the B.B.C. for permission to write and publish parts of the book.

G. PARR

J. W. GODFREY

London 1958

NOTE ON THE REVISED REPRINT

The gratifying need for a reprint so soon after the first publication of this book has limited the authors to making only essential corrections and alterations to the text.

They are grateful to many friends who have taken the trouble to point out inconsistencies and to make suggestions for improvement, and in particular to Mrs. R. Lang, Dr. Michael West, and Mr. H. V. Jeffery for annotations. It is hoped to include all amendments in a later edition if it is called for.

J. W. G.

G. P.

December 1959

CONTENTS

11

PLATES

(*All other figures are in the text*)

CHAPTER 1

TECHNICAL LITERATURE

THE term 'technical literature' covers a variety of publications, all of which have as their object the conveying of information from one person to another. This information, to be of greatest use, must be conveyed as efficiently and as clearly as possible and herein lies the whole art of technical writing.

The output of technical information at the present time is immense and will certainly never diminish; every newcomer to the scientific field may contribute to it sooner or later in his career, and it is a necessary part of his ability and training to be able to express himself adequately. The question asked of a candidate by many appointment boards is 'What have you published on the subject?' and a well-written thesis or report is often taken into account when selecting candidates for administrative posts.

The work of preparing written papers can never be regarded as a minor disagreeable accompaniment to a scientific occupation: it is as much a part of the whole work as the taking of readings or plotting results and, indeed, may take more time than the investigation itself. It is worth while therefore to study methods by which this work can be made lighter, and evolve one that suits the writer's temperament. No one can write effectively by following a set of rules, and the utmost that any manual or textbook can do is to indicate to an author those principles or methods which have been found satisfactory, and to cite those details that form a large part of good writing.

Apart from following accepted principles, a writer can only hope to improve his power of expression by wide and constant reading. The study of prose, good or bad, technical and non-technical, will provide him with a basis on which he can develop his own style. A vocabulary can be acquired by memorizing words, whether in English or any other language, but the fluent use of the vocabulary can only come through studying other writers and profiting from their ability or their mistakes.

Forms of Technical Literature

The form in which technical information is presented varies according to the content and the class of reader requiring the information. Frequently a short memorandum is all that is needed to inform a narrow circle of co-workers who are familiar with the problem under investigation. A familiar example is a letter to *Nature* or one of the other scientific periodicals in which the writer announces briefly some new discovery and ' stakes a claim ' to be first in the field. A memorandum of this type is confined to a short summary of the phenomenon observed and indicates in what way it is likely to be of interest.* The early publication of such a memorandum is of value in saving duplication of effort or in showing fellow-workers a useful line of development.

The Technical Report†

The usual way of conveying information about a project or piece of research is by means of a report which is circulated among all those interested. The majority of reports do not go beyond the organization in which they originate, but it is the practice of large firms to issue selected reports for the benefit of their customers and thereby add to their prestige.

In some organizations a junior may find that an effective way of introducing himself to his superiors is through the medium of a well-written and signed report. The occasional practice of issuing works' reports anonymously or under the name of the head of the department offers little encouragement to junior staff; a writer should be encouraged to stand by his work and append his name to it.

The construction of the report is dealt with in later chapters and further comment will not be given here, except to quote Prof. J. R. Nelson's description :‡

Since a report is fundamentally the communication of information or counsel which is desired and which will be used by someone for a

* In some research departments a memorandum is called a minute, but this word is more usually confined to an official record of a meeting or discussion.

† The word ' report ' is used here to denote a class of technical writing of which the report is an example. Most of the discussion which follows can be applied to all forms of technical literature.

‡ J. R. Nelson, Prof. Emeritus of English, University of Michigan ; Synopsis to *Writing the Technical Report* (McGraw-Hill, New York, 1947).

particular end, its success depends on its being planned carefully to meet all the conditions under which it will serve.

The introduction should present a clear statement of the subject, of the purpose, and of the plan of organization of the subject treated. It often also includes a brief statement of the conclusion or recommendation, and sometimes a summary of the results or findings.

The conclusion should agree and balance logically with this introduction.

The body of the report should be so written as to make evident the structural design announced in the introduction.

Ideally, a report should read coherently and smoothly, and should bear evidence of the writer's mastery of his subject matter in its larger aspects as well as in its minutest details.

The Technical Paper

Reports on certain scientific investigations, particularly if the work is original and novel, can often be used as the basis of a technical paper to be read before one of the learned societies or institutions. The treatment of the subject matter generally requires modification to make it suitable for an audience of a wider range of interests than is covered directly in the report, and in general, the setting down of experimental results in detail is avoided in favour of a descriptive treatment. The mere record of a series of experiments, with an account of the technique and a summary of the findings is seldom acceptable as a paper for discussion before one of the scientific bodies.

The style and make-up of the report will also need to be modified to suit the requirements of the particular society to which it is submitted, and intending authors of papers can usually obtain a printed form of requirements from the secretary.

It is not necessary that all papers submitted to a scientific society shall contain the results of original work, and an occasional ' survey ' paper on a subject of general interest is welcomed. The merit of these survey papers is that they give the audience a balanced account of progress in one of the fields which is not normally covered by regular communications.

The limitations of meeting time compel the Papers Committee of any scientific society to make a selection of the many papers submitted in the course of the year, and the rejection of a manuscript is not necessarily a reflection on its technical merit. Arrangements are usually made for publication of papers in the Proceedings or

Journal of the society when it is not possible to have them read, particularly if it is considered that a useful discussion would not be stimulated by the paper.

The Technical Article

The distinction between a technical paper and a technical article is not well-defined, and many ' reject ' technical papers are accepted for publication by a scientific periodical with only slight modification.

This modification is usually to make the text appeal to a wider class of reader, as it is obvious that the readers of any periodical may vary considerably in their knowledge of a technical subject and in their capacity for absorbing information.

Although it is not possible to be precise, the following differences between technical articles and technical papers or reports may be noted :

The report is usually intended for a specific class of reader, and one with which the author is familiar. An article is designed to have an appeal to a wider class which may have a range of intelligence and interests beyond the author's immediate circle.

In making a report it can often be assumed that the reader has a certain amount of pre-knowledge of the subject. This assumption is not necessarily true for readers of periodicals.

An article can and should introduce a background to the subject, and may be written in a more discursive style than a factual report.

The aim of an article is to attract the reader and to hold his attention. A report is often addressed to a reader whose interest can be taken for granted, and it is only necessary to prevent his losing interest.

Depending on the technical standard of the publication, the style of writing may be more free in a technical article, and colloquialisms are not always out of place.

Instruction Leaflets and Manuals

The writing of an instruction leaflet or manual requires more than usual care if the author is also the designer of the equipment. He becomes so familiar with the details of its working that he omits to put down many features that will be required by the reader, and he tends to assume a greater degree of knowledge than the user of the equipment actually possesses.

A handbook containing operating instructions should always be checked by an independent knowledgeable colleague, who should be able to operate the equipment successfully by following the actual wording of the text. A common fault in instruction leaflets is reference to a non-existent component which may have been omitted in certain models, or describing a component in vague terms, such as ' the switch at the back ', when there is more than one. In one handbook the user was told to switch on and allow ten minutes for warming up, but the method of connecting the equipment to the mains was not mentioned.

In writing instruction booklets on domestic equipment, or apparatus for use by the general public, it is more than ever necessary to keep in mind the varying degrees of intelligence of the users. The average housewife has a low standard of technical intelligence and may even find difficulty in understanding a reference to a ' clockwise direction ', ' left-hand thread ', ' spigot ', and similar terms which do not give the author a moment's thought. Further, no point should be taken for granted in a booklet intended for non-technical users, and it cannot be assumed that they know how to start up an equipment by instinct.

A writer to the *Engineer* has listed the following defects seen in handbooks : *

> The book is too large or too cumbersome.
> The lines of type are too long.
> The arrangement is disjointed and jerky.
> The book is written in a literary " officey " style.
> Utility has been sacrificed to appearance.
> The descriptions are too wordy.

Some of these shortcomings may not be the responsibility of the writer of the handbook, but he should in any case try to exercise a tactful supervision over the whole production if his own efforts in writing a clear handbook are not to be marred by bad presentation.

Technical Sales Information

It is one of the attributes of a good salesman to emphasize the advantages of his company's product while glossing over any shortcomings, but this unbalanced method of presentation will not be endorsed by a technical man whose upbringing has taught him to make impartial statements. A common fault of ' sales talk '

* March 19, 1948.

is the use of words which imply qualities that the product does not in fact possess, e.g. ' absolutely permanent ', ' waterproof ' (for ' water-resistant '), and similar exaggerations.

In some literature the use of misleading descriptions has resulted in legal claims, and for this reason, as well as in the cause of technical honesty, the writer of sales information should be particularly careful in the choice of words.

A leaflet describing a technical product should be checked for accuracy with the same care as a technical report. The use of wrong terms or units will be noted by technical readers, who will have a correspondingly bad impression of the firm's technical staff. The following extract from a technical advertisement shows both lack of appreciation of the meaning of words, and careless use of technical terms :

A very perfect cord-grip is a fundamental feature of its design. Originally developed for a service requirement for a waterproof connector to I.S.S.R.C. 320, e.g. tested to withstand a water pressure of 25 lbs.

Apart from technicalities, the appeal of a sales leaflet can be ruined by neglect of the ordinary rules of good composition, as the following example shows :

We have no hesitation in offering the . . . equipment, and would call attention of would-be purchasers to the following features, when, we are sure, one glance would be sufficient to convince the amateur or the most experienced that it is the ideal machine for the small shop or as an auxiliary in a large shop where it is often found too costly to use a larger machine or otherwise await the one and only machine the firm possesses becoming vacant.

Books

Many books owe their origin to technical papers, articles, or a series of articles in publications, and a book may be considered broadly as a series of articles carefully strung together to make a coherent survey of the subject in a uniform style. This uniformity of style is an important asset to the readability of a book; it is frequently found that a symposium or collated work of several authors, each of whom is an authority on his subject, is nevertheless unacceptable to a reader, who prefers a book in which the theme has been developed by one writer. A heavy duty is laid on the editor of a symposium to avoid repetition or even contradiction in successive chapters, to adopt uniform symbols and nomenclature throughout, and to attempt to level up the method of presentation of the various viewpoints.

The preparation of material for a shorter form of technical writing is good practice for the more arduous work of planning a book, but it is unfortunately true that many subjects which may make a brilliant report or article may not be suitable for publication in book form. The qualities of an ideal book are, briefly: (*a*) it must be needed by a wide range of readers; (*b*) the author should be an authority on his subject and able to write well; (*c*) the contents must be up-to-date; (*d*) the production must be economical, consistent with good printing and illustrations and (*e*) the book should be unique. Some of these qualities are incompatible, which may account for the number of books which fall short of the ideal. A book which contains mainly summaries of other people's work and opinions, however skilfully done, may give the reader an impression of ' scissors and paste ' work which will not enhance the author's reputation.

E. H. Selwyn, writing in the *Institute of Physics Bulletin*,* says:

I think the features which make a good textbook are the following:

(*a*) An account of the substance of the subject claimed in the title written plainly and at a modest level of difficulty for the student.
(*b*) Absence of material which is not of importance to the student.
(*c*) Conveyance of a feeling that the subject is still alive and worth knowing about otherwise than as a mere ' intellectual discipline '.
(*d*) In physics textbooks, a preference for physics rather than mathematics.
(*e*) Enough originality to make the book worth reading by teachers in the hope that they might find something useful in their teaching.

Further notes on the preparation of books are given in Chapter 10.

* March 1959.

CHAPTER 2

THE TECHNIQUE OF TECHNICAL WRITING

THE first aim of technical writing should be consideration for the reader, and this point will be stressed continually throughout succeeding chapters. If there were no readers, the labour of writing would be wasted and it is therefore in the writer's own interest to secure and hold the reader's attention.

Unlike the non-technical author or novelist, the technical writer has a potential readership of those who *want* the information he is imparting, but this does not mean that he can take advantage of their demand and serve it up to them in an unappetizing way. In spite of his need, the reader can easily become discouraged and it is the duty of the writer to present his subject in such a way that the reader is finally left satisfied and informed.

Nearly every writer has had the experience of reading an obscure passage in some textbook or article and has felt a momentary irritation at the lack of precision or clarity; and yet the same writer will blithely commit the very blunders in his own text that caused him irritation in another's. The golden rule in technical writing is therefore ' Put yourself constantly in the place of the reader '.

Types of Reader

Before undertaking any form of writing it is essential to have in mind the type of reader to whom the information is addressed, as this will govern the whole approach to the style and treatment of the material. Unfortunately, with one or two exceptions, it is not possible to draw up a classification of types with as much precision as, say, income groups, and a writer generally has to assess the intelligence and knowledge possessed by his unknown reader by comparison with his known colleagues, students, or non-technical friends. In most cases it is fairly safe to assume a lower degree of knowledge than that of the writer rather than an equal degree. This assumption will prevent the writer using a self-conscious

24

style which is sometimes noted in technical papers read before scientific societies. An author of a book once admitted that in writing the first edition he was thinking more of impressing his professional colleagues than instructing the student. As a result his writing was obscure and above the average comprehension of the very class of reader for whom the book was intended.

In the more specialized forms of technical literature, such as research reports or scientific papers, a fairly accurate estimate can be made of the reader's qualifications, and the writer's main task is to maintain the level of writing throughout the text.

As an indication of the classification which can be made, the following types can be singled out as representative of their class:

(a) *Specialists.* If the reader is an expert in the subject, it will usually be unnecessary to extend the writing beyond the immediate matter in hand. It can be assumed that he has a knowledge equal (and in some cases superior) to that of the writer, and will not require elaborate explanations, nor will he accept evasions or faulty arguments. Such a reader is often the head of the department in which the work is done and will be satisfied with facts concisely stated and the deductions drawn from them.

(b) *Technical Users of the Information.* It frequently happens that a report is drawn up for the use of a reader who has to apply the results to some work or process in which he is concerned. This class may be large, including as it does designers, operators of plant, engineers, and executives in the works departments.

These readers are, in general, more interested in the results than in the means by which they are obtained, and hence the technical details of the work can be subordinated to the main requirement of advice on the necessary action and the effect which will result.

Prof. R. O. Kapp* raises an interesting point relating to this type of reader, which affects the order of presentation of the material in the report:

Suppose, for instance, that a report contains a recommendation the nature of which is not easy to understand and the need for which is not at all apparent to the reader—the person who will have to act on the report. (He may even have a strong objection to the change.) To make the nature of the recommendation clear a number of technical

* R. O. Kapp: *The First Draft.* Paper read to the P.T.I. Group Meeting, Oct. 1953. (Privately printed.)

25

points have to be developed at length, and the need for action only becomes apparent when the reader has understood these technical points. Now it may well be that the reader will not have the patience even to try and understand them (and consequently the nature of the recommendation) until he has become convinced that some action is necessary. There is the writer's dilemma. If the reasons for the action are presented first, they will be incomprehensible ; if the recommendations are presented first they will not be listened to.

This is one of the problems that the report writer is sometimes faced with—where the sequence in which items should be presented according to the logic of the subject conflicts with the sequence dictated by the logic of the whole situation.

(c) *The Technically-trained Reader.* The reader who is familiar with technical terms, but is nevertheless unfamiliar with the subject of the report presents a special problem to the writer, who must not appear to be condescending nor should he take for granted a knowledge that the reader does not possess. For such readers the report can be extended to include relevant information which will explain the conclusions reached, but no specialized words or ' jargon ' (see p. 80) should be introduced without justification or explanation.

As a non-specialist, the technically-trained reader prefers to have the material presented him uninterrupted by mathematical reasoning, and if it is essential to include this as part of the argument it is preferable to put it in an appendix. It is also helpful to use as many illustrations as practicable to break up the text and relieve the otherwise dull appearance of many printed pages.

(d) *The Intelligent Lay Reader.* Although a reader will admit to lack of technical knowledge, it is seldom that he will admit to lack of intelligence. The standard of writing for a non-technical reader is usually more difficult to attain than for the more or less well-defined classes previously mentioned. It must be assumed that his knowledge of English is good, and that it is therefore unnecessary to ' write down ' to him. On the other hand, technical words should be avoided if their simpler equivalent is to hand, even at the expense of a slight loss of accuracy or precision. Purely technical processes do not need describing in detail, but the lay reader is often interested in the reasons for a certain course of action which would be self-evident to a technically-trained reader and possibly omitted from more specialized writing.

There are many in a works organization who would like to be informed of developments and who can appreciate the final result even if they do not understand the means by which it is achieved. Examples of such intelligent lay readers are the administrative and accounting staff, shop operatives, customers, and shareholders. The presentation of technical information to readers of this type could usefully be undertaken in collaboration with the publicity department of the firm. The ' writing down ' of technical material is an aptitude for which some engineers and research workers are unsuited and it may be necessary to supply the information to a skilled writer, leaving him to produce the finished work. A useful arrangement adopted by some firms is to issue a technical report in two levels: the detailed one, and a simplified version for the benefit of the lay reader.

Analogies

Although seldom necessary in advanced technical writing, analogies are of value in explaining technicalities to lay readers, and in some subjects they are essential if the explanation is not to become too involved. Every technical writer is familiar with the analogue of electricity and the flow of water through a pipe, and the only danger of using such explanations is that the less intelligent reader accepts them as literally true, overlooking the warning that the writer should give in advance of the analogy. This literal acceptance is found particularly in juvenile readers or audiences, and it seems inevitable that a popular explanation should be taken at its face value in spite of any qualifying remarks.

The use of an apt analogy is very satisfying to both writer and reader, but it is worth spending time in considering the full implications before embarking on a description which may lead to false assumptions or involve the writer in explaining the explanation.

An example of neat analogy is found in the article by Dr. J. Bronowski on *Radio Astronomy* :*

But the radio stars are, of course, far beyond the range of any beams of ours. We detect them by the radio waves that they themselves send out, just as we see the stars by their own light. For this purpose we use only the receiving half of the radar set: the familiar curved network of wire mesh with an aerial at its focus.

* The *Observer*.

This is the radio telescope; it is precisely the analogue of the reflecting telescope invented by Newton which collects light in a curved mirror instead of a lens.

The wire network is the mirror which collects the incoming radio waves and focuses them on to the aerial; and, like Newton's mirror, its shape is parabolic. The radio mirror need not be made of solid metal because the radio waves are about a million times longer than light waves. The mirror can therefore be a million times as rough.

The late Sir Charles Sherrington, who was a poet as well as a physiologist, showed his gifts in many of his technical writings, and his analogy of the function of the nervous system has been quoted many times as an example of elegant prose writing:*

Imagine a scheme of lines and nodal points, gathered together at one end into a great ravelled knot, the brain, and at the other end trailing off into a sort of stalk—the spinal cord.

Let us also imagine that the activity in this scheme is shown by little points of light. Of these, some are stationary and flash rhythmically, fast or slow; others are travelling points, which stream along various lines at different speeds.

The stationary lights lie at the nodes, which are both the goals whither the travelling lights converge and junctions whence they diverge.

The hour of deep sleep is come. Only in some sparse and out-of-the-way places are the nodes flashing and the light points running. The great knotted headpiece lies for the most part in darkness; occasionally at places within it lights flash or move, but these soon subside.

As we continue to watch the scheme, we observe after a time an impressive change which takes place. In the great head end, which has been plunged in darkness, myriads of lights begin to spring up as though activity from one of the local places had begun to spread suddenly far and wide.

The great topmost sheet of the mass, where hardly a light twinkled or moved, now becomes a sparkling field of rhythmic flashing points, with trains of sparks hurrying hither and thither.

Swiftly the head becomes an enchanted loom where millions of flashing shuttles weave a dissolving pattern: always a meaningful pattern, although never an abiding one.

The brain is waking, and with it the mind is returning.

On the other hand, an analogy can be quite irrelevant to the subject, as in the following:

In contrast to the broom, a vacuum cleaner can be used as a blower, paint sprayer, clothes cleaner, and so forth; that is it is multifunctional.

* Reproduced in slightly condensed form from the late Sir Charles Sherrington's *Man on his Nature*, by permission of the Cambridge University Press.

Just so, blood in contrast to other liquids is capable of performing many functions : conveying gases, carrying foodstuffs, clotting, acting in body temperature regulation. . . .

PLANNING THE WRITING

A technical report* is planned to perform a specific function in a similar way to the planning of a piece of equipment to perform a specific job, and the stages in the preparation of the writing follow closely on the lines commonly laid down for developing equipment.

The work is undertaken to satisfy a specification ; in the equipment, the customer's statement of his requirements : in the report, the question that has been put directly or indirectly to the writer. For example, a report on the Moisture Absorption in Plywood is in effect an answer to the query ' How much moisture does plywood absorb ? ', or ' Does the moisture content affect the use to which plywood can be put ? ' The form of the implied question will have been suggested to the writer by the circumstances under which the investigation was carried out ; and it must be clearly understood at the outset in order to develop the theme correctly and prevent including any irrelevant material.

As soon as a satisfactory answer to the question has been found, the writer is ready to plan a more or less lengthy reply. A simple uncomplicated question calls for only a brief report or even a memorandum, but if a thorough investigation has to be made the report will necessarily be as thorough and will include supporting evidence, correlated information, and the writer's conclusions and recommendations. The extent to which these items figure in the report will be governed by the particular requirements of the work and the reader.

Basic Components

The main items of which the report is composed can be set down as follows :

(*a*) A statement of the conclusions reached, i.e. the answer to the implied question.

(*b*) The evidence on which the statement is based, or the facts disclosed by the investigation.

(*c*) Relevant information obtained during the course of the investigation.

* See footnote to p. 18.

(*d*) The writer's own comments, to assist the reader in evaluating the information.

(*e*) Other relevant information to assist future workers or to deter others from unnecessary work.

Influence of the Reader

At the time of planning the report the writer should have in mind the type of reader to whom it is addressed, and will class him into one of the categories outlined on p. 25.   If, for example, the report is intended for the technical works manager, items (*b*), (*c*) and (*e*) may be subordinated to (*a*) and (*d*).   A general survey of the subject would give more weight to items (*c*) and (*e*).   The reader's intelligence level will also determine the method of presentation in the style of writing, the number of illustrations and the use of appendices or even a glossary.

Ultimate Use of Report

Another question which may be considered at an early stage is the ultimate use of a report.   If it is a confidential one, or for internal circulation only, no special action need be taken, but if it will eventually form a technical booklet for publication outside the firm there may be practical limitations which will govern the amount of material or its presentation—in particular the illustrations.   A detailed graph which will reproduce satisfactorily by one process may be unsuitable for another, and if this is noted beforehand it may save extra trouble in redrawing later.

Many reports can be reproduced in quantity by ordinary office duplicating processes (see p. 190) to a sufficiently high standard to enable them to be distributed outside the organization, and if this is to be done the layout and final arrangement must be made with the firm's prestige in mind.   An untidy and badly reproduced report is a poor advertisement for the technical staff, whatever the value of the contents.

GATHERING MATERIAL

The general level of the writing and the scope of the report having been decided, the next preliminary is the gathering of material. Before undertaking any draft, the writer must make sure that he has all the likely material to hand.   It is just as distracting to find that an item of information is missing as it is to find that a component of a piece of equipment is not in stock when it is wanted.

The material for the body of the report will usually be found in the writer's own notebook,* particularly if he is a member of a research staff, but this is seldom sufficient in itself and will have to be augmented by information obtained from outside sources: in fact, ' looking up the literature ' is an essential preliminary to most investigations.

The sources of external information are:

(a) Books
(b) Periodicals
(c) Other Reports
(d) Patent Specifications
(e) Catalogues
(f) Miscellaneous notes

(a) Books

As aids to technical writing, books can be divided into two classes: reference books, and (for want of a better term) textbooks. The writer of an occasional report can usually consult books in his works' or local reference library, but regular writing is made easier by acquiring a small personal library of reference books, including one of the standard dictionaries. For the meaning of terms outside the writer's own vocabulary, one of the scientific dictionaries such as Chambers's, Van Nostrand's or the 4-volume Hutchinson's *Technical and Scientific Encyclopaedia* is useful. Historical backgrounds are found in Source Books of Physics or Mathematics, and general engineering information in one or other of the year books (Kempe's *Engineers' Year Book* in 2 volumes, or a similar text). A selected list of reference books is given overleaf, and a bibliography of works on technical writing together with books on English composition is given in Appendix 5, p. 318.

A list of up-to-date textbooks can usually be obtained from the leading technical booksellers or the publisher of one's choice and it is possible to borrow copies from a local library on giving due notice.

---

* The importance of keeping a dated record of work in a notebook instead of on odd scraps of paper has been pointed out so many times that this reminder is still necessary.

The libraries of the engineering institutions and learned societies are always accessible to non-members on introduction from a member, and it is possible for members to borrow copies of books in general demand.

The library of the Patent Office in London deserves to be better known among scientific writers for its comprehensive stock of periodicals and books as well as patent specifications. It also has the advantage that it is open in the evenings and on Saturdays. A descriptive article on the facilities of the library appeared in *Electronic Engineering* (1949) **21**, 52.

Reference Books

The following reference books will be found useful :

English Language and Composition

FOWLER, H. W. *Modern English Usage* (London, Oxford University Press, 1930).

PARTRIDGE, E. *Usage and Abusage : A guide to good English* (London, Hamish Hamilton ; New York : 1947).

MURRAY, SIR J., and BRADLEY, H. *Rules for Compositors and Readers* (Oxford University Press, 1950).

Style Manual. (Washington, U.S.A., U.S. Government Printing Office.)

WEST, M., and KIMBER, P. F. *Deskbook of Correct English* (London, Longmans, Green & Co., 1958).

Dictionaries

SIMMERMAN, O. T., and LAVINE, I. *Scientific and Technical Abbreviations* (Industrial Research Service, U.S.A., 1949). (See also p. 91).

The Concise Oxford Dictionary

ROGET, P. M. *Thesaurus of English Words and Phrases* (London, Longmans, Green & Co.).

COLLINS, F. H. *Authors' and Printers' Dictionary* (Oxford University Press, 1953).

TWENEY, C. F., and HUGHES, L. E. C. *Chambers's Technical Dictionary* (London, W. and R. Chambers).

Technical Reference Books

WOLF, A. *A History of Science, Technology and Philosophy* (London, Allen & Unwin, 1938. 2 volumes.)

MOTTELAY, P. F. *Bibliographical History of Electricity and Magnetism* (London, Griffin & Co., 1922) (out of print).

McNICOL, D. *Radio's Conquest of Space* (New York, Murray Hill Books ; London, Chapman & Hall, 1946).

FERCHL, F., and SUSSENGUTH, A. *A Pictorial History of Chemistry* (London, Heinemann, 1939).

32

List of Relevant British Standards

Documentation

Alphabetical Arrangement	1749
Bibliographical Reference	1629
Catalogue Sizes	1311
Layout of Periodicals	2509
Photo-copying Materials	1896
Universal Decimal Classification (abridged)	1000

Drawing Office Practice

Architectural and Building	1192
Engineering	308

Electrical Units (M.K.S.) 1637

Glossaries

Acoustical	661
Aeronautical (in 3 parts)	185
Colour Terms	1611
Computers (automatic)	2641
Electrical Engineering	205
Highway Engineering	892
Illumination	233
Mechanical Engineering	2517

Plastics	1755
Process Control, etc.	1523
Radiology	2597
Railway Signalling	719
Refrigeration	1584
Telecommunications	204
Welding	499

Graphical Symbols

Aircraft	M.24
Electrical	108
-installations	447
Instrumentation	1646
Pipes and Valves	Pt. 1, 1553
Power Plant	Pt. 2, 1553
Telecommunications	530

Paper

Sizes (commercial)	1808
(printing etc.)	730

Printing

Proof correction marks	1219
Inks (colour offset)	1480
Layout of Periodicals	2509

Symbols and Signs 1991

(b) Periodicals

The haphazard reading of a few periodicals relating to the subject in hand is inefficient and will generally lead to overlooking some item of interest. On the other hand an exhaustive search through the whole of the literature may prove equally inefficient, because the return from a large number of minor publications will not be enough to justify the time spent looking through them. Holmstrom* quotes the following figures in support of this argument :

On the subject of lubrication there are about 100 articles per year

---

* *Records and Research in Engineering*, 2nd edn. 1947 (Chapman & Hall, London), p. 214.

distributed among 20 specialized periodicals; there are a further 100 references in publications dealing with related subjects, but the number of publications is 120. There are also as many as 700 publications in which an occasional reference to lubrication appears. In order to cover all references to lubrication it would be necessary to consult nearly 850 publications, but the cream of the information is probably contained in the 140 publications first mentioned.

For example, as a source of information on chemical processes, the searcher would find the following periodicals listed in the classified reference books:

Chemical Age	*Chemistry and Industry*
Chemical Products	*Chemical Trade Journal*
Chemist & Druggist	*Chemical Worker*
Journal of the Chemical Society	*British Chemical Engineering*
The Industrial Chemist	*Journal of the Society of Chemical*
Journal of the Royal Institute of	*Industry*
Chemistry	

The total list of periodicals on chemistry and allied subjects exceeds 50, but it is probable that the useful information will rapidly diminish after the foregoing list has been consulted.

A list of the titles and publishers of British and Commonwealth periodicals together with other useful information is given in *Willing's Press Guide*, issued annually with supplements by Willings Press Service Ltd., 356 Gray's Inn Rd., London, W.C.1. This guide does not indicate the relative importance of the periodical, and to assess this it would be necessary to consult an abstracting journal for the subject required. The many collections of published abstracts are important aids to finding suitable references, and these should always be consulted before any detailed reading is undertaken.

Guides to Technical Literature

The Information and Library Committee of ASLIB (see p. 39) has compiled a list of bibliographical guides to special subjects, from which the following examples are taken:

General Science

THORNTON, J. L., and TULLY, R. I. *Scientific Books, Libraries, and Collectors: a study of the book trade in relation to science* (London, Library Association, 1954).

34

Mathematics and Physics

PARKE, N. G.   Guide to the literature of Mathematics and Physics, including related Works in engineering science (New York, McGraw-Hill Book Co., 1947).

WHITFORD, R. H.   Physics literature :   a reference Manual (Washington, Scarecrow Press, 1954).

Chemistry

CRANE, E. J., and PATTERSON, A. M.   A Guide to the literature of Chemistry (New York, John Wiley & Sons, 1927 ;   London, Chapman & Hall).

DYSON, G. M.   A short Guide to Chemical Literature (London, Longmans, Green & Co., 1951).

Engineering

DALTON, B. H.   Sources of Engineering Information (University of California Press, 1949).

SMITH, J. F.   Instrumentation Literature (Washington, Library of Congress, 1953).

Source Books.   A series of Source Books on the history of the sciences has been published by the McGraw-Hill Co. (London and New York).   Among the titles are :

Astronomy   Mathematics   Physics   Geology

A book—*Historic Researches*—based on articles by T. W. Chalmers in the *Engineer* (Morgan Bros., Publishers, 1949), gives concise accounts of the principal experimental researches in all branches of applied physics and chemistry*.

Abstracts

For engineering subjects the leading source of information is *Science Abstracts*, published by the Institution of Electrical Engineers in two sections, Engineering and Physics, and issued in monthly parts.   These abstracts cover all the leading publications in electrical engineering and applied physics and are usually available for reference at the principal libraries.   In addition there are specialized abstracts relating to telecommunications issued by the *Electronic and Radio Engineer* each month, and reproduced in the *Proceedings of the Institute of Radio Engineers.*

Other abstracts relating to scientific subjects are *Acta Chemica* and *Acta Physica* published regularly by the Pergamon Press Ltd.

* See also the *Source Book on Atomic Energy* (S. Glasstone). (D. van Nostrand, N.Y., 1958.)

and there are also the abstracts of the specialist societies included in their monthly or quarterly transactions.

For those who require information with the minimum of trouble, it is possible to subscribe to an abstract service from *Engineering Index Inc.* of 29 W. 39th Street, New York. This publishing house undertakes to send, for an appropriate fee, a weekly set of abstracts from the leading periodicals on a particular subject printed on 5″ × 3″ index cards, ready for filing. The cost varies with the number of abstracts furnished, and in certain well-documented subjects it may be considerable, but it is a useful and time-saving method of acquiring a standard reference file.

Other forms of abstract are given in monthly publications such as the *Engineers' Digest,** and some of the larger manufacturing firms issue their own series of abstracts for the benefit of their customers.

Unfortunately, the contents of the abstract do not always give an indication of the value of the article, and it is essential to use them only as a guide to those articles which may be worth investigation.

There are two publications which give a complete list of abstracting periodicals: one, *The Bibliography of Abstracts*, is issued by the Royal Society, and the other, *Index Bibliographicus*, is issued in two volumes by UNESCO. Vol. 1, covering science, appeared in 1952 and is obtainable from H.M. Stationery Office or its agents.

In Britain a recently established Information Bureau has been of particular use to firms who do not possess a library or information service of their own; I.O.T.A. Technical Services Ltd., of 38 Farringdon St., E.C.4, will supply selected abstracts and information on any specified subject for an annual fee. In addition it issues a monthly collection of abstracts on all science subjects.

Index Information Ltd., of 221 Elmwood Ave., Glen Rock, N.J., U.S.A., will supply lithographed facsimiles of the contents pages of any technical publication each month. The cost varies from $7.00 per journal per year to $6.25 for large numbers of contents pages.

(c) Other Reports

A number of official reports issued by Government or other scientific establishments may contain information which is not

---

* Published monthly from 120 Wigmore St., London, W.1.

ordinarily available in periodicals. In Great Britain the main organization concerned with circulating information is the Technical Information and Documents Unit of the Department of Scientific and Industrial Research. In America the U.S. Government Research Reports are issued by the Office of Technical Services, a branch of the U.S. Department of Commerce at Washington, D.C. A bibliography of these reports is issued monthly. A similar report service is available in Canada, issued by the Technical Information Service of the Canadian Research Council.

The Department of Scientific and Industrial Research (D.S.I.R.)* also issues a series of selected bibliographies and technical digests, and a certain number of reports can be obtained from H.M. Stationery Office.

Reports and reprints for circulation in the industry are issued by many of the important industrial firms, and these are valuable sources of up-to-date information. Such reports, if issued regularly, will be filed in the Science Library or Patent Office Library.

(d) Patent Specifications

A valuable source of patent information is given in the Abridged List issued regularly by the Patent Office before the war, although this is several months later than the date of the specification. The publication of the abridgements was suspended throughout the war and is now being resumed with a heavy list of arrears. A weekly *Patents Journal* issued by the same office gives a list of titles.

Complete search through the patents on a particular subject is only possible by a visit to the Patent Office, but copies of patent specifications relating to a subject can be supplied by the Librarian on a standing order from a firm. Abridgements of patents from the Commonwealth and America are kept in the libraries at Birmingham, Glasgow, Liverpool, Leeds and Manchester.

Information on patents in general can be obtained from the following:

Patents and Designs Act, 1949 (H.M. Stationery Office).
MATHYS, H. Patents as a Source of Information. *Aslib Proceedings* **4**, 2, 69 (1951).
MEINHARDT, P. *Inventions, Patents and Monopoly.* 2nd Ed. (London, Stevens, 1946.)

* Department of Scientific and Industrial Research, 15 Lower Regent St, London W.1.

The " Fair Copying " Declaration

An author may often wish to obtain a photostat copy of a particular article which will be of value to him for personal reference. Except in certain circumstances the Copyright Act requires him to obtain permission from the owner of the copyright of the article before he can have a copy made; this causes unnecessary correspondence and delay, as libraries will not provide copies without evidence that permission has been obtained.

The Royal Society, at their Information Conference in 1948, proposed a method whereby *bona fide* research workers or authors could obtain copies of scientific papers for their own use, and this scheme has since become widely adopted by scientific societies and publishers under the name of the Fair Copying Declaration. The text of this Declaration, to which the publisher or society subscribes, runs as follows:

We will regard it as fair dealing for the purpose of private study or research when a non-profit making organization, such as a library, archives office, museum or information service, owning or handling scientific or technical periodicals published by us makes and delivers a *single* reproduction of part of an issue thereof to a person or his agent representing in writing that he desires such reproduction in lieu of a loan or manual transcription, and that he requires it solely for the purpose of private study, research, criticism or review, and that he undertakes not to sell or reproduce for publication the copy supplied, provided :

1. The recipient of the copy is given notice that he is liable for infringement of copyright by misuse of the copy, and that it is illegal to use the copy for further reproduction.
2. The organization making or furnishing the copy does so without profit to itself.
3. Proper acknowledgement is made to the publication from which the copy is made.
4. Not more than one copy of any one excerpt shall be furnished to any one person.

It is assumed that the person requiring the copy has taken all reasonable steps to secure the originals, either the publication itself or a reprint, from the author or publisher. Further, the Declaration does not apply to books and other non-periodic or non-serial publications, and is not intended to enable a user to evade his responsibilities to an author of a published work.

The majority of the leading scientific societies and publishers in

Britain and the Commonwealth have subscribed to this Declaration, and a complete list is obtainable from the Royal Society, or from a library.

ASLIB

A valuable aid to tracing sources of information which are not commonly known is the organization known as ASLIB—the Association of Special Libraries and Information Bureaux (3 Belgrave Square, S.W.1). The services of this organization include an information bureau with a special section for industrial enquiries, a book loan service, a panel of translators, a library consulting service, and other activities including book-lists and a *Journal of Documentation*. It should be pointed out that much of the information service is intended for its members (who include most of the British industrial firms) and that the Association does not act as an ordinary enquiry bureau to save trouble on the part of the lazy searcher.

Classifying Information

The material gathered from the various sources mentioned requires classifying into some arrangement that will make it easy for the writer to use it, and herein lies one of the difficulties of the preliminary planning. The writer at this stage may not be decided on the order in which he will present his material, nor on the headings under which it will be presented in the first draft, and it is not therefore possible to draw up a list of detailed headings under which the gathered information should be filed.

As a preliminary it may be necessary to group the information under a few broad terms, such as ' History ', ' Applications ', ' Theory ', ' Numerical Data ', and so on, until the work of drafting has advanced further. In deciding the main headings, the writer is guided to a certain extent by his knowledge of the background of the report, i.e. he will know which of some classifications have little bearing on the final work or whether there is a particular aspect which will require special investigation and collection of material.

At this stage the beginner should be warned against misusing the tempting word ' Miscellaneous ' as a heading in any system of classification. A certain number of items will always resist classifying

39

under well-defined headings and can legitimately be put in the Miscellaneous section, but there is always a temptation to use this section either as a repository of useless items which should be scrapped or as a pending file for items which should be put elsewhere.*

In considering the actual form that the classification should take, the writer should take into account the possibility of the report being the first of a series, or being on a subject that he intends to make his life's work. The information will then be more than a temporary aid to completing a specific task and will become part of his personal reference library. The indexing and filing system will need to be planned more thoroughly, and possibly one of the existing library classification systems could be adopted (see p. 44).

Recording Information

As with most organized work, it is preferable to decide on the way in which the information is to be stored and standardize on this method throughout. The choice initially lies between loose-leaf filing books and filing cards, with quarto or foolscap folders for larger items of information—tables, graphs and tear-sheets.

The loose-leaf book has the advantage that it is possible to collate both laboratory work and gathered material in the same cover, and if a separate sheet is used for a fresh item, the material can be rearranged without difficulty. There is also the advantage that graphs can be filed with the relevant data and small extracts can be pasted in with the text. Finally, the filled book can be stored without taking up too much space, and can be carried in a document case.

The filing cards, which are commonly sold in boxes labelled 'Trial Outfit', are made in three standard sizes : 5″ wide by 3″ deep, 6″ wide by 4″ deep, and 8″ wide by 5″ deep. Index cards, of thicker card with a projecting tab, can be obtained but it is usually convenient to make them by gumming a 'tag-strip' to an ordinary card, marking the tag in any way required. It is also useful to obtain a small quantity of coloured tag-strips, $\frac{1}{4}$″ wide, for identifying special cards or for cross-referencing.

The smaller sizes of filing card will take short abstracts or notes,

* As in the store of an electrician who had a box labelled ' Pieces of wire too short to be of use '.

and the printed abstracts obtained from periodicals can be gummed on them directly.* It is not always necessary to limit one card to one item of information; closely related items can be copied on the same card.

The filing card system is essentially an abstracting system, and should be operated in conjunction with a larger file containing the reprints, photostats, or data referred to on the file card. This implies a form of numbering or coding, so that the associated large file can be compiled in step with the card system; but it may not be necessary to operate two files if the card index is only required for a limited amount of writing.

The chief advantage of using filing cards is the ease with which they can be shuffled and re-classified at will. If certain information is found unnecessary, the card can be scrapped without upsetting the arrangement of the file. It is also a simple matter to show cross-references by fixing a colour-coded tag in a particular position on the top of a card: for example, all cards having a blue tag on the right-hand corner could be related.†

Punched Cards

The punched-card system enables detailed information to be obtained fairly rapidly and easily from among a large collection of items which need not be kept in a classified order. The card used is of any size from 1″ by 1½″ to 10″ by 8″ and has one or more rows of circular or elliptical holes punched near each edge. The top right-hand corner of the card is cut off obliquely to act as a guide for 'right way up'.

The card may be over-printed with headings ready for filling in data, and the holes are usually marked with an alphabetical or number code to suit the user's requirements.

A typical general purpose punched card is shown in Fig. 2.1, laid out to give information classified by letter or numeral.

To operate the system, the position of the holes corresponding to a given code is first decided: it may be alphabetical combinations or two or three letters, or number combinations in the simplest

---

* *Science Abstracts* can supply special proof copies of the abstracts, printed on one side of the sheet only, specially for sticking on filing cards.

† This method and other satisfactory ways of dealing with card indexing are dealt with by Holmstrom : *Records and Research In Engineering* (previously referred to on p. 33).

41

case. The edge of the card opposite the selected hole is then clipped out by means of a hand punch. Holes at the sides of the card can be assigned to special items of information and clipped out accordingly.

If a particular card or set of cards bearing required information is to be picked out, the whole collection is gathered in the hand and checked to see that the cut-off corners are all at the top right-hand edge. A knitting needle is then run through the holes at the positions corresponding to the coding of the required information. On lifting the needle, those cards which have clipped-out holes will

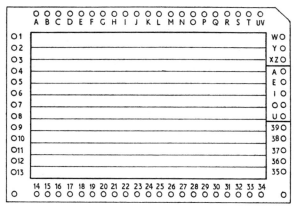

FIG. 2.1. *Typical punched card for alphabetical or numerical sorting.*

fall on the table (Fig. 2.2) and by successive threading it is possible to divide the whole set of cards up into classified groups or to select an individual card from among the pack.

Coding of Cards

If only a limited number of classes is to be coded on the card, it is sufficient to assign one hole to one subject or item of classification, as for example, in separating organic from inorganic compounds.* When classifying names of authors, a simple 26-hole alphabetical arrangement is sufficient, but it is possible to combine a numbering code with the alphabetical arrangement, if the order of the letter in the alphabet is remembered.

* Note that it is not necessary to punch one hole for a class and another for its negative or converse.

42

A commonly used numerical code involves only four holes to give any number from 0 to 14 inclusive by marking them 7 4 2 1. In this code 10 would be indicated by punching 7, 2 and 1. By using several sets of 4 holes in this way very large numbers can be coded with the minimum of punching.

Coding systems have been devised for classifying stocks of components, spare parts, drugs, and chemical compounds. A description of some special applications of punched card systems is given

Fig. 2.2.   *Method of sorting punched cards.*
(*By courtesy of Copeland-Chatterson Ltd.*)

in *Punched Cards : their Application to Science and Industry* by R. S. Casey and J. W. Perry (Reinhold Corpn., N.Y., 1951).

For the ordinary technical writer the punched card system may be unnecessarily complicated, although it can be usefully adapted to the filing of abstracts. Its principal value is in the compiling of statistical data and in the indexing of a large number of items which have various points of difference.

Punched cards and accessories may be obtained from Copeland-Chatterson & Co., London, E.C.4 (" Cope-Chat "), and in America from the McBee Co., Athens, Ohio (" Keysort "), or the E–Z Sort Systems Inc., San Francisco (" E–Z Sort "). More complex systems for mechanical and electronic sorting have been developed by the International Business Machine Corpn. (I.B.M.), Powers-Samas, Remington-Rand, and others.

Indexing Systems

The storage of an accumulated mass of information is useless without a key which will enable any item to be found quickly and accurately. This all-important key is the method of classification or indexing, which involves sorting the material into groups and identifying each component in the group. The classification into groups can be based on attributes such as quality, function, species, and within the group the items can be arranged on a different basis— chronological, alphabetical or functional—as desired.

In classifying information for a specific piece of writing a simple form of grouping is usually sufficient, since the material is seldom too voluminous to handle with ease. It is possible to devise a grouping system which will be efficient for all the material relating to a specialized subject, such as concrete, chromatography, or sound recording, and suitable headings for the groups can generally be found in the index or chapter headings of a textbook on the subject. Individual items can then be arranged according to authors or titles of articles in alphabetical order.

In classifying information covering a wide field, such as electrical engineering, a writer can either extend the grouping system (which may then become unwieldy) or adopt one of the existing widely-used systems for universal classification. One advantage of using a well-known system is that it enables a private filing system to be worked in collaboration with others, and references in other languages are more easily located and filed.

Decimal Classification

Of the widely-used systems, those based on the Decimal Classification are the best known and are used in the principal libraries throughout the world. The original decimal classification was proposed by Melvil Dewey* (1876) and in an improved form is in use in American libraries. The basis of the system is the division of all knowledge into ten groups, denoted by the decimal numbers 0 to 9.

* Dewey's original explanation (*Decimal Clasification and Relativ Index* (1927) Forest Pres, New York) is complicated by his own form of simplifide speling.

44

Each group is then divided into ten sub-groups, using a second decimal number following the first, and so on. The decimal numbers are divided into groups of three figures for convenience, and the initial decimal point is omitted. Related subjects are connected by a sign " + ", e.g. 531·75 + 536·8 and a functional relation between subjects is denoted by " : ", as in :

537·531 : 535·4 : 548·0 = X-ray diffraction by crystals
X-rays Diffraction Crystals

The Universal Decimal Classification, which is used in libraries in Europe, is a modification of the Dewey System and the code is

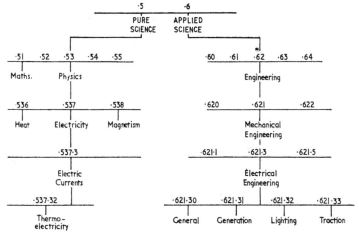

FIG. 2.3. *Tree showing some of the sub-divisions of pure and applied science in the U.D.C. system.*

given in detail in British Standard BS.1000 and class code books CG(DOM).... relating to specific groups.

The primary sub-divisions of the U.D.C. are :

0 Generalities   5 Pure Science
1 Philosophy   6 Applied Science
2 Religion   7 Art
3 Social Sciences   8 Literature
4 Philology   9 History and Geography

Some of the sub-divisions of groups 5 and 6 are shown in Fig. 2.3.

The aim of the originator of the system was to provide a universally recognized coding system for all written material, regardless

45

of language difficulty, which should make the filing and collating of information straightforward and easily accessible to all. Nevertheless, as its opponents have pointed out, the decimal system is far from foolproof and requires a skilled codifier to apply it. The field of knowledge has widened in directions which were never foreseen by Dewey, and this widening has resulted in an unbalance in the coding and strings of figures to denote some subjects of major importance. The risk of ambiguity is indicated by the sections set out in Fig. 2.3, and the choice of the appropriate code number often rests with an individual librarian instead of being determined automatically by the content of the writing.

Other Systems

Holmstrom, in his book mentioned earlier,* describes a system of analytical indexing, the Kaiser system, in use by Imperial Chemical Industries Ltd. Another system has been proposed by H. E. Bliss (*A Bibliographic Classification* (1952) H. W. Wilson, New York), and there are specialized systems designed for chemical nomenclature. Apart from these, the best-known system in use in American libraries and scientific institutions is the Library of Congress System. This classifies the field of knowledge into 20 classes, using letters of the alphabet, with a second letter for sub-divisions of the class and numbers for further sub-divisions. For example, Physics is QC, and Heat is QC252. The British Patent Office also has a system of class marks and 'press marks' for library books and patents which unfortunately are not in agreement between themselves.

An excellent survey of classifying and indexing methods is given in chapters in the book *The Technical Report* by B. H. Weil and others (Reinhold Publishing Corpn. 1954). Other books are listed in the section on Indexing (p. 330).

PREPARING THE FIRST DRAFT

At what stage should the first draft be undertaken ? From the foregoing discussion it appears that it is time to draw up a scheme of writing when the answer has been found to the implied question behind the investigation.

* See p. 33.

There are, however, many investigations which take a year or even several years to complete. Does this mean that no report should be made throughout the period ? Such a delay would involve the writer in extra work in dealing with the accumulation of material, beside provoking comment from higher quarters.

One guide to the timeliness of a report is therefore the amount of material which can usefully be presented in order to give the reader either the information that he wants, or sufficient information to show the lines along which the investigation is proceeding, together with results up to date. It is not desirable to prepare an interim report ' for the sake of showing something ', and the writing should have some definite conclusion, however it may be modified by later progress.

The difficulty of issuing a useful report on investigations which go on for a long time is recognized by most research establishments, and a scheme of issuing ' Progress Reports ' is found to be a satisfactory way of keeping various people informed of developments during a given period. An obvious point which is frequently overlooked is that the report should show clearly the dates covered by the work—in fact, where the possibility of patent action is involved a reference to the date may be vital in the record.

If, however, the investigation is definite in its scope and is completed in a reasonable period, the criterion of when to start writing and what to put down is the knowledge that the contents can be briefly stated in one or two sentences which form the answer to the implied question in the investigation (see p. 49). Unless the answer can be completely framed in the form of a brief summary the report will not be conclusive although it may contain information. In reports and articles of a more general nature (' survey ' articles) a summary may not be possible to prepare in a sentence or two, but the writer should still have a definite plan for the scope and, more important, the limitations of his work. Unless he sets these down at the outset, there is a risk of going on for too long or of bringing in extraneous material which is only slightly connected with the main subject.

The Title

The exact wording of the title must be carefully chosen if the reader is not to be misled. It is the first item that catches his eye and it should tell him at once whether the contents of the writing will be of interest to him. Of almost equal importance is the use of the title for classifying and indexing the material : a misleading title will annoy librarians and abstractors and may result in an article being filed in the wrong place.

A satisfactory title is neither too all-embracing nor too detailed ; short titles may mislead by their very brevity, and long titles are difficult to remember and to quote (for reference). If a short title does not express the contents sufficiently clearly, it is preferable to compromise by combining two statements in the title : the first a short phrase of three or four words indicating the main contents of the writing and the second a longer sub-title giving specific information on the particular aspect covered.

For example, a paper with the title ' Intelligence Tests as a Guide to the Educability of Adult Morons ' might be misquoted and misfiled under ' Intelligence Tests ' only, where the education of the moron is of equal, if not more, importance. The title could be reworded ' Education of Adult Morons ', with the sub-title ' Value of Intelligence Tests ', which would alter the emphasis and give a more balanced indication of the contents.

In books and certain articles of a semi-technical nature a certain latitude in the wording of the title is permitted and even desirable. To a reader who browses in a library or bookstore, the title is often the incentive which makes him take a book from the shelf and look through it, and if the author can encourage him by a provocative title (always within the bounds of scientific accuracy) so much the better for sales. As an example, a book published some years ago dealt with the subject of luminescence and phosphorescence in animals, fish and insects. The author might have called it ' Luminescent Phenomena in Vertebrates and Invertebrates ' but instead he used the happy phrase ' Living Light '.*

Occasionally the exact phrasing of a suitable title presents some difficulty, especially if there are already several publications with similar themes or titles. There is no actual copyright in a title, but no one would willingly copy an existing title for obvious reasons. It is, however, possible that a legal action might lie for ' passing off ' if the title of a well-established work were appropriated by another author. It is seldom profitable to search for a suitable

* C. Harvey, Princeton Press, N.J., U.S.A.

combination of words if they do not come spontaneously, and the writer should leave the problem for a time in the hope that the words will come later or be suggested by some phrase in the writing.

Titles preceded by words such as ' Some Thoughts on . . .' or ' A Few Observations on . . .' belong to the eighteenth century, but may occasionally be revived in special cases. As in the writing, so in the title : conciseness and clarity are always to be preferred.

Divisions of the Writing

The main sections into which a report or article is divided will be determined by the summary and also by the emphasis which may be required on certain aspects of the work. A report, for example, on the technique of a new process would naturally contain more information of a descriptive nature than details of the results, and the number and arrangement of the sections will be arranged accordingly. The actual number and designations of the sections need not be considered as definite in the early stages of preparation— in fact it is frequently necessary to revise the arrangement as the writing progresses—and no attempt need be made to follow them rigidly in working on the first draft.

Conventional Headings

There are certain reports of a stereotyped nature in which the order of the items has been dictated by long-established custom. A student is introduced to this type of report early in his laboratory work when the instructor lays down the order in which an experiment should be written up. The sequence follows a train of thought which is provoked by the natural question ' What are you doing ? ' and which ends by answering the question ' What have you found out ? '. The headings of the report are set down in the order :

Nature of the Experiment (or Investigation)
Apparatus Used
Results Obtained
Conclusions

In the same way, the order of items in a handbook will be arranged to answer the question asked by the user from ' What is this apparatus ? ' to ' How does it work ? '. Translated into headings this becomes :

> Brief Description of Apparatus
> Application
> Operating Principles
> Detailed Description

although it is possible to invert the order of dealing with the apparatus and explain its operation fully before describing its uses.

The writing of instructional handbooks for the user may not need the amount of detailed technical description that would be given in a book for the maintenance engineer or skilled technician. An example of the difference in treatment would be found in a manual for the owner of a radio-gramophone or a car compared with the servicing manual for the use of the dealer. It may be convenient to divide a handbook into two sections so that the user may find all the information he needs without the distraction of detailed technical descriptions.

Special Requirements

Handbooks and reports for Government departments usually have to conform to an existing code of practice which covers the arrangement of title page, contents, and method of display by sections or sub-sections. In preparing reports for these departments a writer will save himself much time and trouble if he consults a specimen for style and presentation, and enquires whether there are any peculiarities in terminology (e.g. ' knob ' for ' handle ') before starting the work.

Many industrial firms adopt a standard style for reports, designed to give a rapid grasp of the contents or to facilitate filing and abstracting. A writer who is given the task of organizing a technical information department should plan the presentation of reports from the beginning so that they will conform to a logical and orderly scheme. Further suggestions for presentation are given in Chapter 6.

The Summary

It has already been stated that the criterion of a successful report lies in the summary. In addition to clarifying the writer's plan it serves two other useful purposes : if placed at the head of the report it saves the reader's time by showing him whether the report is worth reading in its entirety, and it is useful for abstracting and filing.

If the summary is looked on as a report in miniature, the writer can use it to check whether his full draft is well-balanced and contains all the necessary information. If a summary tends to bring out certain features of the work at the expense of others, the writer may find that the same unbalance is reflected in the full report. The writing of the summary as a preliminary to the report is certainly a guide to whether any important part of the work has been omitted, but there is a tendency to make it unduly long if the writer tries to make sure that everything is included.

As a general guide to the preparation of a summary, the following points should be borne in mind :

(i) The summary is the reader's introduction to the contents of the report, and should therefore be sufficiently interesting to make him want to read further. A dry style will often defeat the writer's object of enticing the reader.

(ii) The length of the summary should not exceed 10% of the length of the report. This figure is only an approximate one, but if it is exceeded it is a warning to the writer that he may be giving too much detail.

(iii) The summary should not be padded by unnecessary words, such as 'After an extended series of trials over a period of several months. . . .'

(iv) On the other hand, a telegraphic style must not be used, and the ordinary grammatical constructions must be retained.

(v) Tables and formulae should not be included unless the whole report deals with the derivation of a specific formula or its modification.

(vi) The order of presentation in the summary should correspond with the order of the report.

Finally it should be remembered that the summary should not be too abstruse. As it is intended to serve as a guide, the reader must not be involved in too much mental effort at the start, and a difficult introduction, though full of information, may be too unappetizing.

It is not necessary to make a lengthy summary if the results of the investigation do not warrant it. For example, in dealing with the testing of a particular material, the writer may content himself with saying :

The tests have shown that it would be economical to use a thinner gauge of metal for all cabinets without any adverse effects.

Another form of concise summary which covers the calculation and design of special filter circuits might read:

This report describes the design and manufacture of two simple filters to give a phase-shift of $90° \pm 10\%$ over a frequency range of 2 decades.

It is instructive to analyse the wording of this summary, as an example of compressing information into a single complex and readable sentence. The use of the word 'manufacture' will indicate that the report does not only deal with the theoretical calculations involved, but gives practical details. The nature of the filters is given by the word 'simple', and the limitations or properties of the particular network are defined by the final clause.

Examples of short and long summaries will be found in any copy of *Science Abstracts*, and it is a useful exercise to try and improve on the condensations which have been written by experts.

The following summary is of the telegraphic type, and could have been composed to read more smoothly:

A Wide-band Amplitude Response Curve Tracer

The purpose of curve tracers is explained and discussed. Various solutions are outlined and the curve tracer developed by the author is described. Advantages of changing frequency swing. Limitations of method used. Suggested applications to video amplifiers.

A somewhat breathless summary:

A series of measuring instruments for the measuring of many non-electrical quantities has been developed using a small physical displacement, either static or dynamic, which often may not be reliably measured by non-electrical means, to cause a change in some electrical parameter which may then be easily measured with accuracy, with the additional advantage of remote indication and control if necessary.

The following summary contains the necessary information about the contents of the report, but the method of expression and disregard of grammatical construction may discourage the reader:

An Improved Arc Control Circuit

Recent development has centred on maintaining the arc length constant without continual attention of the operator. A single tube using the arc voltage only for its plate supply and only one control to be set, and thereafter handle any change in the line voltage and at the same time keep the arc within 0.2 in. of the required length without the attention of the projectionist.

The writer feels that these aims have been attained plus a visible means of adjusting the controls, and thus eliminate all guesswork. Reference to the diagram will substantiate these claims.

Some books on technical writing recommend that the summary should only be written after the report has been compiled, but if the writer has his ideas clarified at the outset, they can be set down at any time in summary form ; if the ideas are not clear, the report will reflect his mental state, and the summary may be correspondingly imprecise. Further, the act of composing the summary provides a logical starting point for arranging the subject matter of the whole text, and if the report develops along different lines from that originally planned it is possible to re-check with the summary and note any omissions.

At the early stage of writing the summary need not be polished into its final form, and it is to be expected that it will require modifying before putting it at the head of the finished work.

The Introduction

The introductory phrases to a report are intended to provide a background for the reader who is not familiar with the circumstances or with the reason for an investigation on which the report is based; it is a means of 'putting him in the picture'.

Readers of newspapers will have noted that it is common practice to state the salient points of an article at the head of the column, repeating them again in their correct relationship to the narrative later in the column. It is sometimes useful to adopt this practice, but the writer should avoid making the introduction read like an expanded version of the summary.

Among the subjects that can usefully be outlined in the introduction are :

Reasons for undertaking the investigation or for writing the article
Brief history of recent work of a similar nature
Possible outcome, or advantages which may accrue from the work described
Any special restrictions which might apply in reading the account of the work.

A writer should *never* fall into the error of appearing to deprecate either his work or his capabilities in the introduction to any form of writing. This practice is common in introductory remarks to lectures, and always has a bad effect on the audience who are then inclined to take the speaker at his own valuation.*

If any excuse seems desirable, it may be made at the conclusion of the work when the reader (or the audience) may be more tolerant, but the practice of self-deprecation is undignified in both writing and speaking.

The introductory paragraphs often present more difficulty in composition than the body of the text, and, depending on the temperament of the writer, they may be left until a later stage. There are some who cannot write unless they develop the theme in sequence from the opening sentence to the end; others can write sections of the manuscript as fancy dictates and weld them into a coherent whole towards the end of the work. One author has said that he could only write his books by beginning with the Preface and continuing through Chapter 1 to the end.

The opening sentences of an article, as distinct from a report, are usually more difficult to compose as they must attract the reader's attention and persuade him to continue. It will be noted how many authors of successful books begin the first chapter with a dramatic situation or an arresting sentence.†

Unfortunately this practice cannot be followed in technical writing, but there is no doubt that the introduction to many articles shows a lack of care in choosing the opening words. In writing an introduction it must always be remembered that a professional editor who wishes to prune an author's manuscript turns first to the introduction with the certainty that he can cut out a sentence or two. Authors would save editors the trouble if they pruned them in revising their own manuscripts.

An example of verbose introduction is:

With the centenary of the typewriter still many years hence, an analysis of its development and ubiquitous use would show that it has done for

---

* In speaking of lecturing, Faraday used the following words which apply equally to writing:
' A lecturer falls deeply beneath the dignity of his character when he descends so low as to angle for claps and asks for commendation. Yet I have seen a lecturer even at this point. I have heard him causelessly condemn his own powers. . . . I have several times seen the attention of by far the greater part of the audience called to an error by the apology which followed it '.
† ' Marked cards ! '—*Under the Red Robe* (Stanley Weyman).

clerical work and business transactions what the printing press has done for publishing—it combined clarity with ease and speed of functioning.

A good example of an introductory phrase, which states a truism and then applies it to the subject under discussion is the following:

In general, the accuracy of an experimental measurement will not be greater than that of the least accurate piece of measuring equipment; in particular, exact measurement of the standing-wave ratio in an un-matched length of wave-guide cannot be made unless the inherent standing-wave ratio of the measuring equipment is negligible in comparison with the ratio to be determined.

The Body of the Writing

The plan to be followed in writing the main text of an article or report will have already been outlined by setting down some of the conventional headings (see p. 49), or by the order of arrangement of the collected material. At this stage, the space or weight to be given to the various components may not be decided, and the choice will be influenced by the number of illustrations it is desired to include.

The points to be considered at this stage are:

(*a*) The background of the report. This will determine both the style and amount of material included, and the emphasis to be placed on certain aspects.

(*b*) The ultimate destination of the report. Is it to be published outside the organization? Is it to be a brief interim statement of progress?

(*c*) The method of presentation—influenced by the type of reader and by both the foregoing considerations.

It must be reiterated that it is seldom possible to follow a stereotyped form in writing any but the simplest factual reports and the writer must be prepared to revise or modify his layout almost up to the time of writing the final copy for duplicating. All that he has at the initial stages are the main sub-divisions of the subject with an approximate idea of the weight that should be given to each, and it is on this basis that he begins the task of writing. There are, of course, certain guiding principles that experience has shown to be the right ones for correct presentation of the information, but within these directions he should be free at the moment to select and, what is much more important, to discard material.

The guiding principles of good technical writing are those of any good writing, and can be set down as follows:

(1) The subject must develop logically, i.e. each step in the argument should be related to the previous step, either by contrast or by enlargement.
(2) No new statement should be introduced abruptly without warning.
(3) Unless deliberately introduced for the sake of emphasis or clarity, the arguments should not be repeated.
(4) A good balance should be kept between the various items under discussion, and the writer should not appear to show partiality in a factual report.

W. G. Reeder, in an excellent little book *How to Write a Thesis*,* lists some important violations of the principles of sound scientific statement which may be committed consciously or unconsciously by inexperienced writers. These are:

The author stating his opinion as a fact, without any evidence, or without sufficient evidence to support the opinion
Stating the opinion of a reputed or so-called authority as a fact
Stating the opinion of the majority as a fact
Reasoning from analogy
Reasoning from silence (or negative evidence)
Omission of evidence contrary to the author's theory
Failure to indicate how and where data were obtained
Inaccurate or vague citations or quotations.

A writer who does not pay sufficient attention to the details mentioned in the foregoing lists will inevitably irritate the reader; in fact, the one rigid principle which must be followed in all technical writing is ' Never irritate the reader '.

The Conclusion

In general, the detailed discussion of the results follows on their presentation, but the writer should always be considerate to a busy reader and provide him with a summary of the findings and, possibly, a recommendation as a conclusion to the report.

It might be wondered why a conclusion is necessary if the gist of the report has already been given in the summary at the head. The writer who raises this question in his own mind probably does so because he finds that his conclusion is becoming very similar to the

* Public School Publishing Co., Bloomington, Ill., U.S.A.

summary, and, in fact, this is a common fault to be seen in many technical papers. The best way of illustrating the difference is by quoting from an actual paper :*

The Application of Dielectric Tuning to Panoramic Receiver Design.

Summary : This paper describes a method of utilizing the voltage tuning characteristics of ferroelectric capacitors in a wide-range superheterodyne dielectric-tuned panoramic receiver. Continuous tuning over a 2 : 1 frequency band is obtained in frequency ranges up to 110 Mc/s. Some of the problems encountered are described, and a method of optimizing the parameters of specific materials is discussed. The application of these capacitors to various types of circuitry is briefly indicated.

The Conclusion to this paper runs :

There are many applications in the field of instrumentation in which dielectric tuned tank circuits could be used to advantage, i.e. sweep generators and spectrum analysers. Dielectric-tuned v.h.f. oscillators which may be suitable for use in instrumentation are under development at the present time. The results achieved to date are very good considering the characteristics of the capacitor body material used in the tuning elements.

It is possible that the present difficulty of dielectric tuning—obtaining a large tuning ratio while maintaining a small temperature coefficient— may be considerably reduced through the development of new materials and manufacturing techniques.

It will be seen that the summary is a factual account of the contents of the paper, indicating its scope and limitations (' briefly indicated '). The conclusion is a sound complement to the summary, and indicates the present and future possibilities of the subject discussed, with a brief opinion on the merits of the method.

The following conclusion does not give the reader a clear picture of the outcome of the investigation, and includes a detailed item which should have been phrased better :

The apparatus has now been constructed and is in service. It may be desirable to make R.10 variable[1] thus placing the automatic release time under the control of the operator.

There are two distinct parts of the apparatus, the monitor and the respirator mechanism, as shown by the circuit diagram.[2] It is thus possible to construct the monitor alone without the respirator mechanism.

* Butler, T. W., Lindsay, W T., and Orr, L. W. *Proc. I.R.E.* (1955), **43**, 9, 1091.

Notes :

1. This refers the reader back to a part of the text, which is undesirable in a self-contained section such as a conclusion.
2. Again a reference back, and this statement could well have been included in the main text.

No comment is made on the performance of the apparatus other than that it has been made, nor is any special feature of interest to the hasty reader included, other than the note about making separate parts of the equipment.

Acknowledgements

In making the acknowledgements which conclude the writing, it is usual for the author to mention the names of all those who have helped in the preparation of the material or in the construction of the apparatus. For many willing co-workers who may have spent extra time and trouble, this is often the only reward possible.

If permission has been obtained from a firm for publishing an article, this should be stated, but some scientific bodies deprecate the mention of a firm's name in such a way as to make a veiled advertisement.

The staff of Government establishments usually have to use a conventional form of words such as :

Acknowledgement is made to the Chief Scientist, Ministry of Supply, and to the Controller of H.M. Stationery Office for permission to publish this paper.

and it is usually necessary to add the statement that the views given are the writer's and are not necessarily officially endorsed. This disclaimer applies to other forms of writing than those from Service establishments.

Details of Presentation

Before undertaking the actual writing, several details should be settled on the manner of presentation. If the report or article is a lengthy one, or the forerunner of others on the same subject, the writer is advised to draw up a list of conventions and points of style that he intends to use. Among these are :

(*a*) Method of addressing the reader (see p. 84)
(*b*) Symbols used for equations (see p. 92)

(c) Method of citing references (see p. 95)
(d) Style of tabular matter (see p. 237)
(e) Units and abbreviations used (see p. 91)

As an example of the attention to detail that is required: if a writer gives the results of wavelength calculations in Angstrom units he should make a note that Angstrom units are to be used throughout the text and not change half-way to millimicrons. The symbols of diagrams and graphs should be consistent with the symbols in the text matter, and so on. It is usually convenient to keep a memo pad on which all the units and conventions can be noted at the first time of using.

House Rules

Many organizations which have a steady output of technical literature from various departments draw up a list of ' house rules ' laying down the accepted practice in spelling, abbreviations, references to their products, and other items of use to all technical writers. If such a list is not available, a technical writer will benefit both himself and his colleagues by compiling one.

A useful example which came to the authors' notice is a 76-page booklet issued by Rank-Cintel Ltd. for the use of their staff. This book, under the title of *Grammatikos*, contains ' a collection of notes, accepted ways of doing things, British Standards and personal preferences '.

CHAPTER 3

STYLE AND PRESENTATION

I BELIEVE with justice that there is for every thought a certain nice adaptation of words which none other could equal, and which, when a man has been so fortunate as to hit, he has attained in that particular case the perfection of language.

BOSWELL'S words not only express the ideal that all technical writers should strive to attain, but they also serve to define that quality known as ' style ', of which Swift said more tersely : 'Proper words in proper places make a true definition of style '.

As exemplified by these quotations, style may take quite different forms ; its quality can be more easily recognized than analysed, and it cannot be made the subject of rigid rules. Boswell, by Swift's standard, might be considered verbose and pompous. Swift, by Boswell's standard, might be considered inelegant. The only ground they have in common is the emphasis on the importance of the right word in the right place, and, provided the writer follows this principle, a fluent and clear style can be developed by experience and continual watchfulness.

It might be thought that if Swift's dictum were followed literally technical writing would tend towards a uniform and dry level, with the utmost economy in words and the minimum of embroidery of the subject, but this is not necessary nor desirable. A telegram is an extreme example of economy in words, but no one reads telegrams for choice.

The technical writer has to perform two functions : he must convey the information accurately and logically and he must convey it agreeably and smoothly. The choice of the correct word has been learned in his technical training : the use of the accompanying phrases which make the information palatable to the reader can be learned by studying the style of others and by constant self-analysis. A wide vocabulary is essential to good writing, and we are fortunate that the English language provides such an immense variety of words which can be selected to express subtle shades of meaning.

60

Conveying the Information

However intelligent the reader may be, his capacity for taking in and understanding information is limited. He can receive it better in the form of small quantities steadily delivered than in a lump which will provoke mental indigestion. The writer, from previous consideration of the type of reader he is addressing, must estimate the size of the ' information unit ' and the rate of delivery. He then has to take care that they are maintained uniformly throughout the text, using the aids of illustration, simile, explanatory notes, unusual phrase, and all the adjuncts of good style to keep the reader interested and receptive.

The means by which the information units are conveyed are, of course, the sentence and the paragraph. The short paragraph, which is a characteristic of modern technical writing, has a physiological as well as a psychological value; it serves to break the monotony of following line upon line of printed matter with the eye and gives the reader a momentary rest of which he may be quite unaware until he has had to follow a page or two of close-typed lines. For this reason, the breaking up of the subject matter into paragraphs need not be strictly according to the logical separation of the themes but should be done according to the weight of the matter, i.e. an involved discussion will require more frequent breaks than a simple narrative.

The Sentence

Except in writing for six-year-olds, the sentence is rarely of the simple type, subject—verb—object; in fact, a succession of simple sentences does not attract the reader of technical writing at all, and if the text contains a succession of short statements it will have the effect of a machine-gun:

Heaviside was a wonderful electrical engineer. He was also a mathematical genius. At first he worked in a telegraph office and had to leave because he became deaf. Finally he retired to Paignton, in Devon, and lived alone. He wrote articles and his editors made him condense them. These articles were no doubt hard before they were condensed. They are far harder now.

The only justifiable short sentence in this passage is the last one, which rounds off the paragraph neatly. The rest of the passage

61

could be expressed more smoothly by the simple linking of two or more statements :

Heaviside was not only a wonderful electrical engineer but he was also a mathematical genius. Owing to deafness he had to leave the telegraph office where he first worked and retire to Paignton in Devon, where he lived alone.

He wrote a number of articles which were no doubt hard enough to understand before his editors made him condense them. They are far harder now.

The value of the short sentence lies in the break that it introduces into a rhythm which may become monotonous : the effect is that of pulling the reader up, and it thus contributes to keeping him mentally awake.

The sentence is usually made longer by inserting one or more qualifying or explanatory clauses to amplify the bare statement which it conveys, and it is in adding these clauses that the writer runs the risk of committing the first fault in sentence construction :

The Over-long Sentence

Although the sentence may not contain too many items of information to overpower the reader, the auxiliary phrases may be so many, or so long, as to make him lose the thread of the argument.

Intelligent answers to such questions ought to be within the competence, or at least handy reach, of any museum functionary charged with the administration of works of art in which metal is material ; yet how few such are in a position to inform an enquirer of much more of the technical associations of an object in their care than—to take as examples the cases puzzling enough to the thoughtful visitor, cited above—that (perhaps with a casual mention of the ' lost wax ' process) the bronze has been cast, that the silver has been hammered and then chased, or that the tiny pellets have been shaped and then soldered into place, usually leaving the questioner, whose interest in the object (and in the processes involved in its production) might easily have been stimulated by a more specific reply, little less ignorant than before !

This example suggests that a useful test for the length and complexity of a sentence is to read it aloud. If the writer has to pause for breath, it is certain that the reader has paused for mental breath by the time that point has been reached.

The Overloaded Sentence

A sentence may not be over-long and yet may be overloaded with information. This occurs when the writer tries to impart more than one or two major items of information without giving the reader time to take them in. In this case, the reader may either attach insufficient importance to one of the items or overlook it altogether.

The quality of the half-tone reproduction depends both on the grade of paper used (the glossier the better) and on the fineness of the screen, in general the finer screens giving the better detail, but the limit is set by the absorbency of the paper and the quality of the printing, not every printer being equipped to reproduce half-tones with maximum clarity.

The improvement obtained by breaking up this sentence is evident :

The quality of the half-tone reproduction depends both on the grade of paper used and on the fineness of the screen. In general, glossy paper and finer screens give better detail, but the limit is set by the absorbency of the paper and the quality of the printing. Not every printer is equipped to reproduce, etc. . . .

The " Grasshopper " Sentence

The characteristic of the grasshopper sentence is that the writer jumps from one theme to another, or from one viewpoint to another with no connecting link, and the reader is left wondering where the relevance of the various phrases comes in.

This construction is nearly always an indication of muddled thinking by the writer, or a sign of impatience to put down his information as rapidly as possible without consideration for the reader. It is difficult to understand how a writer who reads over his text conscientiously can allow such jerky prose to pass :

A formidable expansion has taken place in America during the past twenty years, such as phenol-formaldehyde, nylon, bakelite, etc., in the conversion of benzol from coal tar into styrene (a compound of synthetic rubber), in the manufacture of water gas, acetylene from coke, naphthalene used as a fumigant and a reagent in the manufacture of rubber, toluol for explosives, etc., all derived from coal.

Sentence Construction

The majority of obvious faults in sentence construction arise from the writer being too concise and omitting words which are essential to the proper understanding of the information. Many faults can be eliminated by paying strict attention to the rules of

63

grammar, and some of the more common faults are mentioned on pp. 81–84. An example of a condensed sentence which would be improved by adding words is:

The figure shows the basic circuit for 500V use, the indicating instrument being a valve voltmeter of 2V range.

The Paragraph

The defects in sentence construction mentioned previously apply also to the paragraph, which is in effect a sequence of related sentences. Although it is permissible to break up a complete argument into a series of paragraphs, the opening words should be chosen to act as an indication to the reader that the argument is being developed further. Conversely, a change of subject is also indicated by the opening words of the next paragraph, which should indicate either that a fresh section is being discussed or that an opposing argument is being put forward.

The heading or sub-heading should normally be repeated in the opening words of the paragraph. If this is not done, a quick reader may not take in the relation between the text and the heading. An example of an unrelated opening sentence is:

Bars and Plates
When these are free at the ends the fulcrum may be at one of the nodal points.

The extreme case of unrelated sub-headings is often found in newspapers, where they are inserted apparently at random to catch the reader's eye.

One of the difficulties in writing is to determine when a fresh paragraph is necessary. As a general guide it may be said that the more complex the subject, the more frequent the relief that must be given to the reader by introducing fresh paragraphs—a rule that follows the principles laid down for limiting the units of information. On the other hand, a number of discrete statements which are not closely related require a separate paragraph for the convenience of the reader who may wish to pick out the information. This principle is followed in the paragraphing of this and many other technical books. Occasionally the text may be broken up by mathematical expressions, quotations, or passages in different type, all of which have the effect of relieving the monotony. On the other hand, a rapid succession of short paragraphs which contain little more than a sentence or two will produce the same irritation as a series of short sentences themselves.

Apart from paragraphing as a relief to the reader, it is essential to start a fresh theme with a fresh paragraph, choosing the opening words to indicate the change of theme. The development must then take place on the same logical lines as in the construction of the sentence, avoiding abrupt changes in viewpoint or introduction of irrelevant material (' grasshopper paragraphs ').

The following is an example of a grasshopper paragraph in which the writer fails to develop the theme indicated by the sub-heading: The small numbers refer to notes below.

Oxidation

This [1] is the absorption of oxygen by a substance such as the formation [2] of iron or aluminium oxides. Examples are given of the latter where the material in a finely divided form self-heats and fires due to oxidation [3]. Again, the green colouring matter of plants (chlorophyll) under the action of light decomposes the carbon dioxide in the air and returns the oxygen to the air [4]. Coal is the degradation product of plants and gives up its energy in the form of heat by combustion [5].

1. The sub-heading is not repeated : a minor fault of style which should have been corrected. A better opening would have been :
   ' Oxidation is the term describing the absorption of oxygen by . . .' (if oxidation was the absorption of oxygen, which it is not).
2. This may be a misprint for ' such as in the formation ' but it is doubtful, judged by the style of the writing.
3. This is an *effect* of oxidation, and not an example of the formation of oxides. The opening words imply several examples, but the next sentence has no relation to the preceding one.
4. Unrelated to the subject of the paragraph, which is oxidation.
5. This is an example of oxidation, but is not related to the original statement by contrast or by similarity.

PUNCTUATION

In speech, the exact meaning of words and phrases is conveyed with the help of pauses of varying duration and by inflexions of the voice. Both these aids to understanding are capable of a wide range of variation to suit the subject matter and the audience.

In writing, both pauses and inflexions have to be conveyed by a limited number of signs, or ' punctuation marks ', from which the reader has to deduce all the changes in expression or emphasis

E   65

that the writer wishes to convey. Occasionally these signs can be helped out by the use of special type or by underlining words, but the printed page cannot compare with the spoken word unless the writer has this limitation in mind and adapts his style to the change of medium.

It has been said that one of the tests of correct punctuation in written words is to read the passage aloud, but, as will be seen from the above observations, this test is of doubtful value, as a good reader can supply missing punctuation with inflexion of the voice. Reading aloud will certainly show up any serious omissions in punctuation, and may even indicate by loss of breath when the sentence has gone on too long, but it should not be taken as a criterion of successful punctuation.

The trend in recent years has been to reduce the number of punctuation marks in the written text, particularly in technical writing. Compare this sentence of Clerk Maxwell's, written in 1873, with a modern revision:

There are other classes of phenomena which are more complicated, and in which cases of instability may occur, the number of such cases increasing, in an exceedingly rapid manner, as the number of variables increases.

The reader would have little difficulty in grasping the meaning of this sentence if the number of commas were reduced, and in the modern tendency it might be re-written:

There are other classes of phenomena which are more complicated and in which cases of instability may occur, the number of such cases increasing in an exceedingly rapid manner as the number of variables increases.

In certain sentences over-punctuation may actually confuse the reader instead of helping him, as the frequent pauses implied by the commas may suggest a sequence of important qualifying clauses to which he may give undue consideration.* In the sentence above, ' in an exceedingly rapid manner ' does not deserve the separation implied by the commas, for if it had been replaced by the word ' rapidly ' it would have conveyed the same meaning without pause: ' the number of such cases rapidly increasing . . .'

* The liberal use of punctuation marks is referred to as ' close ' punctuation, in distinction to the modern ' open ' punctuation. Clerk Maxwell's passage is closely punctuated.

Like good style, punctuation cannot be made the subject of rigid rules, and the art of successful punctuation is to guide the reader into taking in the meaning of a sentence with the minimum of mental effort. *If a punctuation mark does not serve a definite and useful purpose it is better omitted.* An author should not rely on the printer or the printer's reader to supply missing punctuation marks which he has been too lazy to add, though this is frequently done in good printing houses. On the other hand, an author should not form the habit of going back over his manuscript to add punctuation that was omitted at the first writing.* This hardly merits the term ' revision ', for, if the writing is punctuated naturally to aid the reader in the first place, there should be no need for further additions, particularly as these usually consist of commas, added for good measure. The foregoing sentence illustrates the use of a series of commas to indicate the pauses in reading a complex sentence, and the reader may be interested in debating whether the omission of any one would affect the ease of taking in the meaning.

The following notes deal with some specific uses of punctuation marks, but are not intended as a comprehensive guide. The subject of punctuation generally is dealt with in books on English composition, and notably *The King's English*, *The Macmillan Handbook of English*, and the *Rules for Compositors*, mentioned in the Bibliography.

Full Stop (Period)

Apart from its obvious use in ending a sentence, the period usually follows an abbreviation. The modern tendency is to omit the period in abbreviations of scientific units and in certain shortened forms of technical words which have become commonly used. The letters standing for well-known public bodies are now generally written without periods in American practice (e.g. RCA, TVA), but in England they are sometimes retained (as in L.C.C.) unless the letters form a pronounceable word such as UNESCO. A list of abbreviations not requiring a period is given on pp. 90 92.

A period is not used after the title, heading, or sub-heading to a paragraph.

The omission of certain words from a quoted passage is indicated

* Oscar Wilde is reputed to have worked on a proof all the morning and to have taken out a comma. In the afternoon he put it back again.

67

by three periods : . . . Strictly speaking, the omission of any word should be so indicated, but writers are not always meticulous in indicating their selection in this way. A familiar example of selective quotation is the amended review ' I can truthfully say that I have never read such a book before and never wish to read another like it ', which becomes ' I can truthfully say that I have never read such a book before . . .'

Commas

The comma, being the most common mark of punctuation, is the most liable to abuse. Like the horn on a motor car, too frequent use leads to irritation and careful writers, like careful drivers, should seldom need it.

The following are the accepted constructions requiring commas :

(*a*) For separating qualifying clauses in a sentence. The first sentence of this section is an example.

(*b*) For separating adjectives or nouns in a series :

. . . operations such as polishing, grinding, boring, and light machining

The comma before ' and ' is usually omitted in modern writing; some compositors will omit it when typesetting.

(*c*) For separating words commonly read together, to avoid confusion :

as if the writing were punctuated correctly

has a different meaning from

as, if the writing were punctuated correctly,

(*d*) In separating complementary or opposite phrases :

This ensures, not only that . . ., but that . . .

(*e*) To avoid ambiguity with words having two meanings, such as ' for ' (preposition) and ' for ' (= because)

A writer is often tempted to put a comma after a long introductory or qualifying clause, feeling that the reader requires some rest :

Studies of the factors affecting the oxidation resistance of crankcase oils, will show . . .

It is well known that the angle to which a tool for cutting metal should be ground, varies from . . .

This violates the rule that the subject should not be separated from its verb by a comma, but may be justified for the reason given. It is preferable to try and re-cast the sentence.

Semi-colons

These are comparatively little-used punctuation marks: Prof. Kierzek, in the *Handbook of English*,* gives their occurrence in the text of seven American writers as 10–17% of the number of commas. The accepted use of a semi-colon is to give a longer pause than a comma without the finality of a period; it follows that the second part of the sentence in which it is used should be closely related to the first and not introduce a new theme.

The semi-colon is usually convenient to indicate a degree of correlation or contrast between the clauses which it separates:

In a telephone system the meaning of the message received depends on the sender; in a sensory system the meaning depends on the receiver.

Colons

In earlier writing the colon was usually followed by a dash :— which added weight to its function of pointing out the succeeding clause. When the :— was preceded by the word ' viz.', the writer had done all that he could to draw the reader's attention to what was to follow. It is primarily a mark of enumeration:

The Committee's recommendations can be summarized as follows: (*a*) Grade 1 . . .

or of direct introduction to a closely related clause:

Similar effects have been observed in experiments on animals: the response is neither simple nor regular.

Hyphens

The hyphen is commonly found linking two words to form a compound adjective or noun, e.g. six-inch, wave-band . . . In this application hyphens have generally been accepted as an intermediate stage in the combining of two words to form a single compound. The word ' wavelength ', which 50 years ago was separated into two words, became ' wave-length ' and subsequently ' wavelength '. Many similar terms are in the process of being compounded in such

* See Bibliography, p. 319.

stages, which may account for the difference in convention between certain printers and authors.

The use of a hyphen in compound words such as adjective-nouns or noun combinations avoids ambiguity. There are many examples, mostly humorous, of the results of omitting the hyphen:

Wanted: a baby clothes finisher

The rule given in the *Compositors' Guide* states definitely: 'Where either a noun or an adjective, or an adjective and noun in combination, are used as a compound adjective a hyphen should be used '.

Special examples of the use of the hyphen in technical writing are:

(*a*) If two alternatives are given, both compound words, the hyphen is retained after the first term:

Short- or long-wave antennas . . .

(*b*) The hyphen is used to denote the extremes of a range of values:

Connect to a 220-240 volt supply

means a supply of which the voltage can vary between 220 and 240 volts. On the other hand, two fixed alternative values are denoted by a solidus (/):

Connect to a 220/240 volt supply

means either 220 or 240 volts, but no intermediate value.*

The solidus is also used in place of the hyphen in such expressions as signal/noise ratio, where it indicates division, and in cycles/sec (c/s), but the hyphen indicates multiplication rather than division, as in ft.-lb. *The solidus must not be used within abbreviations, as* m/m. See note on p. 91.

There is still considerable freedom in the choice of hyphened words, and some publications have a preferred list which their writers are expected to follow. Examples of preferred hyphenating, from the Institute of Physics list, are:

| after-effect | ground-level | water-bath |
| boiling-point | post-mortem† | wave-guide |

---

* These are I.E.E. recommendations, but to avoid ambiguity why not use the word ' or ' ?

† Used adjectivally, as also hydrogen-ion.

cathode-ray	screw-thread	horse-power
cotton-wool	short-circuit	gamma-rays
end-point	to-day	test-tube
freezing-point	to-morrow	filter-paper
glass-wool	watch-glass	lamp-black

A longer list will be found in the *Rules for Compositors*. Most prefixes, such as re-, anti-, post-, have a hyphen separating them from the succeeding word; other prefixes may be followed by a hyphen when there is a doubling of the vowel or consonant.*

The Dash

The dash is distinguished from the hyphen in printed matter by its length, but the distinction is not so clear in typescript. If a dash is required in typing it should be indicated by a space before and after the hyphen mark.

Although the dash is criticized by the stylists, it makes a convenient alternative to the comma or parentheses, and can be used for extra emphasis on occasion. Its significance is in the abruptness implied by its use, and for this reason it should not be used too often. In the sentence:

In practice this means that not one but many—as many as possible—observations must be made . . .

commas or parentheses could not be substituted for dashes without a loss of forcefulness.

Parentheses

These are called ' brackets ' in everyday speech, but the printer prefers to use the Greek term for ' round brackets ' and confines the word ' bracket ' to the ' square bracket ' : [ ].

Whether round or square, brackets usually enclose additional clauses in a sentence which, although helping to clarify the meaning, are not vital to the sense of the information conveyed. The clause within the brackets should be capable of being omitted without harm being done to the sentence.

Square brackets are, by convention, confined to comments,

---

* The American method of distinguishing the second vowel by a diaresis (Coöperate, reënter) is a useful alternative. The *O.E.D.* gives cooperate and coordinate without any marking.

71

missing words, or explanatory text supplied by the quoter of an abstract or quotation:

A famous Victorian mathematician [Lewis Carroll] immortalized their manner of operation for all children . . .

The use of brackets in mathematical expressions is discussed on p. 234.

Quotation Marks

The primary use of quotation marks, as their name implies, is to indicate the exact words uttered by an author from whom a quotation is being made. It is of great importance, therefore, that the text enclosed by the quotation marks is an exact transcript of the original. Many writers omit or modify the wording in a quotation and thus seriously offend the author of it by imputing a meaning different from that expressed in the correct version. Each separate quotation, although from the same passage, requires its own quotation marks, and words which are not part of the original should not be included between the marks. The question whether the punctuation mark precedes or follows the final quotation mark can safely be left to the printer.

At present there is no general agreement on the use of single or double quotation marks. The Oxford University Press in its *Rules for Compositors* recommends single quotation marks for the first quotation and double marks for quotations within a quotation. The Cambridge University Press, until recently, recommended the exact opposite.

The *U.S. Government Style Manual* recommends that all words given an unusual meaning should be in double quotation marks. The authors and printers of this book have used single quotation marks for ordinary words used in an unusual sense and double marks for jargon or unfamiliar technical terms:

The cell contains a " depolarizer ", or compound which has an affinity for nascent hydrogen.
The longer the path traversed by the beam, the greater the ' splash ' on arrival at the screen.

If an author has no strong views, the style of setting should be left to the printer, who will follow his established House Rules.

SOME FAULTS OF STYLE

While it is not possible to classify all the faults in writing which, singly or together, brand it as being in poor style, it is possible to list some of the more obvious defects in presentation which a careful writer can avoid. These can be related to the following headings :

(a) Bad or careless construction, making the sense of the writing difficult to follow
(b) Faults in grammatical construction
(c) Misuse of individual words

A carelessly constructed sentence or paragraph need not be ungrammatical : many of the examples previously quoted contain no grammatical errors but irritate the reader nevertheless. An unusual form of construction in a sentence may serve to bring out a point or vary a style which is becoming monotonous, but is permissible only if the reader is stimulated and not puzzled.

All forms of bad construction can be avoided by continual watchfulness. A better term, perhaps, is ' awareness '. Throughout the whole preparation of the manuscript the writer must be aware of what he is writing, aware of what he has written previously, and aware of the effect that his words are going to produce on the reader. It is this awareness that will prevent him from taking things for granted or from making slips which are apparent at once to the reader.

An effective phrase was coined by Robert Graves and Alan Hodge in the title of their book : *The Reader over your Shoulder*. A writer who can train himself to remember the reader over his shoulder will avoid such obvious flaws in style without much trouble.

Verbosity

A poor writer errs in using either too many words or too few. The tendency to use long-winded phrases in scientific papers is a habit acquired from reading papers by other poor writers and probably arises from a desire to impress the reader and to conceal the writer's uncertainty. A scientific paper may be long without being wordy, provided that the words are efficiently used to convey the information and not to wrap it up in a cloud of woolly padding. The technical author who writes:

There may be a protracted hiatus in providing potential at the consumers' terminals

instead of

> The supply may be cut off for some time

may be impressing the reader with the extent of his vocabulary but merely becomes tedious.*

The main encouragements to verbosity are the use of the passive instead of the active voice ('It is believed by the writer' instead of 'The writer believes'); the use of abstract instead of concrete nouns (nouns ending in 'ness', 'ment' and others),† and the use of woolly phrases. These three defects, singly or together, are found in nearly every piece of badly-written technical prose.

Examples of woolly phrases are given in most textbooks on the writing of good English (see Appendix, p. 318), and only a few need be quoted:

In the region of . . .	by no means inconsiderable . . .
With a view to . . .	to no small degree . . .

The *Lancet*‡ gives some examples found in medical writing:

Aetiological factor (cause)	In large measure . . . (largely)
A variety of . . . (many)	Experimental dog (dog)
Subsequent to . . . (after)	In a few instances (occasionally)

One author of a paper begins his summary:

Details are given of an experimental study made in view of reducing the pulse shape distortion to a minimum.

and another hopes that

it should be possible to obtain some measure of distortion cancellation.

which combines the woolly phrase with the abstract one.

It may happen that the writer who resolves to banish all such phrases from his work finds difficulty in using suitable alternatives and may find his style becoming too direct. Many of the

---

* Possibly the author of this actual phrase was meaning to be facetious? But verbal gambolling of this type is equally out of place in a scientific paper.
† But, of course, cement is a concrete noun.
‡ Supplement to the *Lancet*, 1937, Jan. 2.

introductory phrases which are considered woolly by the purists serve a useful purpose in making a smooth transition from one paragraph or section to another. The fault in using the woolly phrase lies not so much in the combination of the words as in using it to avoid precise statement.

The temptation to indulge in woolly writing occurs most often at the beginning and end of a piece of technical prose. The Introduction is one of the most difficult parts of a technical article, particularly if it is intended for a wide readership, and the writer tends to pad out the Introduction as being an easy way to start.

The following example illustrates the point. It occurred in an introduction to an article on light metal industries:

With the centenary celebration of the invention of the typewriter still many years hence, an analysis of its development and ubiquitous use would show that it has done for clerical work and business transactions what the printing press did for publishing—it combined clarity with ease and speed of function.

This advantage might, by the cynical, be considered aesthetic but the typewriter has advantages which would mollify even them. Its invention wrought the creation of a light industry which weighs heavily in the favour of those economies lucky enough to feature it. Those which have it, foster it, those which lack it, seek it.

Most modern business procedures either have typewriters as their basis or include them as an integral part. The typewriter industry, therefore, in this country is crescent, although subject to the availability of steel.

This example also illustrates the importance of awareness on the writer's part. If he had been conscious of the sound of the words he would hardly have allowed such a jingle as ' those which lack it, seek it '. Note also the use of the word ' crescent ' in its true, though seldom used, meaning. Is it superior to ' growing '?

Over-compression

At the other extreme is the fault of over-compression. By omitting such links as relative pronouns, conjunctions, and even nouns the writer becomes obscure in another sense. Correct grammatical constructions require a certain minimum of words and nothing is gained by reducing them below this minimum. Examples of over-compression frequently occur in instructions, as in:

The flask is filled with dilute acid, warmed and then filtered or in such simple statements as

The tensile strength of steel is greater than copper

The writer excuses himself by saying that the reader ' will know what is meant '—an assumption which may be true but which is certainly impertinent.

Over-compression leads to other forms of bad grammar which are cited later, and may even in part be responsible for the use of the adjectival noun.

Adjectival Nouns

The use of nouns as adjectives is a common practice in newspaper headlines, where economy of space compels the sub-editor to try to convey the maximum information in one or two lines. Thus we have such expressions as:

Italian Assassin Bomb Plot Disaster

and many others which can be noted in the press each day.

In technical writing, the adjectival noun is becoming popular, due, as Dr. J. R. Baker says,* to the influence of English-speaking German scientists on the literature. The Germanic sentence construction, as in ' *die einzigen, durch unmittelbare Beobachtung sicher zu ermittelnden Stellen* ' is paralleled by a writer who puts ' adenosine triphosphate activated actomyosin contraction '. There are probably two other influences which persuade a writer to adopt this style : the first is that by so doing he is giving the impression of terseness and accuracy and the second is a conscious or unconscious laziness which avoids using the extra words and prepositions of the correct grammatical construction.   As Dr. Baker remarks of the example quoted above : ' These are words put together without the slightest attempt at clarity or any consideration for the reader. The phrase is worse than merely illiterate : it is rude.'

On the other hand there are many noun-adjective constructions which are unavoidable because the alternative phrase would be clumsy or waste space unnecessarily, especially if the phrase is repeatedly used in the text. The term " curve relating anode current change with grid voltage " has been adequately replaced

* English Style in Scientific Papers, *Nature*, 1955, Nov. 5, p. 851.

by " anode-current grid-volts characteristic ", the hyphens making the relationship clear.

Ambiguity

Ambiguous words or phrases are those capable of more than one meaning, and it is a peculiarity of ambiguities that they are noticed by the reader although usually unnoticed by the writer. The reason for this is probably the usual one—that the writer is aware of what *he* means but does not trouble to enquire whether the statement can be read in another sense.

Ambiguities can arise through over-compression, as in the headline quoted on p. 76. The sub-editor who composed the headline ' Warships Sabotage Fear ' overlooked the use of ' sabotage ' as a verb as well as a noun. A similar ambiguity occurs in the possessive pronouns in the following:

A barrister described to-day a conversation he had with an airman before he was arrested and charged with the murder of his sister.

Some words capable of bearing two distinct meanings should not be introduced into the same portion of the text. Examples are the use of ' current ' as in ' current demand ' confused with the electric current, and ' case ' which may mean a packing case or the subject under discussion.

An interesting example of ambiguity in successive sentences is:

Zoologists could only visit the hot springs in E—— with the permission of the local khaliphat . . . since they are reserved for the exclusive use of women bathers. An attempt was made to bring back a number of specimens alive in a vacuum flask so that further investigations could be made.

Occasionally the reader is misled into mentally giving a wrong sound to a word:

Short lengths of lead wire are provided for external connexion

or

The sound is multiply reflected from the walls.

An unusual inversion in the order of words may make the reader hesitate before taking in the meaning:

. . . while changes in the art may make obsolete standards initially well chosen.

77

Anthropomorphism

During the past fifteen years a tendency has grown up among technical writers, particularly those who are simplifying explanations for instructional purposes, to endow various mechanisms and components with human attributes. Thus a car is spoken of as 'not liking a steep gradient' or an electronic device as 'looking at the input signal '.

In some cases this method of expression is a useful way of simplifying an explanation; in others it is not. There is always a temptation to adopt it to save words and it is a habit that can easily be acquired by a writer who cannot be bothered to select the more orthodox words of description. As an example of how a reader can be bewildered rather than helped by this method of explanation, the following occurred in an elementary article on electronic circuits :

> Q. How does a transformer make a loudspeaker look like a resistance ?
> A. The transformer does not ; a speaker, so far as the valve is concerned looks like a resistance anyway. A speaker is essentially a motor, in that electrical energy is supplied to it and mechanical energy is produced.

Misuse of Words

The misuse of words arises either from muddled thinking or actual ignorance of the meaning of the word. Some words have acquired an alternative (wrong) meaning through constant misuse, and the writer often has to decide whether he will follow the practice or try to keep the purity of the language.

As an example of words put down without any appreciation of their meaning, the following sentence from a textbook can be analysed :

There are two definitions of heat : specific and latent, and there are two common measurements of heat : Fahrenheit and Centigrade.

The words 'specific' and 'latent' are not definitions of heat, nor are Fahrenheit and Centigrade measurements of heat. They are not even measurements of temperature : they are the names applied to two methods of marking the scale of temperatures on a thermometer. Before attempting to explain, the writer must be sure of the words he is using.

Another example from a book :

Since the eye is the sense chiefly used in perception, the majority of instruments are visual.

Here the writer should have put ' organ ' for ' sense ', or altered the opening to read ' Since the visual sense is the one chiefly used in perception . . .' The second part of the sentence is over-compressed to the point of absurdity, and the word ' visual ' is misapplied. The writer meant to say ' the majority of instruments are made to give a visual indication '.

A list of commonly misused words is given by Sir Ernest Gowers* and others, and the following are typical examples :

Blue-print does not mean a plan
Describe should not be used for ' explain ' or ' designate '
Following often misused for ' after '
Literally should only be used sparingly and in its correct sense
Practically does not mean ' almost '
Quantity should not be confused with ' number '
Similar is not the same as ' same '

Other words whose meaning has become distorted are :

Alibi for ' excuse '. It is doubtful whether this word will ever recover its true meaning.
Infer for ' imply '. This error is found in all forms of writing, and the same remark applies.
Compare for ' contrast ' (verb)
Fraction for ' part '.

Other examples will be found under ' Clichés ' (p. 81).

In a competition held by the *Spectator*† for examples of the most irritating misuses of English words and phrases, the following were quoted :

aggravate *for* annoy   less *for* fewer
disinterested *for* uninterested   mutual *for* common
fruition *for* completion   ' quite unique '
infer *for* imply   ' three alternatives '
literally (giving wrong emphasis)

The word " Data "

This word is given a special section to itself, since it occurs so frequently in technical writing and is so frequently followed by the

* *Plain Words*, H.M.S.O., London.   † Nov. 16, 1956.

singular verb. It is the plural form of " datum ", (Lat.) meaning ' the thing given ', and thus signifies the collection of facts from which the writer is drawing conclusions. As he seldom draws conclusions from a single fact, the word is more often used in the plural and requires the plural verb.

For some reason there is an aversion to using the plural construction, and the phrase ' This data provides ' is more frequently seen than ' These data provide . . .' If the writer finds difficulty in constructing a phrase which is grammatical and which does not at the same time look clumsy, he can avoid it by using such alternatives as ' From the data . . .' or ' The data obtained gave . . .' (in which the singular and plural forms of the verb are the same). The following wrongly-worded phrase :

The data obtained from the sample batch is to be published in the next month's report. It should be of use to those intending to instal a plant of this type

can be simply and grammatically corrected by altering to :

The data obtained from the sample batch will be published in next month's report and should be of use . . .

Jargon

The *O.E.D.* definition of this word as ' applied contemptuously to the . . . terminology of a science or art ' should be a warning against using unfamiliar scientific terms in writing for semi-technical or lay readers. More specifically, a word is jargon when it is only understood by a narrow circle of readers who are specialists in a subject, and when it is used to impress the uninitiated. Common examples of jargon are found in the literature of amateur radio transmitting enthusiasts, in musicians, followers of sport, artists, and others who require a vocabulary of their own. As an example of jargon which is only intelligible to the initiated there is the following :

Coming, as they do, at a time when Webern had foregone triadic functionality, but prior to the formation of twelve-tone operationability, these three pieces are the lowest possible approximation to truly *ad hoc* musical composition. It is the absence of a pre-defined functional unit that gives rise logically to the features that are mistakenly called idiosyncratic : extreme brevity, non-repetition, and maximum differentiation of individual tone elements, giving rise to an unprecedented exploitation of the sonic resources of the medium.

Other examples of jargon may be found in books on psychology.

Clichés

A word or phrase which is used repeatedly without regard for its true significance soon becomes a cliché (Fr. : a stereotype block from which many impressions are made), or a stereotyped word. Although most clichés occur in the so-called journalistic writing, there is a temptation to use them in technical writing, particularly as certain words tend to become fashionable. Many clichés have no other fault than that they are used too often : ' in the case of ', ' in the foreseeable future ', and many other phrases become wearisome through repetition.

Once a word has become fashionable, there is a tendency to use it regardless of whether it is apposite or not. Examples are :

. . . new methods of using chlorine have opened new *fields* for the removal of tastes (in water)

and the almost universal use of the word ' tool ' for any process or device which assists in research or thinking :

X-ray crystallography, the chief *tool* of structural analysis, is curiously amorphous.

How can a tool be amorphous ?

Other words such as ' bottleneck ',* ' unit ', ' prototype ' will, it is hoped, fall into disuse through over-use.

Grammatical Faults

A technical writer is expected to be familiar with the rules of syntax and grammatical construction, and no attempt is made in this section to instruct him in English composition. Nevertheless, as many authors of textbooks on English have pointed out, there are a few slips in grammar which recur more often than others, even with experienced writers, and these are set down so that the less experienced may guard against them.

---

* The unknown writer who first used the phrase ' the biggest bottleneck in the production ' deserves to be remembered.

Misuse of Participial or Gerund Phrases

Both the participle and the gerund of the verb end in ' ing ', and are the forms of the verb which are used as nouns, adjectives or adverbs. The participle itself does not constitute a verb, and it is therefore ungrammatical to write ' The unit fitting into a standard 19″ rack ', as a complete sentence.

A participle must always have a proper ' subject of reference '. A sentence like the following is incorrect because the word to which the participle refers grammatically is not that with which it is connected in sense : ' Born in 1890, a part of his education was received at College '.*

These unrelated participles are frequently found in descriptions of processes:

After boiling, the flask was stirred carefully . . .

Requiring to find the heat produced in the conductor, the equation is modified to . . .

Wrong Relatives

The pronoun ' it ' and the relative pronouns ' this ', ' these ' are often made to do duty for a longer phrase which would make the meaning clearer and also make the sentence more grammatical.

The precipitate was washed for five minutes and then treated with a dilute solution of caustic soda.   This gave a similar result to the previous specimens.

The efficiency of such a machine increases as the difference in temperature between the hot and cold body.   This obeys the second law of thermodynamics.

The magnesium volatilizes and absorbs the last traces of gas.   In this way it is as near a perfect vacuum as possible.

The Split Infinitive

In spite of frequent statements some confusion still exists in the minds of some writers on what exactly constitutes a split infinitive. The infinitive form of a verb is split when an adverb is interposed between the word ' to ' and the verb, as in ' to quickly run '. It is not intended here to discuss the demerits or even the origin of

* C. T. Onions, *An Advanced English Syntax*, Kegan Paul, Trench & Co., 1932, p. 133.

this so-called ungrammatical construction, but it is generally accepted that in good writing the split infinitive should be avoided *except* where the sense of the words or the smooth reading of the passage makes it preferable to split. The writer who rigidly follows the rule that an infinitive should not be split often betrays himself by a clumsy arrangement of words which will produce a worse effect on the reader than if the infinitive had been split.

The practice can be summed up in Bernard Shaw's words: ' Every good craftsman splits his infinitive when the sense demands it '. See below.

Pseudo-split Infinitive

Many inexperienced writers try to avoid a split infinitive which is not actually present. There is no objection to interposing the adverb between ' to be ', or ' to have ' and the rest of the verb form, as in '. . . to be easily converted . . .' or '. . . to have steadily increased . . .', and if the order of the words is changed into '. . . easily to be converted . . .' the smooth flow of words is interrupted to no purpose. This method of avoiding a non-existent split infinitive is frequently seen in newspapers.

Repetition

There is no necessity to consciously avoid * using the same word several times in a given passage: in fact it is difficult to avoid repetition with technical words having a precise meaning and no synonym. With non-technical words, repetition is a useful means of emphasizing a key word or even providing a sense of drama :—

All his tricks had now been played out, and had failed, or their temporary success had contributed too little to make that last necessary difference. He had tried the glory of militarism, and failed. He had tried ' true socialism ' and failed. He had tried the New Order, and failed . . .
As the days darkened, he had tried (as Spear said he should have tried) the appeal of blood, sweat and tears . . . and that had failed too.

(*The Last Days of Hitler*, H. R. Trevor-Roper)
Macmillan & Co., London

It is far more important to avoid careless repetition of words or phrases because they happen to come easily to the pen. This does

* Note that the split infinitive is better than ' consciously to avoid ' or ' to avoid consciously '.

not mean that the writer should go out of his way to find alternatives, as with the reporter who wrote an account of a football match without once using the word ' ball '. It is possible to recast a sentence so that the repeated words are not used, and this implies exercising the sense of ' awareness ' mentioned previously.

A writer who was aware of the effect on his reader produced by the following sentence would rewrite it in the final draft:

Symmetrical Varistors have application to protective purposes such as lightning protection, such as thyrite, the trade name of one form, and to acoustic shock prevention, such as in parallel with a telephone receiver to cut down key clicks.

Allied with repetition of words is the repetition of particular forms of construction which appeal to the writer's sense of style. These are effective when used occasionally, but will become wearisome if introduced into every paragraph. Once a writer becomes conscious of his habit and is put on guard the fault is easily overcome.

PRESENTATION

The Approach to the Reader

The method of approach to the reader, or the form in which the information is conveyed, is governed by the relationship between writer and reader and the level of the discussion.

In writing a factual report or account of experimental work, it is generally accepted that the impersonal style is most suitable and the past or present tense of the verbs is used according to the content of the information. For example, the findings of a research team might be set down in the form:

Cortical potentials have been examined in 17 patients with either postoperative or parathyroid insufficiency. The same EEG pattern has been observed in all patients: little alpha rhythm, an increase in the amount of fast activity . . .

In many cases where treatment has relieved the symptoms and the EEG has, by the authors' standards, become normal, overbreathing elicited the original hypoparathyroid picture.

A statement of facts, or instruction to an operator, is usually written in the present tense, as:

Electrostatic induction is the commonest form of interference. With an unbalanced amplifier, that is, when discrimination is poor, the only cure is to surround the subject with an earthed Faraday screen. . . . The intensity of the interference usually diminishes as the square of the distance from the source.

The reader may be referred to in the third person, as in :

When the engineer has collected all the items which will be listed in the specification he will have the problem of arranging them in some definite order. He may notice that he is listing a number of parts with similar functions. . . .

The text of this book is written for the greater part in impersonal style, with occasional changes to the imperative style.

Imperative or Conditional Style

This is the method of writing well adapted to instructional hand-books or laboratory procedure, and, as the name implies, is in the form of directions :

(a) Switch on the apparatus and allow ten minutes for warming up.
(b) Clean, and, if necessary, re-chloride the electrodes.
(c) Refill the saline bottle, and check other solutions.

The conditional mood is a less direct approach to the reader, and may at times soften the harder imperative :

The leads from the amplifier may be attached to the electrodes by crocodile clips (alligator clamps), or they may be soldered to the tip of the electrode. The leads should be light and flexible in order that they may not disturb the electrodes when swinging about.

Note : The careful writer will take care to give reasons for any instruction, whether direct or permissive. Very few obey an instruction willingly without understanding the reason for it, and the explanation may also help the reader to understand the exact degree of importance to attach to specific directions.

The Personal Approach

It is still considered bad writing, if not presumptuous, to use the first person singular, and its use may jar on the reader as much as the reiteration of ' I ' offends his ears in conversation. On the other hand, some literary advisers permit the use of ' I ' whenever desired by the writer, particularly if he is describing personal experience. If the writer is a recognized authority on his subject he may safely use ' I ' knowing that his reputation will protect him from charges of arrogance. On the whole, it is safer to err on the side of modesty.

When I had translated what I considered to be Faraday's ideas into mathematical form, I found that in general the results of the two methods coincided, so that the same phenomena were accounted for and the same laws of action deduced by both methods . . .

(W. Clerk Maxwell)

A different problem is presented by the use of the plural pronoun ' we '. Its use is clearly sanctioned on three occasions:

(a) The Royal ' we ', which the writer is unlikely to be in a position to use.

(b) The editorial ' we ', which has become the attribute of periodical, newspaper and other editors. It is often extended to the staff of the periodical, especially if they are authorized to express the views of the proprietor or editor.

(c) The true plural pronoun relating to two or more authors writing in collaboration.

The pronoun is more often used in a confidential manner to imply close co-operation between the author and the reader: ' we ' are studying this subject together—let us see what happens.

The use of ' we ' in this sense may be acceptable, especially in textbooks, but there is danger of its use being carried to absurdity, as in:

Let us take a tin and fill it with water, and then if we bore a hole in the side near the bottom, we shall see the water come out in a curved jet.

Occasionally the writer is tempted to use the editorial ' we ' to denote himself: a practice which has little to commend it.* The danger in adopting this method of writing is that the writer and reader may eventually become confused as to who is meant, as in the following extracts from an introduction:

The personnel of a modern instrument factory has many uses during wartime. We have shown beyond doubt that we are capable of making instruments by mass production, and one has only to walk round a modern factory to be convinced. We were recently shown round a factory where 85% of the staff were female . . .

* A delightful example of the absurd use of ' we ' by an author is in Cobbett's *Cottage Economy* (1823): ' We rose comparatively well in the morning, yet were restless, our stomach was acid, visage pale, and eyes bloodshot '.

Here the author intends the first ' we ' to denote the people of Britain, but the second ' we ' relates to himself in his editorial capacity, and this change of viewpoint is maintained in the concluding paragraph of the same preface which begins:

We would like to acknowledge our thanks to . . .

Author and Writer

Confusion often arises in the reader's mind when the author of an article refers in his text to the writings of another author. If, after naming him, he refers to him as ' the author ', the reader may be in doubt as to which is the author in question.

It is usually possible to avoid ambiguity by referring to oneself as ' the writer ', using the word ' author ' to refer only to the work of another.

Needless to say, this comment cannot apply to this book, where the authors are speaking to writers who are also readers. If the authors called themselves the writers and referred to their readers as writers, parts of the book would be unintelligible.

A dangerous practice is to use ' we ' when the writer is associated by implication with a company or scientific society, as the reader may infer that statements are made with the authority of the body concerned. It is safer to add a disclaimer at the end of the text: ' The opinions given are those of the writer. . . .'

Choice of Words

It is important to remember that the choice of words used in a given text must be governed by the vocabulary of the reader for whom it is written. The selection of suitable words becomes progressively more difficult as the level of intelligence decreases, particularly in technical prose, and it is probable that the selection is given so little consideration by writers of handbooks that many words are imperfectly understood by the reader although they may be considered to be ' in common use '.

The work of Vernon* gives some surprising results: nearly half the population of Britain cannot give the meaning of words such as ' automatically ', ' equivalent ', ' expansion ', or ' analysis ' some of which will be used in a handbook for laymen. If no alternative can be found for a technical term, it is preferable to add an

* The Intelligibility of Broadcast Talks, P. E. Vernon, *B.B.C. Quarterly*, 1950-1, 5, 4, 206.

explanatory sketch rather than to assume that the meaning will be clear from the context. See also Chapter 1, p. 21.

Where technical terms are unavoidable in the text of a book intended for a wide range of readership it is helpful to add a glossary at the end. The knowledgeable will be able to do without it, and the ignorant will appreciate it.

Spelling

The spelling of certain technical (and even non-technical) words is often the cause of controversy when reference to a standard dictionary should speedily settle the argument. As an example, the word ' connexion ' is given with this preferred spelling in the *Oxford Dictionary*,* but it has been held that the ' x ' instead of the ' ct ' is of American origin. Similarly the word ' disk ' is better spelt with a ' k ' (*O.E.D.*), and this form of spelling is not American but relates to the original Greek.

Nevertheless, it is understood that long custom is hard to alter, and those writers who are habituated to the spellings ' connection ' and ' disc ' may find it hard to change. When the manuscript is set in type the printer may superimpose the custom of his ' house rules ' on the writer's preference and it is not always desirable to insist on one style of spelling without adequate authority.

The following list gives acceptable alternative spellings for some words. The first column gives the preferred spelling, but the ruling is not rigid. The important point is to be consistent and preserve the same spelling throughout, not only in the individual manuscript but in all technical literature issuing from the same source. This convention can be conveniently noted in the list of conventions mentioned in Chapter 2 (p. 58).

List of Accepted Spellings

Preferred	Alternative	Preferred	Alternative
centred	centered (Am.)	dispatch	despatch
connexion	connection	focused	focussed (2)
cipher	cypher (1)	grey	gray (Am.)
deflexion	deflection	inflexion	inflection
disk	disc	inquiry	enquiry

* *The Shorter Oxford English Dictionary* says : L(atin) *connexionem* . . . the etymological spelling *connexion* is most used in England!

88

Preferred	Alternative	Preferred	Alternative
install	instal (3)	paralleling	parallelling
manila	manilla	show	shew (4)
net	nett	siphon	syphon

Notes :

Am. denotes the spelling usually found in America.

1. The word 'cypher' is occasionally used for the cryptographic message, and 'cipher' for 0.
2. Focussed is occasionally used for optical focussing, and focused for electron focusing.
3. Install is sometimes attributed to American spelling.
4. Shew is usually considered old-fashioned, but see G. B. Shaw's writings.

'ize' or 'ise'

There is a tendency in England to soften the sound and appearance of words ending in 'ize' by using the 'ise' termination, in spite of the etymology and dictionary guidance. Many writers have no definite views and are content to leave the spelling to the printer's discretion. The following list gives some words generally accepted as ending in 'ise'.*

advertise	enterprise	premise
advise	excise	reprise
apprise (1)	exercise	revise
comprise	improvise	supervise
compromise	incise	surmise
demise	merchandise	surprise
devise (2)	mortise (3)	televise

The following are usually spelt with 'ize' :

carbonize	ionize	oxidize
centralize	localize	polarize
criticize	magnetize	realize
economize	minimize	recognize
equalize	neutralize	sensitize
galvanize	normalize	standardize

but, as said above, many of these words will be found with 'ise' terminations.

Notes :

1. Apprize (to value) is more often spelt *appraise*.
2. This is the spelling of the verb in Gt. Britain.
3. The noun is usually spelt *mortice* in Gt. Britain.

* An odd instance of differentiation in spelling is the word 'fuse', which is spelt 'fuze' when referring to the military use as a slow-burning igniter.

ABBREVIATIONS

In technical writing it is not good style to use abbreviations for words, although it is permissible to refer to organizations and well-known scientific terms by initials.

When used in a sentence, the names of quantities should be written in full, e.g. 'about ten amperes' instead of 'about 10 amps.', but it is allowable to write 'a 10-h.p. motor', as the word 'horse-power' is seldom spelt in full, and the abbreviation is universally recognized.

The contraction of a word into its familiar form is also unpermissible, even though the colloquial form is accepted as part of everyday speech: for example one should not write 'photo' in a text. Many words are in the transition stage from colloquial to accepted usage, e.g. 'test gear'. The more dignified form, e.g. 'test equipment', should be used in writing for technical publications of a high standard.

As said above, the name of a unit or quantity should be written in full in the text, and the abbreviation used when it is expressed in calculations or formulae. A list of the principal units and their accepted abbreviations follows.

Note that the following units are not abbreviated:

Gauss   Gilbert   Newton   Oersted   Maxwell

The abbreviations for use in technical literature are laid down by British Standard 1991 : 1954. The general notes relating to the writing of symbols and abbreviations can be summarized as follows:

(a) Periods (full stops) are omitted in all single-word units and quantities, except where there is risk of ambiguity (e.g. 'in.' for inch, not 'in'). Care must be taken to distinguish between words and units, e.g. min for minute but min. for minimum.

(b) Abbreviations are the same for both singular and plural.

(c) Periods are used with abbreviations representing more than one word: 'e.m.f.' (plural: e.m.f.s).

(d) The use of capital letters for abbreviations is discouraged, *except* in abbreviations of proper names (G.P.O.) and where it has become standard practice to use them (C.G.S.).

(e) Italic type is used for lower case symbols only, except that in electrical quantities italics are used for both capital and lower case letters.

90

(*f*) A solidus (/) shall be used to indicate 'per', except in well-established abbreviations such as 'r.p.m.', 'm.p.h.'
The period is omitted before the solidus.
A hyphen must never be used as a substitute for a solidus.

Note : The solidus should *never* be used as a break after a prefix :
'm/sec' cannot be used as an abbreviation for milli-seconds, nor is m/c correct for 'megacycles'.

A useful *Glossary of Abbreviations*, giving the names of most of the scientific and commercial organizations (particularly in the telecommunications world) has been compiled by S. T. Cope, Librarian of the Marconi Company. Copies are obtainable from the Research Laboratories of the company at Great Baddow, Essex. Over 25,000 abbreviations of all types are found in the *Complete Dictionary of Abbreviations* by R. J. Schwartz (New York, T. Y. Crowell ; London, Geo. G. Harrap).

List of Common Abbreviations

This list is compiled from recommendations by the British Standards Institution and the senior scientific bodies in Gt. Britain. The American standards agree closely with these recommendations. Numbers in brackets against an abbreviation refer to the notes overleaf. The same abbreviation applies to both singular and plural.

Angstrom unit	Å (1)	inch	in. (3)
calorie	cal	litre	l (4)
candle-power	c.p.	lumen	lm
cubic centimetre	cm³ or c.c.	metre	m
cubic metre	m³ or cu.m	micron	μ
cycles per second	c/s (2)	million	M (5)
decibel	dB	minute	min
diameter	dia.	potential difference	p.d.
electromotive force	e.m.f.	pound	lb
electron volt	eV	power factor	p.f.
feet per second	f.p.s. or ft/sec	radian	rad
		radius	rad.
foot	ft	root mean square	r.m.s.
foot-candle	f.c.	second	s or sec
grain	gr	square metre	m² or sq.m (6)
gram(mc)	g	ultra-violet	u.v.
horse-power	h.p.	volt-ampere	VA
hour	h		

Notes :

The words 'alternating current' are abbreviated to a.c. when used adjectivally, but are otherwise spelt in full. The same rule applies to 'd.c.'. The words 'a.c. (d.c.) voltage' are not permissible.

(1) The initials A.U. are permitted for this unit if the printer has no Å available.

(2) The term 'cycle' by itself is deprecated. The continental term 'hertz' for cycle per second is often found.

(3) Note that with abbreviations which may be confused with words the period is retained after the abbreviation.

(4) This abbreviation should be written in longhand in the typescript if there is any risk of confusion with 1.

(5) In conjunction with the £ sign, the M is placed after: £M.

(6) These alternatives apply to all units of length. See also 'cubic metre'.

List of Common Electrical Symbols

electromotive force	E	conductance	G
potential difference	V	admittance	Y
current	I	power	P (2)
charge (quantity)	Q (1)	angular frequency	ω
inductance	L	90° operator	j
capacitance	C	phase difference	ϕ
resistance	R	dielectric loss angle	δ
reactance	X	permittivity	κ
impedance	Z	permeability	μ

Notes :

(1) In addition to denoting quantity, the letter Q is used for apparent power and for the circuit magnification factor (Q-factor).

(2) The former symbol for power (W) is used for energy.

The operator j is set in roman type and not italic. The 120° operator is sometimes λ and (I.E.E. recommendation) **a**.

For electrical quantities and symbols, see also p. 146.

A list of letter symbols and mathematical signs adopted by the American Institute of Radio Engineers appears in *Proc. I.R.E.* 1957, **45,** 8, 1140. This agrees closely with British practice.

Latin Abbreviations

Where a reference is to be repeated for the reader's benefit, or where the source of information is frequently referred to by the writer, it is sometimes customary to use Latin abbreviations in place of writing the reference again in full. These abbreviations are seldom used accurately unless their meaning is fully understood, and are therefore set down in detail with suggestions for their proper application :

op. cit. (opere citato) ' in the work cited '
loc. cit. (loco citato) ' in the place cited '

Both these terms are used to save repetition of the full title and particulars of an author's work which has already been mentioned earlier in the text. They are convenient *if used close to the previous full reference,* but the reader should not have to search back through many pages to find the actual source of the reference ; it is better to repeat the full wording if the quotations from it are widely separated.

ibid. (ibidem) ' the same place '
id. (idem) ' the same '

These have substantially the same meaning as ' *op. cit.*', and should only be used when a number of references to one source are given on the same page of the text. *Idem* is preferably written in full and not contracted to *id.*

Unless the position and number of references warrant the use of these abbreviations, they are better left out.

Other abbreviations which are found in certain writings are :

vide supra ' see above ', sometimes contracted to ' *vide* ' or ' *v* '
vide infra ' see below ', sometimes contracted to ' *vide inf.*' or ' *v. inf.*'
et seq. ' and the following ', sometimes written ' *sqq* '

but they can offer no advantage over the use of the plain English equivalent.

Certain contractions are commonly and usefully used : there can be no objection to *i.e. (id est)* = that is, and *e.g. (exempli gratia)* = by way of example, but the writer should be careful to distinguish their meanings and not write one for the other, as is frequently done.*

The common but vague abbreviation ' etc.' should not be found often in accurate writing ; it gives no information and is a cover for lack of precision.

References

In preparing a scientific paper the writer usually needs to provide a list of references to other papers or books on the subject. This

---

* The *Rules for Compositors* recommends that the Latin abbreviations be set in roman type (appropriately), but they are more usually found in italic type.

list should be prepared with the sole object of helping the reader, and for this reason it should be a select list and not one designed to impress him with its length.

The sophisticated reader of scientific papers will know that it is possible to obtain ready-made bibliographies on a particular subject and may suspect the writer of adding a long list of references which he has not himself checked.

There is sometimes a tendency to make the references take the place of a preliminary explanation, or even to save the writer trouble in putting down other arguments. The editor of *Electronic and Radio Engineer*, in speaking of improper use of references, says :*

> They [authors] use them so that the reader is forced to read earlier papers before he can understand what they write. Sometimes the whole paper rests on the assumption that the reader is familiar with the previous one ; sometimes an essential step in the argument is passed over by a reference.
> We regard this as laziness on the part of the writer. It is his job to write so that he can be understood without outside reference by the kind of people for whom he is writing.
> When a reference is used to avoid including information on a paper which should be there, there are two kinds which are especially useless. One is to the ' unpublished report ' ; the other is to an obscure conference, the Proceedings of which are exceedingly hard to come by !

The references, therefore, should be chosen with the following aims :

1. To indicate the source from which the writer's statements, critical or otherwise, are derived and to give proper acknowledgement to another's work.
2. To provide a source of additional information on sections of the subject which have been treated in a summarized form.
3. To encourage the reader to go further into those parts of the subject which may be of particular use to him.

References given under one or other of these conditions are a valuable adjunct to the text, and to make them of maximum use to the reader they should be arranged according to one or other of the following conventions :

1. The source of a quotation used in the text may be conveniently shown by a footnote and an asterisk if there are not too many.

* *Electronic and Radio Engineer*, 1957, **34**, 10, p. 357.

The use of a succession of printers' marks *†‡ . . . is deprecated, but see overleaf.

2. A collection of references bearing on the contents of one chapter or section may be grouped at the end with identifying symbols.

3. A selected collection of references, some of which may refer to the text matter and some which may be added for 'further reading' can be grouped under a heading such as 'Bibliography', 'Reference List'.

Arrangement of References

There are two methods of setting down the essential information in a reference, both of which are in common use; they differ only in the order of arrangement of the items.

The first gives the items in the following order:

Title of Paper Author's Name and Initials Journal Year Volume Page (1st and last)

The second, which is gaining in popularity, gives the name of the author first:

Author Initials Title of Paper Journal Year Volume Page(s)

Examples:
1. A Simple Electronic Switch A. W. Russell *Electronic Engineering* 1942 Vol. 15 pp. 284–285
2. Russell, A. W. A Simple Electronic Switch *Electronic Engineering* 1942 Vol. 15 pp. 284–285

When referring to a book, the arrangement is as shown in the following example:

Abramson, A. *Electronic Motion Pictures* (Berkeley, Cal., Univ. of California Press, 1956) p. 78.

and the number of the edition, if not the first, is added after the title of the book.

References to a patent should quote the patentee, country of origin, patent number and date of final or other application,

Example:
Baird, J. L. Br. Pat. 546,740; 6 Oct. 1942.
Besant, G. U.S. Pat. 1,768,888 filed Mar. 23, 1955.

Certain shortened forms of quotation are acceptable: for example, the words 'vol.' and 'Part' can be omitted, and the first page only

95

need be given instead of the span of the pages. These shortened forms are more convenient when the text matter is set in type, as the printer can make use of various forms of type face to indicate the volume and even the author's name. For example:

RUSSELL, A. W.   A Simple Electronic Switch *Electronic Engg.* 1942 **15** 284

Note that the volume number is always set in heavy type and the title of the periodical in italics. If the text is typewritten, these distinguishing features are not available and the alternative is to underline the title of the periodical and use the words ' vol ' and ' p '. It is not desirable to underline the volume number in typescript that is intended for setting in type, or the compositor will be confused.

Marking References

As said earlier, the use of printers' marks to indicate references should be confined to a limited number set at the foot of a page or column. The marks are also permissible if there is a risk of reference numbers confusing the reader, as in mathematical expressions or numbered equations (see Footnotes, p. 102).

British Standard 1629 : 1950 gives the accepted methods of setting out references in full and covers all forms of reference. American practice conforms closely to the British.

The printers' marks, when used, are arranged in a definite order which should be followed carefully by the author to avoid mistakes in the proof reading. This order is : * † ‡ § ∥ ¶ ** . . .

A more common method of marking the reference is by using small figures in the text, sometimes enclosed in brackets (35) but more usually set above the line, e.g.[2] The position of the reference mark should preferably be chosen so that it does not distract the reader—at the end of the sentence, rather than in the middle of the phrase. The same commonsense rule applies to footnote marks, but it is not always followed.

The reference numbers should run consecutively throughout the paper or article, but in books it is sometimes convenient to renumber the references with each chapter. This system leads to confusion if there is any cross-reference between chapters, and a method including the chapter number (e.g. [3.2]) might be adopted. Holmstrom renumbers his references afresh on each page of the book and quotes the page number against the reference number in the compilation at the end of the book.*

Another method of citing references, which is found in medical and biological texts is that known as the Harvard or Royal Society method. This quotes the name of the author in the text, followed by the year of publication of the paper quoted : Jones (1945). When the name of the author is not worked into the sentence it is added at the end of the appropriate statement :

. . . but this has since been shown to exist (Smith, 1935)

If the author quoted has published several papers in the same year, they are distinguished by the letters a, b, c . . .

At the end of the paper or chapter all the references are listed in *alphabetical order of authors' names*, with the papers of each author arranged in chronological order; the suffix letters then distinguish the particular paper referred to.

It is difficult to see the advantage which this method of arranging references has over the more direct linking of the number and the corresponding reference in the list. In this, as always, the convenience of the reader is the prime consideration.

Titles of Periodicals

The following rules have been formulated by a British Standards Committee for adoption :

1. Titles consisting of one non-compound word are written in full.
2. The abridged form of the title should retain all words other than articles, prepositions, and conjunctions.
3. The normal method of abbreviation is by omitting the last letters of the word (at least two), and adding a period.
4. Nouns are spelt with a capital letter and adjectives with a small letter, except for geographical or proper names.†
5. Plurals are indicated only where necessary.
6. Compound words are abbreviated in each part, the parts being separated by a hyphen.
7. When the title begins with the name of a person, the name is retained in full.

* *Facts, Files and Action*, Pt. II (London, Chapman & Hall, 1957). Note on p. xiii.

† In the authors' opinion, this ruling should not apply literally to publications of a scientific body with recognized initials, such as the Institution of Mechanical Engineers. The *Proceedings* of this Institution might be referred to as *Proc.I.m.E.* under this ruling instead of the more familiar and logical *Proc.I.M.E.*

G   97

These rules are given in summary form only, and for full information B.S. 1629 : 1954 should be consulted. A fairly complete list of abbreviated titles is given regularly in *Science Abstracts*, and, of course, in the *World List of Scientific Periodicals*.

The general rule for abbreviating is : Never shorten a word beyond the point at which it can be identified with certainty.

Common Abbreviations for Titles of Periodicals

Akust. Z.	Akustiche Zeitschrift Leipzig
Amer. J. Phys.	American Journal of Physics N.Y.
Amer. J. Sci.	American Journal of Science N.H., Conn.
Ann. Phys. Lpz.	Annalen der Physik Leipzig
Arch. Elektrotechn.	Archiv für Elektrotechnik Berlin
Arch. techn. Messen	Archiv für technisches Messen Munich
A.W.A. Tech. Rev.	Amalgamated Wireless (Australasia) Technical Review
Bell Lab. Rec.	Bell Laboratories Record N.Y.
Bell Syst. Tech. J.	Bell System Technical Journal N.Y.
Brit. J. Radiol.	British Journal of Radiology London
BTH Activ.	BTH (British Thomson Houston) Activities Rugby
Bull. Ass. Suisse Elect.	Bulletin de l'Association Suisse des Electriciens Zurich
Bull. U.S. Bur. Min.	Bulletin of the Bureau of Mines Washington
Canad. J. Res.	Canadian Journal of Research Ottawa
Chem. and Ind.	Chemistry and Industry London
Chem. Ztg.	Chemiker Zeitung Köthen
Circ. U.S. Bur. Stand.	Circular of the U.S. Bureau of Standards
Elect. Comm.	Electrical Communication N.Y. and London
Elect. Engg.	Electrical Engineering N.Y.
Elect. Rev.	Electrical Review London
Electronic Engg.	Electronic Engineering London
Engl. Elec. J.	English Electric Journal Stafford, Eng.
ENT	Elektrische Nachrichten-Technik Berlin
ETZ	Elektrotechnische Zeitschrift Berlin
E u M	Electrotechnik und Maschinenbau Vienna
Found. Tr. J.	Foundry Trade Journal London
G.E.C.J.	G.E.C. (General Electric Co.) Journal London
Gen. Elec. Rev.	General Electric Review N.Y. and London
Helv. Phys. Acta	Helvetica Physica Acta Basle
Hochfr. u Elektroakust.	Hochfrequenztechnik und elektroakustik Leipzig
Industr. Chem.	Industrial Chemist London

Iron Coal Tr. Rev.	Iron and Coal Trades Review London
Izv. Elektroprom. Slab. Toka	Izvestia Elektropromnishlennosti Slabogho Toka Moscow
J. Acoust. Soc. Am.	Journal of the Acoustical Society of America N.Y.
J. Appl. Phys.	Journal of Applied Physics N.Y.
J. Chem. Soc.	Journal of the Chemical Society London
J. Inst. Met.	Journal of the Institute of Metals London
J. Inst. Civ. Engrs.	Journal of the Institution of Civil Engineers London
J. Inst. Elec. Engrs.	Journal of the Institution of Electrical Engineers London
J. Jr. Instn. Engrs.	Journal of the Junior Institution of Engineers London
J. Opt. Soc. Am.	Journal of the Optical Society of America N.Y.
J. Res. Nat. Bur. Stand., Wash.	Journal of the National Bureau of Standards Washington
J. Sci. Instrum.	Journal of Scientific Instruments London
J. Televis. Soc.	Journal of the Television Society
J. Wash. Acad. Sci.	Journal of the Washington Academy of Sciences Washington
Light and Ltg.	Light and Lighting London
Mech. Engng.	Mechanical Engineering N.Y.
Met. Z.	Meteorologische Zeitschrift Braunschweig
Metro-Vick Gaz.	Metropolitan-Vickers Gazette Manchester
Mod. Plast.	Modern Plastics N.Y.
Mot. Ship	Motor Ship London
Oil Col. Tr. J.	Oil and Colour Trades Journal London
Phil. Mag.	The Philosophical Magazine and Journal of Science London
Photogr. J.	Photographic Journal London
Phys. Rev.	The Physical Review N.Y.
Phys. Z.	Physikalische Zeitschrift Leipzig
P.O. Elec. Engrs. J. (P.O.E.E.J.)	The Post Office Electrical Engineers Journal London
Proc. Amer. Phil. Soc.	Proceedings of the American Philosophical Society Philadelphia
Proc. Inst. Rad. Engrs. N.Y. (Proc. I.R.E.)	Proceedings of the Institute of Radio Engineers N.Y.
Proc. Phys. Soc.	Proceedings of the Physical Society London
Proc. Roy. Soc.	Proceedings of the Royal Society London
Quart. J. Roy. Met. Soc.	Quarterly Journal of the Royal Meteorological Society London
Rev. Sci. Instrum.	Review of Scientific Instruments N. Y.
Rly. Elec. Engr.	Railway Electrical Engineer N.Y.
Schweiz. Bautzg.	Schweitzerische Bauzeitung Zürich.

Strowger J.	Strowger Journal Liverpool
Tekn. Tidskr.	Teknisk Tidskrift Stockholm
TFT	Telegraphen- Fernsprech- Funk- und Fernsehtechnik Berlin
Trans. Illum. Engng Soc.	Transactions of the Illuminating Engineering Society London
Trans. Roy. Soc. Edin.	Transactions of the Royal Society of Edinburgh Edinburgh and London
VDI	Zeitschrift des Vereines deutscher Ingenieure Berlin
Z. phys. Chem.	Zeitschrift für physikalische Chemie Leipzig
Z. tech. phys.	Zeitschrifte für technische Physik Leipzig

Consistency

Where a symbol or abbreviation is used for the first time it is convenient to make a note on a separate sheet of paper for future reference during the writing. The same symbol will then be used throughout the text. Consistency in symbols and abbreviations is particularly important, as the reader will be misled by any variation, thinking it to refer to some modified expression.

Abbreviations for common units are frequently changed in the text: for example in the first printing of this book the writers used ' inch ', ' in.' and ", an inconsistency which was speedily pointed out by the critics (see also p. 91).

Names of other authors or workers in the subject should be checked carefully for correct spelling and initials.* ' A. D. Smith ' in one section should not become ' Alan Smith ' in another. Courtesy titles are sometimes added, particularly if the author is a Professor, but their omission is not considered a mark of disrespect.

Proprietary goods should be named with capital letters unless the writer is sure that the name has been accepted as a generic term with the approval of the manufacturers. For example, Perspex is not a generic term, but " thyratron " has now been taken into the language to denote a particular type of gas-filled tube.

Section Numbering

It is the practice in some technical papers, books and reports to number the sections or paragraphs according to a decimal system,

* Remember that a man's name is to him the sweetest and most important sound in the English language—*Dale Carnegie*.

commencing with 1 and numbering succeeding sub-paragraphs 1.1, 1.2 and so on. Sub-sub paragraphs add a second figure: 1.1.1, 1.1.2 . . . In deciding whether to number the paragraphs of a report, a writer may have to conform to the custom of his organization, but if given a free choice he should consider whether the addition of numbers to the sections helps the reader to find his way more easily through the text. If no use is made of the numbers in references, the reader may wonder why they were added.

There is justification for numbering the sections of a handbook in which several items may appear on one page and the numbered sections enable the reader to find the information without reading down the page. Another use of numbered sections is in handbooks which are subject to revision; the page or section may be replaced without disturbing the pagination, but this implies that the book must be indexed according to sections and not according to pages.

The reader is accustomed to look at page numbers—he is not so accustomed to looking for section numbers. It follows therefore that an index should be presented in the most familiar form, and if section numbers are used they should always be accompanied by page numbers. In a book which also contains mathematical equations the need for avoiding confusion is all-important.

Numbering Equations and Figures (Illustrations)

In publishing terminology illustrations are usually referred to as 'figures'; any ambiguity in mathematical texts is avoided by calling the numerical figures 'numerals'.

The practice of numbering equations and figures consecutively throughout a handbook is giving way to a more convenient method of numbering them in relation to the chapter. The advantage to both the writer and the editor is that alterations may be made at any time in the preparation of the work without having to re-number throughout. The advantage of numbering equations with respect to the chapter is that the reader can more easily refer to them and associate them with the subject matter. In the early stages of preparing a manuscript it is convenient to number not only the equations and figures but also the pages with reference to the chapter, particularly if the writing is done in various sections out of order in the final arrangement.

Footnotes

The object of a footnote is to provide additional information on the subject of the text, either by way of further explanation or to remind the reader of a related matter. References which are not collected into a bibliography at the end of a manuscript can be conveniently added as footnotes to the appropriate page.

In general, a descriptive footnote should not contain material of primary importance—such material should have been included in the text—and its omission should not affect the value of the information on the page. Some authors prefer to add numerous footnotes,‡

---

‡ See for example *Enigmas* by Cdr. R. T. Gould (London, Geoffrey Bles, 1944) or *The Spoor of Spooks* by Bergen Evans (London, Michael Joseph, 1955, or this book.

---

others limit them to occasional comments of interest. In deciding to add a footnote, the writer should be guided by the principle ' Ought it to form part of the main text ? '

Writers of textbooks may conveniently add a series of notes at the end of each chapter. These will help the reader with further information without distracting him with unnecessary detail in the text.

Until recently it was recommended that footnotes should be inserted in typescript immediately underneath the reference mark, a thin line being drawn above and below the footnote to distinguish it from the text (as shown in the example on this page). It is now agreed that it is preferable to add it to the *foot* of the page. If the typescript is being duplicated it is in the correct position; if the typescript is intended for the printer the compositor will be helped by having the footnotes in a conspicuous place throughout the text.

Appendices

Appendices are of particular value in presenting information which includes detailed descriptions or mathematical arguments on which the conclusions are based. A non-specialist reader may be discouraged from reading a report by the sight of mathematics; even a specialist reader will be more interested in the results than in the steps leading to them. Both mathematics and argument may be relegated to the end of the text, leaving the main theme standing out more clearly. Other items which may be added in the form of an appendix are tables of figures for reference, glossaries, and bibliographies. If a report has taken some time in preparation it may be useful to add the latest information in an appendix during the final stages of presentation.

In mathematical texts it is not always necessary to supply a set of logarithm tables as an appendix. Most mathematicians have them.

List of Contents

In a short report or paper it is sufficient to list the main headings and sub-headings with the page on which they are found (see p. 266). If the work is divided into chapters, a suitable layout would be:

CHAPTER 7. EDITORIAL PROCEDURE

> *The Editor and his Function—Technical Editing—Estimating and Casting-off—Proof Reading—Layout and Make-up*

the headings in the chapter being listed as shown.

List of Illustrations

In general, a list of illustrations may not be helpful to the reader unless he is particularly interested in finding a circuit diagram or a particular detailed drawing. The main use of a list is to indicate what should be present in the book, and this function is particularly important if there are separate plates printed on paper which differs from the text paper.

The distinction between a figure and a plate is that figures are usually printed on the paper with the text matter and plates are inserted separately in the text. It usually happens that the quality of the text paper is inadequate for reproducing the details of a good half-tone illustration, and this is printed on a high quality ' art ' paper with a glazed surface and subsequently inserted in the text at the correct place. A list of such plates is therefore useful for the reader to check that they are present.

Final Checking

It has frequently been said that a finished manuscript should be put into cold storage for a period before being re-read and re-written. Unfortunately the pressure to release new technical information does not allow this advice to be followed, but it is none the less worth following as far as circumstances permit. A manuscript should always be submitted to the critical comment of one or more of the writer's colleagues, and their criticism may save apologies or corrections after the material has been published.

There are many points of detail which may be overlooked, and the last stage of production should be a careful and systematic check of all the features that are a mark of a well-prepared manuscript. This check is made more certain if the writer works to a prepared list of queries, and a specimen questionnaire is given below. Some of the details do not apply to shorter forms of writing and will only be required for handbooks or monographs.

Check-list for Manuscript

Page reference in this book

1. Text Matter

Is the title consistent with the scope of the writing ?	47
Does the summary agree with the major points in the text ?	51
Is the introduction too wordy ?	53
Could the opening sentences be omitted with no loss ?	54
Is each section logically related ?	56
Is the paragraphing adequate ?	64
Are there sufficient sub-headings ?	64
Do they agree with the content of the paragraphs ?	64
Has every sentence been checked for grammar ?	73
Are there any ambiguous statements ?	77
Are the symbols clearly explained ?	92, 231
Are the units given where necessary ?	90
Are the mathematical expressions clearly set out ?	230
Appendices ?	102
Has a glossary of special terms been added ?	88

	Page reference in this book
Are additional notes fastened securely in the text ?	285
Is the author's name on the manuscript and illustrations ?	...
Does the list of Contents agree with the chapters ?	...

CHAPTER 4

ILLUSTRATING THE TEXT

THE illustrations should always be regarded as an integral part of a technical paper and accordingly be planned at the same time as the body of the text matter is drafted. Occasionally it is permissible to add relevant illustrations of interest if they relieve the monotony of a long printed passage or even to catch the reader's eye, but in general superfluous illustrations add to the cost of production without benefiting the reader.

The writer may argue that the question of cost is not one that concerns him and that his object is to convey the information in the most efficient manner. If, in his opinion, twenty figures are required they should not be reduced to fifteen at the caprice of an editorial staff. The counter-argument to this is that cost must inevitably be considered when any written matter is reproduced for circulation, and if it is borne in mind at the outset the selection of the illustrations will be more carefully undertaken, with less risk of their being cut down in number. It frequently happens that two drawings are used to illustrate a point in the text where one would serve, if properly planned and labelled. Sketches which only serve to duplicate the information already put down in words can be left out, unless required for later reference. Composite illustrations can often be used in place of a number of smaller scattered ones, provided that they do not fail in their object by being over-complicated.

In choosing illustrations, the writer should put himself in the position of a photographer who has a camera with a limited number of exposures on an expensive film; he will not waste them by snapping unnecessary views.

Photographs

The analogy with the photographer is appropriate when considering photographic illustrations, as these are the most costly and troublesome to reproduce. For this reason they should be kept to a minimum and only used if no other type of illustration is suitable, for example in reproducing photo-micrographs, fine detail views of equipment, or oscillograms, which are essential to understanding the text.

A photograph showing the external view of equipment without useful detail is wasted in a technical paper, although it is often used in catalogues and sales literature. Though pictorially satisfactory it conveys no information to a reader who is interested in height, accessibility, or what is behind a panel. The photograph of Fig. 4.1 is an example of an informative photograph which shows something more than the front view of the equipment—a high-frequency heating apparatus with the cover lifted and a batch of products in place.

FIG. 4.1. *A photograph having functional value.*

Pictures showing a human figure manipulating controls or carrying out an operation are of value in an instructional book, but are not always acceptable in a formal technical paper. The addition of a girl posed in front of complex apparatus may make the picture more inviting but such an addition rarely improves the efficiency of a technical report. A foot-rule would be more useful in most cases. In fact, a writer who directs the taking of photographs for illustration would do well to include a scale as a matter of routine —it can be blotted out if not required and adds an important piece of information for the reader. An ordinary steel rule does not photograph well, and a special 'yard-stick' should be made from a length of wood of 1 inch square section with the four sides calibrated in convenient metric and inch scales with bold black and white markings.

Photographs for Reproduction

When photographs are to be reproduced by the half-tone or other printing processes the limitations of the process and the paper on which the illustration is printed require careful selection of the photographic print.

Prints should be made on glossy paper, be clear (but not necessarily of high contrast), and not contain excess of fine detail. *Great care should be taken to avoid marking or creasing the print.* Lettering on the back, unless made with a very light mark, will show through the surface of the print and may mar the finished reproduction. The most satisfactory way of labelling prints is to type the figure number and any special notes on a separate sheet of paper which can be gummed to the back of the print by one edge and then folded over to form a protective cover.

Illustrations made by photographing existing printed half-tone blocks (see p. 209) should never be used unless absolutely unavoidable. The re-photographing of a half-tone print may produce a ' moiré ' pattern which will spoil the appearance of the finished illustration.* Line drawings can, however, be copied without much difficulty from a printed reproduction if it is not too small. It must be remembered that photographic copying may result in coarsening the detail of intricate drawings.

Exploded Views

A photograph of an assembly showing all the separate component parts in their relative positions is known as an " exploded view " and is of particular value in maintenance or instruction manuals. There are various methods of obtaining these photographs, and the writer should direct the placing of the components in collaboration with the photographer if the assembly is complicated. In one method, the components after dismantling are mounted in their relative positions by wire or wooden supports which are afterwards painted out on the negative. This method has the advantage that a three-dimensional effect can be produced with the components shown in as many planes as desired, but the placing and obliterating of the supports is tedious. Alternatively, sheets of glass or Perspex may be used with the lighting so arranged that there is no reflexion

* But see note on p. 193, Chapter 5.

from the surface. In some cases it is possible to photograph the individual components separately and assemble them in position by cutting them out from a finished print. Fig. 4.2 shows a switch treated in this way, the parts being printed separately and stuck down on a stiff board for re-photographing. Care must be taken in cutting round the prints, and particular care not to alter the scale of the individual photographs.

An article on Exploded View Photography by J. Blaxland appeared in the *British Journal of Photography*, April 14 and 21, 1950, pp. 182, 196 and a shorter article by J. W. McFarlane appeared in the *American Annual of Photography*, 1948, p. 32.

Fig. 4.2. *Exploded view of a rotary switch made up from separate prints.*

Use of Filters

Although the taking of technical photographs is best left in the hands of a professional photographer (and a good studio photographer is not necessarily a good technical photographer) the technical writer may be called on to take photographs of equipment or of experimental apparatus which will not wait for the professional, before it is dismantled. No detailed instructions on photographing can be given here, but it can be remarked that professionals still prefer to use ¼-plate or ½-plate cameras for work of this type. When photographing coloured objects it should be remembered that a radical change in the appearance of the finished print can be produced by using appropriate filters in front of the lens. For example, a greenish-blue background can be made darker by using a red filter.* The colour of resistors or other components can be

* The exposure with a panchromatic plate will be increased up to 4 times in artificial light. For hints on technical photography, see David Charles. *Commercial and Industrial Photography* (Chapman & Hall, 1958).

rendered darker or lighter by the appropriate filter; another use is in the suppression of background lines in graphs drawn on blue or green lined paper. Note that it is impracticable to separate red or deep orange from black by the use of a plain filter, although it is possible to reproduce red as a lighter tone by using special lighting and plates.

Line Drawings from Photographs

Since photographs are troublesome to reproduce, it is worth considering whether a black-and-white ('line') drawing can be

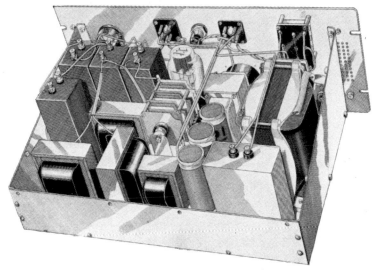

Fig. 4.3.   *A line drawing prepared from a photographic print.*

prepared to serve almost the same purpose. Here again the question of cost must be considered, as the time taken by an expert illustrator in preparing a line drawing from a photograph may prove as expensive in the final result. It is nevertheless preferable to use line drawings wherever a photograph is not essential, as they can be reproduced at less expense and on paper of an inferior finish. Line drawings, for example, can be reproduced on duplicating paper by using a special stencil. It is possible to produce a good

111

line drawing from a photographic print by means of a bleaching-out process; the result is comparable with a perspective drawing and it has the advantage that it can be achieved by an engineer-draughtsman who is not skilled in perspective drawing.

The photograph is printed on smooth matt paper to the finished size required, slightly under-exposed so that the black portions are not too heavy. The picture outlines and details are then inked over, using waterproof black ink, the shadows being indicated by line shading. When the ink is dry the print is immersed in a photographic bleaching solution until the original background has disappeared. The inked-in lines are not affected by the bleach and the print can be re-photographed or used directly for producing a line block. If the photograph contains unwanted shadows or grey tones the inking-in may be made easier by using contrasty paper for the print. A specimen illustration done by this method is shown in Fig. 4.3.

Identifying Components

The labelling of parts or components shown in a photograph should not be done on the picture itself but on the white area surrounding it. If letters are printed or inked on the picture there is a risk of their being overlooked or mistaken for lettering actually engraved on the object. Fig. 4.4 illustrates some of the faults to be avoided in placing letters on the print; the letters which are immediately obvious to the reader are A, B and C on the upper border, and this position of the lettering is the preferred one. For symmetry the letters should be aligned, and arrows drawn from them to the part indicated. Note that the colour of the arrow can be changed when the colour of the background makes it desirable (as in Fig. 4.5). Letters placed on the components themselves (D, E) are more difficult to pick out, and if it is essential that they are placed on the component the letter should be printed in black on a white circular surround. It should be noted that the letter R on the print might be mistaken for a maker's identification letter, and is more confusing for this reason. Finally, the letters G and H on the vertical right-hand edge of unit B are too small to be clearly identified.

Although it is a good practice to label all significant features clearly, there is a limit to the amount of lettering which can be added to a photograph or drawing without confusing the reader and thus defeating the object of the labelling. It is a source of irritation if the reader has to search for a letter on the print among a number of labels, figures and letters, and in marking the print some systematic arrangement is always preferable. Words should be printed to stand out clearly from the adjacent picture and descriptive phrases should be kept as short as possible; they can be elaborated in the text or in the caption under the picture.

The identifying of a large number of assorted components packed into a small space is always a problem for the writer of instruction

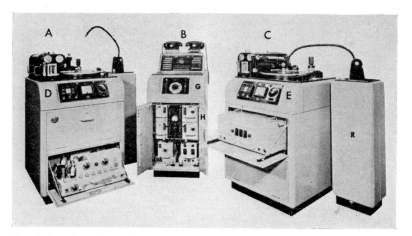

FIG. 4.4.   *Examples of lettering on prints, showing the importance of positioning.*

manuals. It is sometimes possible to separate a photograph into two or three portions which can be related like an aerial survey map, or the photographs can be taken during assembly of the equipment to show components which are partly hidden in the finished job. As far as possible the letters should be kept clear of the components for reasons which have been mentioned previously, and one method of marking them clearly is shown in Fig. 4.5.

Sheets of transparent adhesive material containing a series of black numerals on white background circles are made by Artype Inc., Barrington, Ill. and marketed in Britain by Hunter Penrose Ltd., Farringdon Rd., London, E.C.1. This aid, however, would be difficult to use with closely spaced components. The method

FIG. 4.5. *A satisfactory method of identifying component parts.*

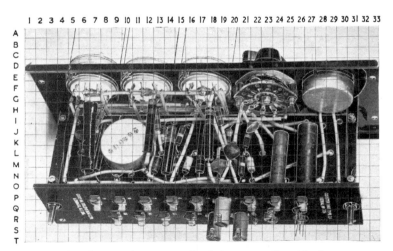

FIG. 4.6. *Identification of component details by means of a grid reference system.*

shown in Fig. 4.6 lends itself to all types of photograph containing intricate detail, and is an adaptation of the well-known ' grid ' principle for map references.   It has the advantage that the spacing of the grid lines can be varied to suit the number and arrangement of the components and it is also possible to identify the smaller items such as screws and screw holes with a sufficiently close grid. Where a number of photographs of particular equipment are reproduced the grid may be printed on a transparent sheet of celluloid and arranged to fold over the photograph being studied, but care must be taken to avoid ambiguity in the text when referring to the grid numbers for a given photograph.

Pictorial Drawings

In preparing the illustrations for a report or paper intended for the engineer reader the writer is safe in assuming that he is accustomed to reading engineering drawings and does not need help in interpreting them.   A great deal of technical literature, however, is read by men trained in other branches of science* who need something more than the orthodox outline drawing to grasp the meaning of an illustration, particularly if it shows the construction of apparatus or its mode of working.

For this reason it is better to present the illustrations in a more pictorial form, using perspective and shading to give the reader an opportunity to take in the meaning without undue effort.

Methods of obtaining perspective from photographs have already been suggested, and further notes on perspective drawing will be found in various books (p. 137).   The preparation of good perspective drawings should be left to the draughtsman-artist, but if one is not available the writer should try to relieve the severity of a line drawing by adding touches which will make it more acceptable to the reader.   An example of the improvement which results from using a pictorial style is shown in Fig. 4.7.   The illustrations are taken from a textbook in which the original figures were accurate but lifeless, and the new versions make the text more attractive.†

There is a totally erroneous belief among some writers that because

---

* For example, physicists, biologists and others whose training does not include drawing office practice.

† *University Physics* (2nd Edn.), Sears and Zemansky. Addison-Wesley Publishing Co. Inc., Cambridge, Mass.

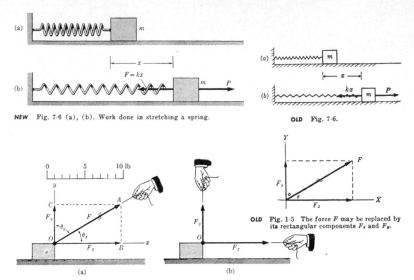

NEW Fig. 7·6 (a), (b). Work done in stretching a spring.

OLD Fig. 7·6.

OLD Fig. 1·5 The force F may be replaced by its rectangular components F_x and F_y.

NEW Fig. 1·5 (a), (b). The inclined force F may be replaced by its rectangular components F_x and F_y. $F_x = F \cos \theta_x$, $F_y = F \sin \theta_y$

FIG. 4.7. *Showing how a plain diagram is improved by using a pictorial style.*
(*By courtesy of the Addison-Wesley Publishing Co.*)

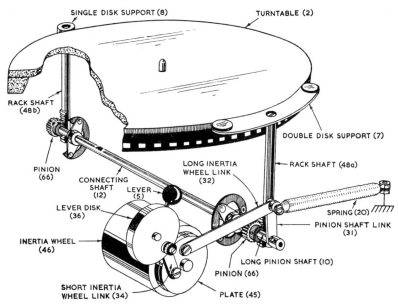

FIG. 4.8. *An example of pictorial shading in a functional drawing.*
(*By courtesy of the British Broadcasting Corporation.*)

the subject matter of a report or article is technical there is no need to ' dress up ' the accompanying illustrations. All readers appreciate an attractive or interesting presentation of intrinsically dry material, and because a man is technically trained he does not lose all liking for form and colour.

As far as possible, therefore, the illustrations should be designed to be artistic as well as useful, and careful shading will often help to improve the appearance of a finished drawing. Fig. 4.8 gives an example of shading methods applied to a mechanical working drawing.

PICTORIAL PRESENTATION OF DATA

As in the case of the engineering drawing, there is a large number of readers who have a superficial scientific knowledge but who may not be capable of appreciating data presented in a strictly scientific form. Most readers in industry are familiar with graphs and can understand their general significance but their knowledge may not extend to analysing the data or interpreting it in detail. Again, if the information is conveyed in a pictorial style it is more easily taken in and remembered, even by an expert accustomed to reading more complex presentations.

Tables v. Graphs

The choice often has to be made whether the information can best be presented in the form of tables or graphs; for example, if it is desirable to emphasize fluctuation in values over a given period, precise figures being of secondary importance, a graph would be preferable to a table. Examples which readily occur are temperature charts or sales charts. On the other hand, if the figures are to be used by the reader in working out results or obtaining further information, the graph is seldom sufficiently accurate. A worker in a factory who has to apply different dimensions to suit different conditions would require them in tabular form.

The choice in some cases may be affected by the knowledge or professional background of the user. Many business men can interpret the overall picture presented by a graph but find difficulty in interpolating values from it.

A graph is obviously required when presenting experimental results, as a table does not indicate the reliance that can be placed on the individual readings, nor does it show the rate at which the quantities are varying. In displaying the results calculated from a formula, a table is sufficient, provided that the reader does not require to apply the calculation to a wider range of values than is set out in the table.

Construction of Graphs

An important consideration in the construction of graphs is the choice of scale. It should not extend beyond the points of interest and it should be selected so that the graph will occupy the greater

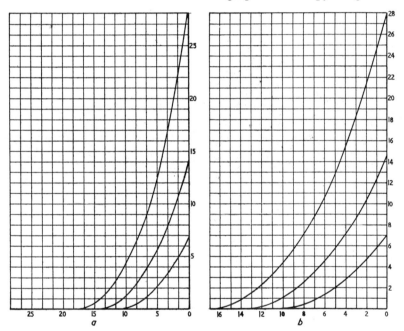

FIG. 4.9.   *Curves drawn to illustrate poor choice of scale* (a), *and the improvement by altering scale values* (b).

part of the sheet (Fig. 4.9). Only in exceptional cases should a scale be used which is not a convenient multiple or sub-multiple of 10. If it is required to enlarge a section of a graph by drawing it to an altered scale, the change in scale values should be clearly indicated and the break in continuity should be shown by drawing a horizontal line or by leaving a gap on the paper.

A useful illustration of the choice of scale is in the graphs used to indicate the performance of an electronic device such as a radio receiver or amplifier. The frequency response is needed to show the relative sound intensities which the device will produce on a loudspeaker over the range of audible frequencies. This is best shown in a graph as in Fig. 4.10a, which indicates that extreme bass tones will be weak compared with the treble. Such a graph

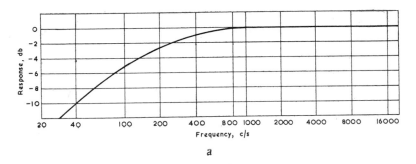

a

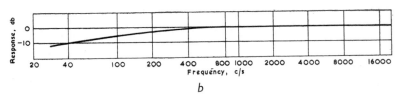

b

FIG. 4.10. *Frequency response curves plotted to different scales, showing how the response can be exaggerated.*

is based on two concepts: first, a varying quantity is related to a set of fixed conditions; second, the trend of the frequency response is visible at a glance.

The choice of scale for this graph has considerable significance. It will be noticed that the frequency scale is logarithmic, equal divisions representing a doubling of frequency values. Apart from theoretical considerations, this scale permits plotting a wide range of values in a small compass. The range of the response scale is dictated by a practical consideration in that the average listener will detect changes in sound volume if the changes exceed two decibels.

119

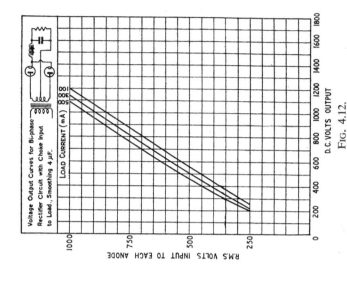

Fig. 4.12.

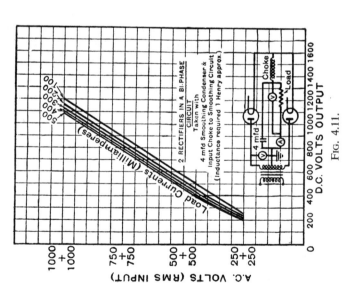

Fig. 4.11.

Bad and good construction of graphs. In Fig. 4.11 the information distracts the reader and the curves are too close. The information has been separated from the graph and the layout is more open in Fig. 4.12.

This scale must therefore be used if the curve is to give a true indication of performance. Fig. 4.10b shows what happens if the response is plotted on a ten-decibel scale; the graph is as accurate as the preceding one, but the choice of scale creates a false impression of performance.

Marking Graphs

If the graph accompanies a typewritten or duplicated report, it may not be possible to bind it close to the text matter relating to it. The draughtsman should be careful to add sufficient information to the graph to enable the reader to understand it without frequent reference back to the text matter. This additional information should include:

Brief conditions of test
Explanation of symbols used on the curves (see Fig. 4.13)
Explanatory heading

This information should not be placed where it can distract from reading the graph itself, as in Fig. 4.11. This sheet contains all the relevant information for interpreting the graph but it is untidily arranged. Other points for criticism are the unorthodox marking of the vertical scale, the bunching of the curves, and the background to the circuit diagram. The curves have been re-drawn in Fig. 4.12: omitting the 200 and 400 lines makes interpolation easier for the reader,* and the information has been set at the head of the sheet where it does not obtrude. The vertical scale has been re-numbered and re-worded to avoid the confusion of a double set of figures.

If it is essential to show a large number of curves which would lie closely together on the sheet it is preferable to make two or more graph sheets, although it is possible to show the distinction between a few closely-drawn curves by using different symbols for the points (Fig. 4.13). Alternatively the lines may be broken, dotted, or chain-dotted, but it is important to keep the same convention among several sets of graphs to avoid misleading the reader.

Fig. 4.14 is an example of a well-drawn set of curves on logarithmic paper; only the cardinal lines have been marked in, as the closeness

---

* Electronic engineers will appreciate that the closeness of the original curves implies a narrower tolerance than is usually found in manufacture.

121

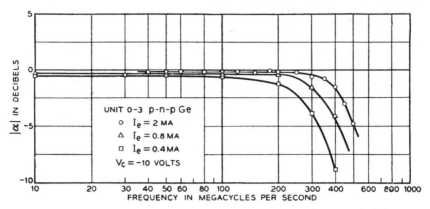

FIG. 4.13. *Distinguishing between closely-drawn curves by use of differing symbols.*

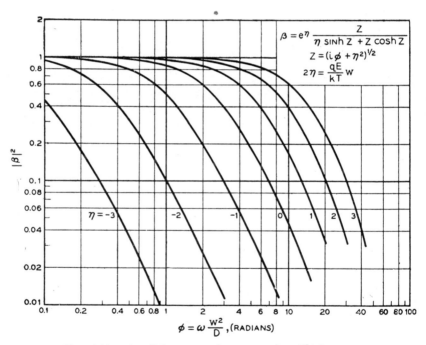

$$\beta = e^{\eta} \frac{Z}{\eta \sinh Z + Z \cosh Z}$$

$$Z = (i\phi + \eta^2)^{1/2}$$

$$2\eta = \frac{qE}{kT} W$$

$$\phi = \omega \frac{W^2}{D}, \text{(RADIANS)}$$

FIG. 4.14. *A well-drawn set of curves on logarithmic paper.*
(*From Bell System Technical Journal, 1956, by courtesy of the Bell Telephone Laboratories.*)

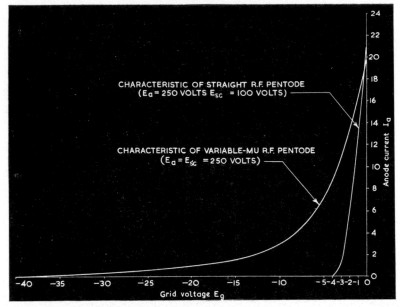

FIG. 4.15. *Scale lines can be omitted in illustrative graphs. This figure has been printed from a 'reverse' block in which the original black lines appear as white.*

of the lines on full logarithmic paper is confusing, and the slight thickening of the lines at 1 and 10 makes the scale more readable.

Graphs which are used for illustrative purposes sometimes have the scale lines omitted (Fig. 4.15). In the particular example shown the bare effect of too much white space has been avoided by printing the block in ' reverse ' (see p. 209). Graphs showing a trend of variation are frequently drawn as in Fig. 4.16 when it is not possible to express the results by a curve drawn through the points. Such a graph is sometimes

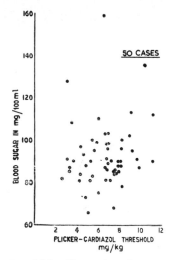

FIG. 4.16. *Illustration of a target diagram, used for indicating the spread of a number of experimental readings.*

123

termed a target diagram, and is useful in showing the departure from normal in a series of tests on manufactured products.

Occasionally the nature of the results requires a special form of graph paper to display the experimental readings. The polar diagram of Fig. 4.17 is in effect a graph of amplitudes plotted against angular bearings from a given datum line; it is not usually necessary to calibrate the radial scale at each line. If three graphs are to be shown in relationship but with separate scales it is possible to use

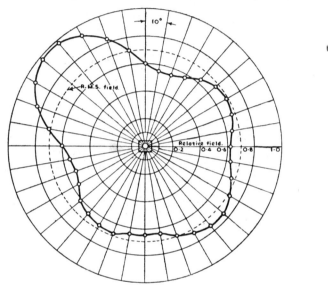

FIG. 4.17. *An example of a diagram drawn on polar graph paper : the radiation pattern of a television transmitter.*
(*By courtesy of the British Broadcasting Corporation.*)

isometric or trimetric construction for the co-ordinate lines. An example of this display was shown in an article in *Electronic Engineering* (1947), **19**, 12.

Correlation Charts

A graph such as that illustrated in Fig. 4.14 may serve two purposes: its original purpose is to record results of measurement or investigation; its second purpose is to provide data from which variations in the quantities may be calculated. The first purpose is that of a graph, the second is that of a correlation chart.

Normally, charts are designed to solve problems involving three or more variables; they can be either in the form of intercept or alignment charts.

If the solution is found by the intersection of all the variables, the chart is defined as an intercept chart : if two of the variables are known, the third is found by the point of coincidence of all three.

In the alignment chart three lines, one for each variable, are divided into a number of values (Fig. 4.18); if two variables are

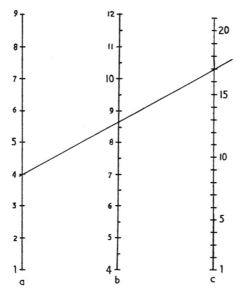

FIG. 4.18. *A simple form of alignment chart for three variables.*

known, and their values are joined by a straight edge, the third is found at the intersection of its scale with the straight edge.*

For an alignment chart to be of practical use it must be simple in construction. A highly complex chart may involve more effort in solving a problem than the mathematical calculations it was designed to avoid. The degree of accuracy depends on the scale used, and this must be taken into account if the chart has to be

* This is sometimes called a linear nomogram, or "abac". For further details on constructing these nomograms, see *Nomography*, by A. Stevens (John Wiley & Sons, N.Y., 1948).

reduced for reproduction; for example, if graduations on a scale or the curves themselves are closer together than a millimetre, accurate results would be impracticable. The accuracy also depends on the straightness of the edge used in reading off linear nomograms; an ordinary office ruler is not good enough.

The rules suggested for the production and reproduction of graphs apply equally to charts, but because they are designed to solve mathematical problems the rules must be applied more strictly. A great deal of work may have been necessary to produce the chart; careless presentation may make it worse than useless.

Pictograms

A method of presenting comparative data in a simple and easily understood manner is by the use of pictorial charts, or *pictograms*. In these a pictorial or stylized outline is used to represent the subject discussed, and relative variations in value are shown by altering the size or area of the outline.

The *Isotype* is a special form of pictogram devised by Otto Neurath of Vienna, and now sponsored in Great Britain by the Isotype Institute, of Rathbone Place, London, W.1. It is intended to convey information pictorially to readers of a wide range of intelligence by using a series of standardized shapes in colour or black. These symbol-shapes are so designed to be self-explanatory as far as possible, and the art of setting out the chart is to convey the message in as simple form as possible.

Bar Charts. The bar chart (Fig. 4.19a) is used to show the comparison between two or more quantities, the height of the bar being made proportional to the actual value. The width of the bar has no special significance and is chosen to make the bar of suitable proportions; about one-tenth of the maximum height is a convenient dimension.

Although in the simple bar chart the area of the bar has no relation to the quantity represented, it is possible to draw the chart so that the actual area of each bar is proportional to the quantity shown, e.g. acres under cultivation, square feet of timber imported.

In such cases it is important to avoid misleading the reader by using special forms of area such as squares or circles. If, for example, the output of a given plant has doubled in a given period, the increase might be shown by two squares, one of which is twice the area of the other (Fig. 4.19b). The impression on the reader, however, is certainly not that of doubling the output. Doubling the linear dimensions of the square would be equally misleading, as it results in a fourfold increase in area.

The same ambiguity applies to circles of area in the ratio of 2 : 1 (Fig. 4.19c), and to volumes such as spheres and cubes (4.19d).

The bar chart may be made more interesting and more pictorial by adding a representation of the article described, e.g. packing cases, radio cabinets, coils of cable. Fig. 4.20 shows an artist's

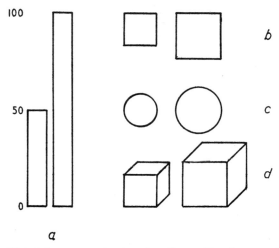

FIG. 4.19. *Pictorial representation by a bar chart. The shapes on the right can give a misleading impression of the difference between two quantities.*

rendering of a bar chart relating to the costs of printing and produc-tion of books during five years.

Circular Charts. An alternative to the bar chart is the circular chart, in which the component quantities are shown as sectors of a circle.* The dimensions of the sectors are calculated by taking $360° = 100\%$ and measuring off the angles corresponding to the percentages of the components.

These sectors should be clearly labelled to help the reader to understand their significance without referring to the caption or the text. This does not mean that the diagram should be loaded with explanatory titles, but sufficient information should be given to make

* Also known as the " pie " diagram, or " piece of cake " diagram.

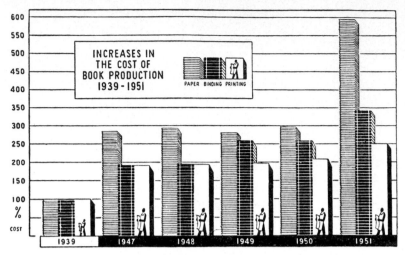

FIG. 4.20. *A bar chart artistically improved to produce a more striking impression.*
(By courtesy of the Publishers' Association.)

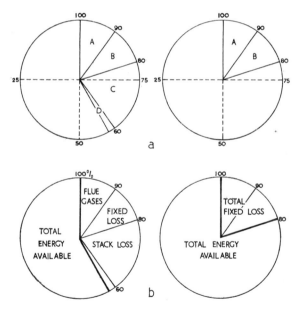

FIG. 4.21. *An example of a circular chart,* (a) *drawn so as to require elaborate explanation* (b) *labelled to be self-explanatory.*

the chart easily read. Fig. 4.21a shows a circular chart drawn with correct proportions, but which defeats its object of conveying the information to the reader at a glance. The use of letters on the chart requires an accompanying explanation, and the reader has to move his eyes unnecessarily to find the meaning of the sectors.

The upper diagrams are scientifically correct but lack punch ; the reader is further confused by the unnecessary scale markings at 25, 50 and 75.

The object of the chart is to show the increase in energy available by preventing waste in fuel consumption, and it will be seen from the lower diagrams (Fig. 4.21b) that elimination of loss in the stack will give a total available energy of 80%. Since this is the point to be emphasized, the sectors should be outlined in heavy line and the reader can see immediately the difference between the diagrams.

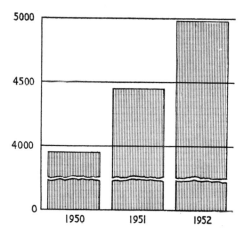

FIG. 4.22. *The bar chart can be made misleading by suppressing part of the scale.*
(*After D. Huff: 'How to Lie with Statistics'.*)

Misleading Pictograms

The subject of misleading charts is amusingly dealt with in *How to Lie with Statistics* by D. Huff (W. W. Norton & Co. N.Y., 1954) from which Fig. 4.22 is adapted. If a bar chart has the greater part of its length suppressed the relative heights will give a false impression of increase ; in the example shown the maxima differ by only 500 but the effect is to show an increase in the proportion of

1 : 2 : 3. Similar misleading charts may be made by exaggeration of the vertical scale, compression of the vertical scale, or similar dodges. The technical writer who values his scientific reputation will resist all attempts to falsify his data in this way, although the temptation to an enterprising sales department is great.

ENGINEERING DRAWING

There are so many commendable textbooks on engineering drawing that it is proposed to give here only a brief survey of salient principles having general application.

Orthographic Drawing

First-angle Projection

In both engineering and architectural drawing, much use is made of the orthographic view in which the *plan* represents the horizontal

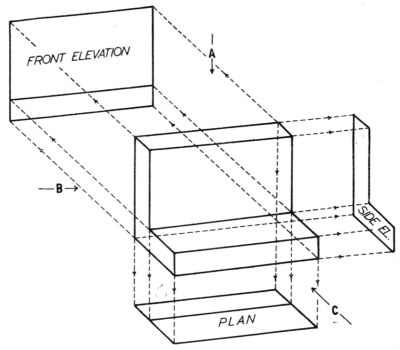

FIG. 4.23. *Illustrating the three views of an object and how they are obtained.*

130

plane of the object as viewed from above, and other views are drawn as *elevations*, e.g. front, end or side. These elevations are drawn by projecting lines through the outline of the object either away from or towards the view point (V.P.) (Fig. 4.23).

In the so-called *first-angle projection* these lines are drawn *away* from the V.P., the plan being placed at the bottom of the drawing. Referring to Fig. 4.23, the plan is projected from A, the end, or side, elevation from B and the front elevation from C. The arrangement of the drawings is shown in Fig. 4.24, the left-hand end elevation being on the right of the plan and the front elevation

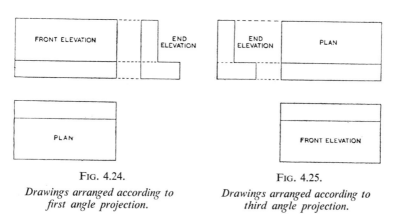

FIG. 4.24.
Drawings arranged according to first angle projection.

FIG. 4.25.
Drawings arranged according to third angle projection.

above it. This is the standard form for first-angle projection; in practice the various views are recognized by their position on the drawing, and captions are not essential.

Third-angle Projection

Until recent years most European countries have used the first-angle or English projection, but many English firms are now using *third-angle projection*, and the British Standards Institution accepts both first and third-angle projection. With third-angle projection, the construction lines shown dotted in Fig. 4.23 are drawn *towards* the view point. The result is that the end elevation now appears to the left of B, the front elevation below and to the right of C, and the plan above A. The practical arrangement is shown in Fig. 4.25. If third-angle projection is used on British drawings it should be specified in the caption.

131

Combined Projection

This method uses the features of both first- and third-angle projections, the plan being placed below the elevation, as in first-angle projection. The elevations are drawn to third-angle projection. Combined projection is widely used on drawings of buildings.

Isometric Drawing

The purpose of isometric drawing is to illustrate three faces of an object in pictorial fashion so that the object can be easily recognized, and at the same time contain full dimensional information.

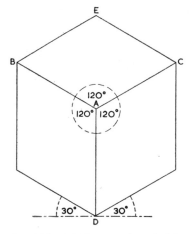

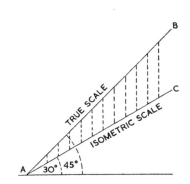

FIG. 4.26. To illustrate the principle
of isometric projection.

FIG. 4.27. The relation between true
and isometric scales.

It is, therefore, a compromise between orthographic projection and perspective.

Imagine a cube tilted and with the view point at a corner, A, Fig. 4.26. Three edges of the cube converge at this point, forming lines AB, AC, AD; the angles BAC, BAD, and CAD all being 120°, the lines projected from A are either 30° or 90° from the horizontal. Since all other edges are parallel to one or other of the projections from A, they too are either 30° or 90° to the horizontal. The lines AB, AC, AD are called the *isometric axes*, and all lines parallel to these axes are called *isometric lines*; lines not parallel to the axes are termed *non-isometric*. In the figure,

132

the isometric projection of the top of the cube is indicated by the rhombus ABEC. But the top of a cube is obviously a square, so that if the cube shown in Fig. 4.26 were tilted through 90°, the rhombus ABEC would be a square resting on one corner, and lines AB, etc., would form an angle of 45° to the horizontal. As drawn, these angles are 30°, hence the relationship between true and isometric scales can be obtained by plotting as in Fig. 4.27, where AB represents actual lengths and AC projected lengths.

The use of isometric projection and scales is not always convenient when applied to workshop practice. It is, therefore, usual to construct isometric drawings from the true scale, in which case the user is saved the trouble of applying the conversion factor needed for isometric projection. There is thus a distinction between isometric *drawing* and isometric *projection*, although in practice both may be referred to as isometric drawing. Discrimination between the two is essential only when scaling is important.

The value of the isometric view in simplifying the interpretation of an engineering drawing is illustrated by Fig. 4.28. The orthographic views of a casting are shown in Fig. 4.28a, and these drawings, while accurate, could only give a clear picture of the object to a trained engineer-draughtsman. The same object has been drawn isometrically in Fig. 4.28b, and the shape of the casting is at once seen. The drawing of isometric views is made easier by using triangular graph paper, which is obtainable from drawing office equipment suppliers. The background lines of the paper on which the drawing of Fig. 4.28b was made are shown in part at the corners of the figure. Special templates for drawing ellipses can also be obtained,

Variations of Isometric Projection

The idea of isometric projection is by no means modern, as it was studied by Professor William Farish of Cambridge well over a hundred years ago. Its general application to engineering drawing. however, belongs to the present century, and a number of different systems have been devised to encourage its use.

The Leete System. This system is based largely on the use of mechanical aids, such as templates for drawing ellipses and hexagon nuts. Use is also made of special scales, set-squares and charts, all of which are designed to facilitate the work of pictorial representation in three dimensions.

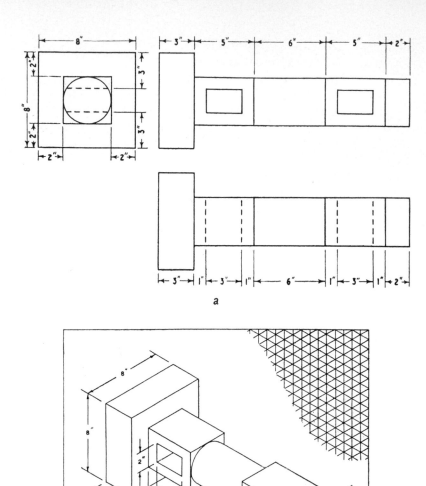

FIG. 4.28.   *Showing the value of the isometric scale in helping the unskilled reader. The orthographic drawing* (a) *does not readily give the clue to the shape of the object. In* (b) *the shape is clear. The triangular scale markings at the corners show the background on which the drawing was constructed.*

The general principles of isometric projection as previously outlined are retained, vertical edges of the object being vertical on the drawing and horizontal at 30° from the true horizontal of the T-square. Dimensions are obtained by the use of the isometric scale.

The Walters System. The chief feature of this system is that three-dimensional views can be drawn without the use of special appliances. Normal isometric projection is used for right-angular objects and ellipses are constructed by the compass four-point method (see Fig. 4.28).

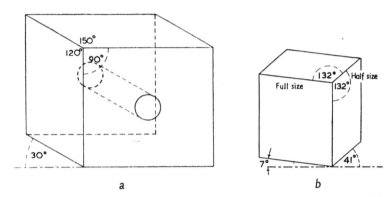

a   b

FIG. 4.29. *A cube with central hole drawn in oblique projection;* (b) *a cube drawn in dimetric projection. The dimensions along the oblique axis are halved, as indicated on the drawing.*

Oblique Projection

The essential feature of oblique projection is that two axes of the projection are at right angles. This is illustrated in Fig. 4.29a. An angle of 30° or 45° is generally used at the base, mainly for simplicity; other angles are used as required, the choice resting on desired emphasis of a particular surface, e.g. a larger base angle in the figure would increase the emphasis on the top view.

Dimetric and Trimetric Projection

In isometric projection the three isometric axes are equally inclined to the plane of projection. If two only of the axes are equally inclined, the projection is called *dimetric* (Fig. 4.29b), and if all three axes form unequal angles with the plane of projection, the projection is *trimetric*. A special trimetric scale has been designed

135

by J. P. Simpson and J. Stewart to enable drawings to be made for three combinations of angles.*

Planometric Projection

With this projection, either the plan or the top view of an object is used as the foundation of the drawing, the elevations then being projected at a suitable angle, say 45°, as in Fig. 4.30. Such projections are useful in displaying large horizontal areas of buildings, together with fittings, piping, etc., contained in such areas.

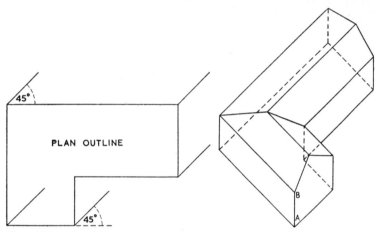

FIG. 4.30. *An object drawn in planometric projection and in axonometric projection.*

Axonometric Projection

These projections are made in much the same way as planometric projections, but the plan is turned through an angle, the object appearing to be pivoted at one corner, say A (Fig. 4.30), so that vertical edges such as AB now appear as vertical lines on the drawing. Here again, the method is suitable for illustrating interior detail and is frequently used instead of perspective.

Perspective Drawing in Engineering

The application of the simple principles of perspective drawing to engineering has been accelerated in recent years, largely because orthographic projections are not readily understood by workers engaged in projects such as aircraft and automobile production.

* See *Electronic Engineering* (1944), **16**, 478.

Credit for the introduction of this system into engineering drawing is largely due to Mr. George Tharratt. The American aircraft industry was quick in realizing its advantages, and the system became known there as *production illustration.* One of the difficulties in introducing the system was that draughtsmen trained and skilled in orthographic projection were often lacking in artistic sense, whereas perspective drawing is more in the province of the artist than of the engineer. It became necessary, therefore, to train personnel in production illustration. Since the illustrations are engineering drawings rather than artistic creations, the first requirement for personnel is engineering knowledge and the second requirement artistic sense and ability to draw.

Production Illustration is thoroughly explained in a book bearing that title by J. Treacy (John Wiley & Sons, N.Y.) and also in *Pictorial Drawing for Engineers* by A. C. Parkinson (Pitman & Sons, London). These books are representative of a number dealing with pictorial drawing. The principles of perspective drawing and methods of application are set out in the *Handbook of Perspective* by A. J. Warren (Crosby Lockwood & Co. London).

Dimensioning

Dimensions up to 2 feet are usually expressed in inches: for example, $3\frac{3}{8}''$, $17\cdot36''$, but $2'\ 3\frac{1}{2}''$. On drawings, the decimal point

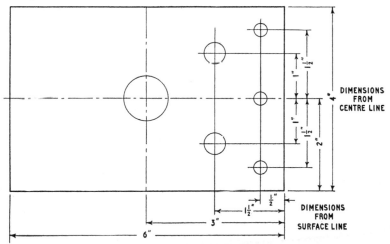

FIG. 4.31. *The correct method of drawing dimension lines.*

137

is never preceded by 0 : thus, ·86 and not 0·86. In printed text, it appears as 0·86.*

Metric dimensions on drawings should be in millimetres or metres, e.g. 16·25 mm or 3·8 m. The decimal point should be placed central to the figure thus ·7, not .7 nor ˙7.

Dimensional lines are usually drawn thinner than outlines or detail and may be based on the surface outlines or on the centre lines (Fig. 4.31). Projection lines drawn from surface lines should be thin and stand just clear of surface lines. Dimensional arrow heads should be sharp and partly filled. If pointer or directional arrows are used in addition to dimensional arrows each should be separately defined as in Fig. 4.32.

DIMENSION   POINTER   DIRECTION

FIG. 4.32.   *Shapes of arrow heads.*

An example of incorrect dimensioning is shown in Fig. 4.33. The

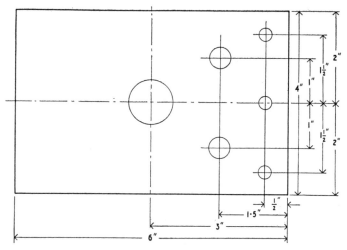

FIG. 4.33.   *An example of a badly dimensioned drawing.*

vertical dimensions are placed in wrong order, the overall dimension appearing close to, instead of remote from, the outline. Also, the 2″ dimension is given twice : if the outline is four inches and one

* These apparently contradictory conventions are recommended by British Standards Institution for reasons the authors do not pretend to understand.

dimension two inches, the other half must be two inches and should not be shown on the drawing.

In the horizontal dimensions, fractions and decimals are mixed for the same unit of dimension; finally, the arrow heads used are directional and not dimensional.

Dimensions for Radii. When possible, dimensions for small radii are shown outside the outline as in Fig. 4.34. The centre of the radius may be marked with a small dot, and dimensions from the outline projected as indicated in the diagram.

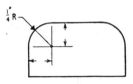

FIG. 4.34. *Method of dimensioning small radii.*

Dimensions of Irregular Contours

Dimensions of irregular contours are best shown by ordinates as in Fig. 4.35. Dimensions are from a datum line drawn through

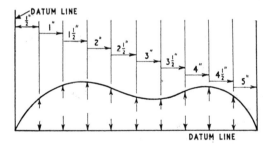

FIG. 4.35. *Dimensioning irregular contours.*

the contour limits. Steps are projected from this datum line and measured from a second datum line on one side of the object. Since the ordinates may be closely spaced, dimensions and measurement steps should be staggered as shown.

Limits to dimensions should be quoted in actual figures and not in terms of plus or minus, for example $\dfrac{2 \cdot 16}{2 \cdot 12}$, not $2 \cdot 14 \pm \cdot 02$.

INSTRUCTIONAL DRAWINGS

Instructional drawings have many and varied applications, such as in training, construction, and operation in specific branches of engineering industries. The keynote of all such drawings is, or should be, simplification. The technical writer must consider how much information each drawing contains, and whether the drawing will be readily understood by his readers. For purposes of training, completed drawings are usually undesirable; whenever possible, they should be broken down to step-by-step illustrations, just as complicated electrical diagrams are re-drawn in simplified circuit form.

Constructional Drawings

Construction drawings may be orthographic or pictorial, according to purpose and to the skill of the personnel who have to use

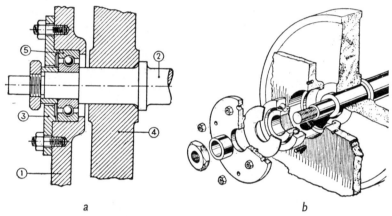

a   b

FIG. 4.36. Left : *Orthodox sectional view, and* (right) *exploded view of part of a gear-box.*

(*From Pictorial Drawing for Engineers* (*Parkinson*) *by courtesy of Pitman & Sons, the publishers.*)

them. Much use is now made of *exploded views* and *cut-away* or *sectional views*, of which two interesting examples are shown in Fig. 4.36. The orthographic drawing (*a*) would be adequate for the trained engineer; a semi-skilled mechanic might well find (*b*) much easier to understand when assembling the machine. It will be noted that (*b*) combines the exploded view with a cut-away of the main parts of the machine.

Operational Drawings

The purpose of operational drawings is to indicate how a machine

FIG. 4.37. *Sectional view of motor and gearing reproduced in*
four-colour half-tone

(*By courtesy of Vactric Ltd.*)

[*Facing p. 140*

or a system works; such drawings are, therefore, purely instructional. An interesting example is shown in Fig. 4.37 which lends support to the argument that a good illustration needs no text to describe it. In this illustration, full use is made of colour and sectioning to show the details. See also under Colour (p. 163).

Drawing Sheets

In large drawing offices it is customary to use drawing and tracing sheets in a number of selected sizes. These sizes should bear relation to the width of rolls as produced by the mills; this is normally 30 inches or 40 inches. Other considerations are adequate trimming margins and filing facilities. The sizes recommended by the British Standards Institution are as follows:

Sheet Size (inches)	Drawing Size or Borders (inches)
72 × 40	70 × 38
60 × 40	58 × 38
53 × 30	52 × 29
40 × 30	39 × 29
40 × 27	39 × 26
40 × 15	39 × 14
30 × 22	29 × 21
30 × 20	29 × 19
27 × 20	26 × 19
20 × 15	19 × 14
15 × 10	$14\frac{1}{4} \times 9\frac{1}{4}$
13 × 8	$12\frac{1}{4} \times 7\frac{1}{4}$
10 × 8	$9\frac{1}{4} \times 7\frac{1}{4}$

The border sizes shown do not allow for binding margins.

It is convenient for drawing offices to have their stock size sheets printed with border lines and with corner panels to suit the class of work. Requirements vary extensively from firm to firm, but panels used most frequently give details of:

Number	Changes
Staff Initials	Scale

Stock Parts

The printing of standard layouts for drawing sheets in large numbers is usually beyond the scope of drawing-office print rooms; the work can be done economically, however, by most lithographic printers and the cost is amply justified by the saving in drawing

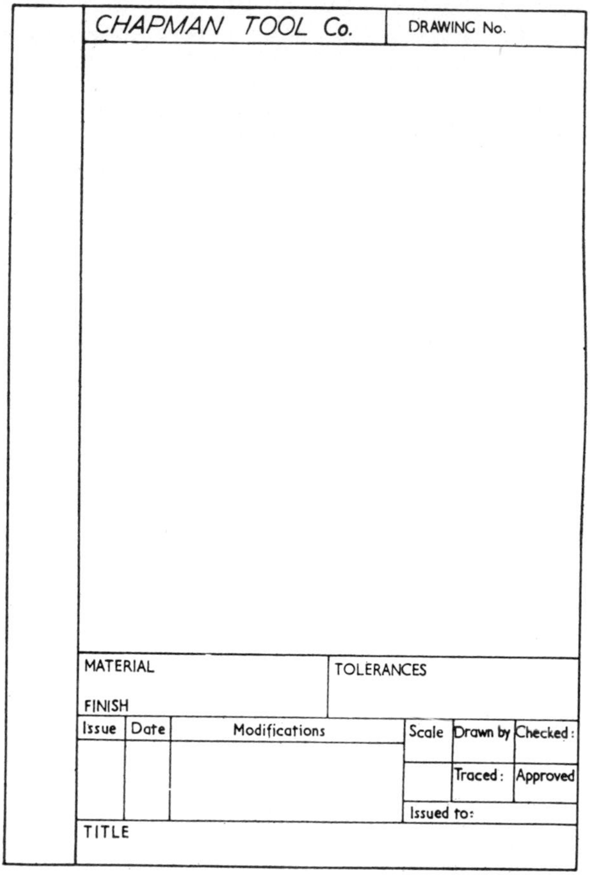

FIG. 4.38. *Specimen layout for a drawing sheet for small detail parts.*

office time. A typical layout for a drawing of small components is shown in Fig. 4.38.

Drawing Board Sizes

The standard sizes of drawing boards in Great Britain are:
Half Imperial 23 × 16 inches Double Elephant 42 × 29 inches
Imperial   31 × 23   ,,   Antiquarian   54 × 32   ,,

Boards are also obtainable measuring 42 in. × 32 in. to fit sheets 40 in. × 30 in.

Graphical Symbols

The main graphical symbols recommended for use in Engineering Drawing Offices will be found in the list of British Standards given on p. 33.

ELECTRICAL DRAWINGS

The operation of an electrical device or installation can be illustrated in so many different ways that no single definition can be applied to the term electrical drawing. It has become general practice to classify electrical drawings under three main headings, which, in order of increasing complexity are: *Block Schematic, Circuit Diagram* and *Wiring Diagram*. In addition, there is a *layout* or *plan* drawing, but since this merely serves to illustrate the disposition of apparatus on a given site, or on a chassis, it is mechanical rather than electrical in conception. Other types of diagram which are distinguished by name in British Standard terminology are:

Installation diagram: A diagram which depicts the separate units of all or parts of an installation, together with all their interconnecting cables and wires and the necessary junction boxes.

Wiring layout: A diagram indicating the physical layout of wiring. (This is sometimes called a bench wiring diagram, a term which is objectionable as it can be confused with the wiring diagram of a bench).

Component layout: A diagram or illustration showing the whereabouts of various components.

Functional diagram: A diagram to illustrate the function of a piece of equipment.

Servicing diagram: A diagram specially drawn to show details of special interest to people servicing equipment, e.g. voltages on tags, etc.

Routed schematic diagram: A circuit diagram which also acts as a wiring diagram and shows uniquely the point-to-point connections of all the wires.

Block Schematic Drawings

The continuity of many electrical circuits can be shown most readily by means of block schematic drawings. In these, each complete unit of the apparatus is indicated by a block symbol. To use a familiar example, consider a simple public address system, making use of a microphone and record player feeding four loud-speakers through a single amplifier (Fig. 4.39a). Several features of this simple drawing are worthy of attention because they embody principles that can be applied to most electrical circuit drawings.

First, the sequence from *source* to *destination* is drawn from left to right; this is important, because when a reader is following the text in left-to-right order he scans the diagrams in that way.

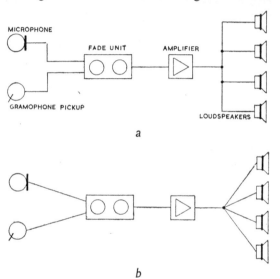

FIG. 4.39. (a) *A block schematic drawing, and* (b) *the same drawing simplified.*

Second, the use of block symbols simplifies drawing; the symbols can be confined to rectangles, triangles or circles with legends, but symbols indicating the shape or function of certain components are preferable. Once the use of such symbols becomes firmly established within an organization, lettering can be omitted.

Third, single connecting lines simplify drawing effort and enhance the readability.

The example in Fig. 4.39a, suffers from a common fault in that economy in drawing effort has been sacrificed for symmetrical appearance. This figure has been redrawn in Fig. 4.39b: in this, the lines on the input side are reduced from six to two, and on the output side the distribution to four destinations from a common point is more effectively displayed.

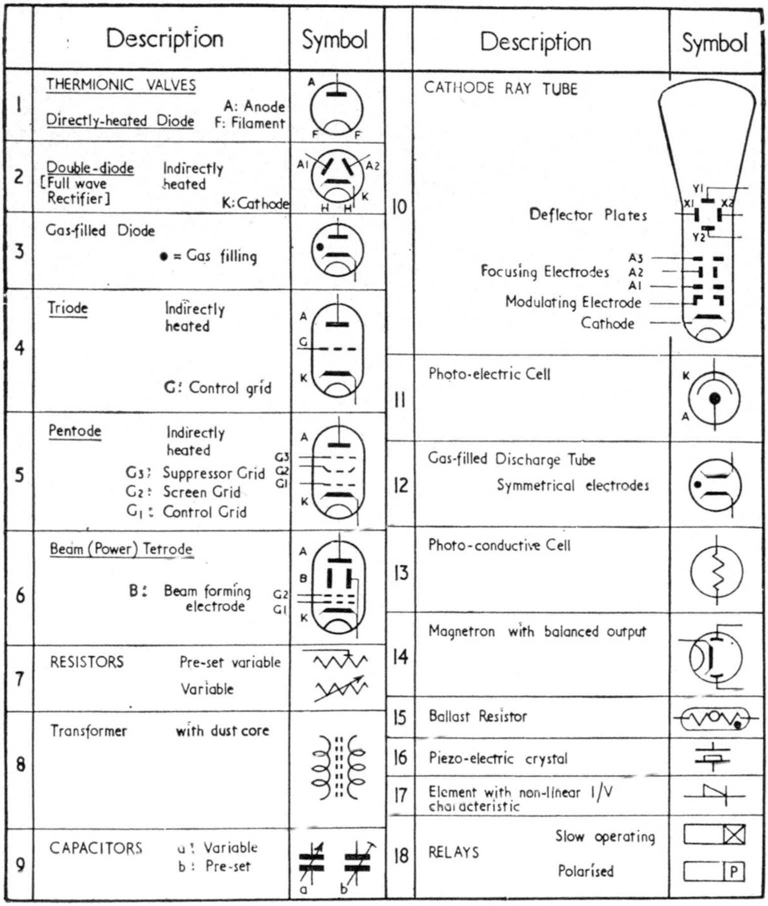

	Description	Symbol		Description	Symbol
1	THERMIONIC VALVES Directly-heated Diode A: Anode F: Filament			CATHODE RAY TUBE	
2	Double-diode Indirectly [Full wave heated Rectifier] K: Cathode		10	Deflector Plates	
3	Gas-filled Diode ● = Gas filling			Focusing Electrodes A3 A2 A1	
4	Triode Indirectly heated G: Control grid			Modulating Electrode Cathode	
			11	Photo-electric Cell	
5	Pentode Indirectly heated G3: Suppressor Grid G2: Screen Grid G1: Control Grid		12	Gas-filled Discharge Tube Symmetrical electrodes	
6	Beam (Power) Tetrode B: Beam forming electrode		13	Photo-conductive Cell	
			14	Magnetron with balanced output	
7	RESISTORS Pre-set variable Variable		15	Ballast Resistor	
8	Transformer with dust core		16	Piezo-electric crystal	
			17	Element with non-linear I/V characteristic	
9	CAPACITORS a: Variable b: Pre-set		18	RELAYS Slow operating Polarised	

FIG. 4.40. *Selected electronic symbols for circuit diagrams.*

Circuit Drawings

The definition of a Circuit Drawing, according to British Standard 530, is 'a diagram which depicts in simple form, by means of symbols, the essential components and the interconnexions required to provide the information necessary to show the operation of the circuit.

	Description	Symbol		Description	Symbol
1	CONDUCTORS Main		20	TRANSFORMERS	
	Subsidiary				
2	CONDUCTORS ⓐ Connected		21	Auto:	
	ⓑ Crossing				
3	Underground Line		22	RESISTORS	
4	One or more conductors forming a circuit: e.g. 3-phase 4-wire.			Non-inductive	
			23	Inductor [Iron-cored Choke]	
5	Group of circuits following the same route − No. per circuit		24	CAPACITORS	
				E: Electrolytic	
6	Terminal Board		25	CONTACTS Various forms	
				[Auxiliary Switches] Open:	
				Closed:	
7	LINK with separable contacts		26	Relay contacts	
	bolted contacts		27	Relay: General symbol	
8	Fuse		28	LAMPS	
9	Surge Diverter [Lightning arrester]			s: Signal	
10	EARTH		29	Indicating Instrument with appropriate letter	
11	GENERATING STATION General symbol		30	Ceiling Outlet	
			31	Socket Outlet	
	Steam or I.C.		32	Thermostat	
12	Sub-station − General Symbol			INSTALLATIONS	
13	MACHINE − General Symbol		33	Fixed Heater	
14	D.C. Generator or Motor with compounding or compoles		34	Switch	
			35	Pendant Switch	
15	A.C. Generator 3-phase 4-wire		36	Conductor Rail	
			37	Overhead line pole	
16	Induction Motor 3-phase Squirrel cage Y−connected		38	Steel Support	
			39	Lattice Support	
17	Rectifier − General Symbol			TRACTION	
18	Mercury-arc Rectifier		40	Section Insulator	
19	Metal Rectifier Full-wave Bridge connected		41	Ear	
			42	Collector Shoe	
			43	Contactor	

FIG. 4.41. *A table of selected electrical circuit symbols.*

A circuit diagram will usually be drawn so as to show this as clearly as possible, and therefore will not necessarily depict the various items and their connexions in their actual spatial relationships '.*
The commonly used electrical and electronic symbols are shown in the diagrams of Figs. 4.40 and 4.41.

For the purposes of this discussion a circuit drawing is defined as a diagram depicting all essential components and interconnexions, arranged to show clearly the working principles of the device and the theoretical relationship of components without regard to their physical disposition; the diagram should give enough information to permit replacement of components without reference to other documents.

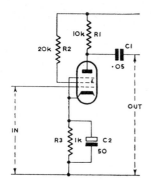

FIG. 4.42. *A circuit diagram of a single valve stage.*

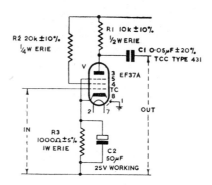

FIG. 4.43. *The same diagram with full information on the components added.*

The last sentence materially affects the amount of information that a circuit diagram should contain, and implies the inclusion of component values, ratings and tolerances; these may not be necessary in a textbook or even in a technical journal, but are indispensable in an instruction manual. The service or maintenance engineer is probably the most frequent user of circuit diagrams, and his work is simplified if he can use the same document for diagnosis and subsequent action.

The problem is how to accommodate all this information on an

* The authors think that this says too little in too many words. The purpose of a circuit diagram is not confined to showing the operation of a circuit; this satisfies the designer and probably the student, but is inadequate for the constructor or for the service engineer.

average size drawing sheet. For the purpose of circuit study, it is essential that component symbols should be well separated as in Fig. 4.42. If full maintenance information is to be given on the drawing itself, it will appear as in Fig. 4.43. This is satisfactory for the simple single-stage amplifier depicted, but the principle could not be applied to an electronic device having hundreds of components.

The solution to the problem lies in providing the additional information in tabular form. For some drawings the table may be on the same sheet as the diagram; for others, a separate sheet will be necessary. The information required may be summarized as follows:

> Component Reference Numbers
> Component Values
> Component Ratings
> Component Tolerances
> Component Types
> Component Locations

Component References and Values on Circuit Diagrams

Component reference numbers and values are usually essential on all circuit diagrams. Reference numbers bear the code letter of the component, e.g. R for resistor, and are followed by sequential numbers or letters, starting from the left of the diagram. This sequence may often break down, because modifications in various stages of design often necessitate additional components; thus it is that on a finished drawing R43 may appear in close proximity to R1, and R42 on the extreme right of the diagram. The code letter and reference number should be of equal size and printed in line, except in purely theoretical circuits subjected to mathematical analysis. Where this applies, reference numbers should be 'inferior' or 'dropped', to conform with the text (see p. 233). In circuits containing several hundred components there is much to be said for dispensing with the code letters to save space; the symbols give adequate distinction between components.

Component values should, whenever possible, be printed on the opposite side rather than adjacent to the reference number as in Fig. 4.42. On electronic circuit diagrams, values should be given in numbers only; it is not necessary to include units such as ohms, microfarads and henrys. It is necessary to indicate multiples or divisions of these values, and the following practice is recommended in B.S. 530:

Resistances	Up to 999 ohms	number only.
	1,000 to 999,999 ohms	number of kilohms., e.g. 47k
	1 megohm and above	number of megohms., e.g. 1·5M
Capacitances	Up to 999 picofarads*	number in picofarads, e.g. 50p
	1 microfarad and above	number only.
Inductances	Up to 999 microhenrys	number in microhenrys, e.g. 500μ
	1 to 999 millihenrys	number in millihenrys, e.g. 750m
	1 henry upwards	number only.

Observing these recommendations will materially reduce drawing effort on complex circuits and save space.

Component Tolerances

Component tolerances relate to values and are applied in particular to resistances and capacitances. They are expressed in terms of percentage above or below a nominal value and must be determined by the designer. Thus, if the value of a resistance may be anything between 44 and 50 kilohms, the designer would specify 47k $\pm$ 5% and the tolerance should be defined in that way. As a point of interest, this conflicts with the method of expressing dimension tolerances (p. 139).

Component Ratings

Component ratings apply in particular to the maximum power dissipation of resistors and the maximum safe working voltages for capacitors. They are quoted in watts and volts respectively.

Component Types

Information on component types should include the name of the

---

* American practice is to use the abbreviation ' $\mu\mu$F ' for picofarads, but the advantage of the single letter is obvious.

149

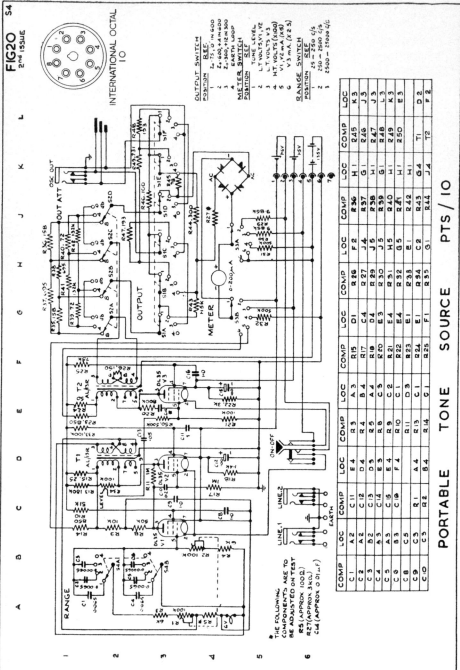

FIG. 4.44. *A circuit diagram with a map reference for use with component list.*

manufacturer in abbreviated form and the complete code allotted to the component, e.g. T.C.C. M2N.

Component Location on Circuit Diagrams

In recent years the increasing complexity of circuit diagrams has necessitated the adoption of some means for locating individual components; this is particularly important when the working of the circuit is explained in the text of an instruction manual. The method recommended and used extensively in current practice is to insert a table above the drawing as shown below.

R	1 30 50	2 3	3 13 5	12 18	15 53	20	R
C	1	3 4	5 6	8 11 15	14 19	24	C
MISC		L1 TR1			MR2		MISC

With this method, the reader can locate a given component reference number by scanning the diagram vertically from the table. The system is adequate for relatively small circuits, but becomes cumbersome and impracticable when a very large number of components is involved. An alternative method is shown in Fig. 4.44. Here the table is replaced by a map reference system, and each component allocated a location code in the comprehensive component table.

Code Letters for Components on Circuit Diagrams

The following list is based on recommendations made by the British Standards Institution.

When more than one component of a kind appears on a diagram, sequence should be numerical unless the component has the function of a switch. Thus, R1, R2, but SA, SB; RLA, RLB; LKA, LKB.

151

Table of Code Letters

Aerial	AE	Fuse	FS
Battery	BY	Inductor	L
Capacitor	C	Jack	JK
Earth	E	Key	K
Lamp	ILP (indicating or illuminating)		
„	PLP (pilot)		
„	RLP (resistor)		
Link	LK		
Loudspeaker	LS		
Metal Rectifier	MR (also any other rectifier drawn as a triangle)		
Meter	M (with prefix as necessary, e.g. VM = voltmeter)		
Microphone	MIC		
Piezo-electric crystal	XL		
Pickup	PU		
Plug	PL		
Relay	RL (uncoded ; for coded relays, see Detached Contact System)		
Resistor	R (fixed)		
„	RV (variable)		
Socket	SKT		
Switch	S		
Transformer	T		
Valve	V	Vibrator Power Supply	VB

Component Tables on a Circuit Diagram

The problem of accommodating all the information previously suggested on a single sheet is not incapable of solution, and one method is illustrated in Fig. 4.45. The layout should be compared with that in Fig. 4.44.

The component ratings, types and tolerances are incorporated in one column, headed *Type*.* In general this circuit drawing conforms to British Standards and all symbols were drawn by stencils and all lettering by letter guides. The preparation of a table of this size on the drawing board by stencils takes a considerable time, which can be reduced by using a Vari-Typer and cartridge paper. If the circuit is prepared on the same medium, the table can be attached to the circuit by office gum. (See Mechanical Aids.)

---

* It will be noticed that all the recommendations made in previous paragraphs have not been applied ; for example decimal points are preceded by noughts, and there is inconsistency in capacitance values.

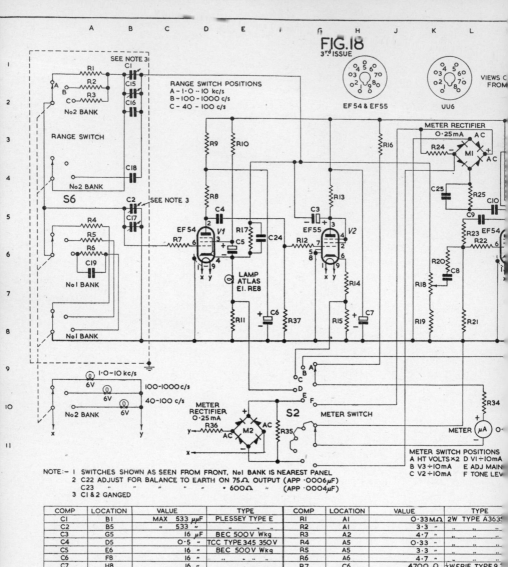

FIG.18
3rd ISSUE

RANGE SWITCH POSITIONS
A - 1·0 - 10 kc/s
B - 100 - 1000 c/s
C - 40 - 100 c/s

EF 54 & EF 55

UU6

VIEWS C
FROM

SEE NOTE 3
No2 BANK
RANGE SWITCH
No2 BANK
S6
SEE NOTE 3
No1 BANK
No1 BANK

METER RECTIFIER
0·25mA

LAMP
ATLAS
E1. RE8

1·0-10 kc/s
6V
6V
100-1000c/s
40-100 c/s
6V
No2 BANK

METER
RECTIFIER
0·25 mA
S2
METER SWITCH
METER

NOTE:— 1 SWITCHES SHOWN AS SEEN FROM FRONT, No1 BANK IS NEAREST PANEL
2 C22 ADJUST FOR BALANCE TO EARTH ON 75Ω OUTPUT (APP ·0006μF)
C23 " " " " " · 600Ω " (APP ·0004μF)
3 C1 & 2 GANGED

METER SWITCH POSITIONS
A HT VOLTS×2 D V1÷10mA
B V3÷10mA   E ADJ MAIN
C V2÷10mA   F TONE LEV

COMP	LOCATION	VALUE	TYPE	COMP	LOCATION	VALUE	TYPE
C1	B1	MAX 533 μμF	PLESSEY TYPE E	R1	A1	0·33MΩ	2W TYPE A363
C2	B5	" 533 "	"	R2	A1	3·3 "	" "
C3	G5	16 μF	BEC 500V Wkg	R3	A2	4·7 "	" "
C4	D5	0·5 "	TCC TYPE 345 350V	R4	A5	0·33 "	" "
C5	E6	16 "	BEC 500V Wkg	R5	A5	3·3 "	" "
C6	F8	16 "	" " "	R6	A6	4·7 "	" "
C7	H8	16 "	" " "	R7	C6	4700 Ω	½WERIE TYPE 9
C8	K7	0·1 "	TCC TYPE 345 350V	R8	D5	0·1MΩ	" "
C9	L5	0·1 "	" - M2N	R9	D3	47000 Ω	" "
C10	M5	0·1 "	" 345 350V	R10	E3	1·0MΩ	" "
C11	N6	16 "	BEC 500V Wkg	R11	E8	10 Ω	½W ERIE TYPE 10
C12	O8	250 "	" 12V Wkg	R12	G6	4700 "	½W ERIE TYPE 9
C13	P8	16 "	" 500V Wkg	R13	G4	15000 "	2W ERIE TYPE 1
C14	Q10	8 "	TCC TYPE CE 25P	R14	H7	330 "	½W " TYPE 100
C15	B2	2-25 μμF	PLESSEY TYPE A3	R15	H8	10 "	½W " "
C16	B2	15 "	TCC TYPE SCT1	R16	J3	2MΩ	½WERIE TYPE 9
C17	B5	2-25 "	PLESSEY TYPE A3	R17	E6	2500 Ω APPROX	SELECTED ON T
C18	B4	0·00025 μF	TCC TYPE SCT3±2%	R18	K7	0·1MΩ	LHAP 10410-24
C19	A7	0·00025 μF	" " "	R19	K8	0·1 "	½W ERIE TYPE 9
C20	U2	·02 μF	UIC TYPE SM1007±1%	R20	K6	0·1 "	" "
C21	T4	·02 μF	" " "	R21	L8	0·1 "	" "
C22	T1	500μμF	TCC TYPE M2N	R22	L6	4700 Ω	" "
C23	T1	500 "	" "	R23	L5	1·5MΩ	" "
C24	E6	10 "	TCC TYPE SCT1	R24	K3	2000 Ω	" "
C25	K4	10 pF	" "	R25	L4	480kΩ	½W TYPE A362
L1	P9	20 H	BULGIN TYPE LF40	R26	N3	33000 Ω	½WERIE TYPE 9

PORTABLE TONE SOURCE PTS/13 CIRCUIT

FIG. 4.45 *A complete circuit diagram with*
(British Broa

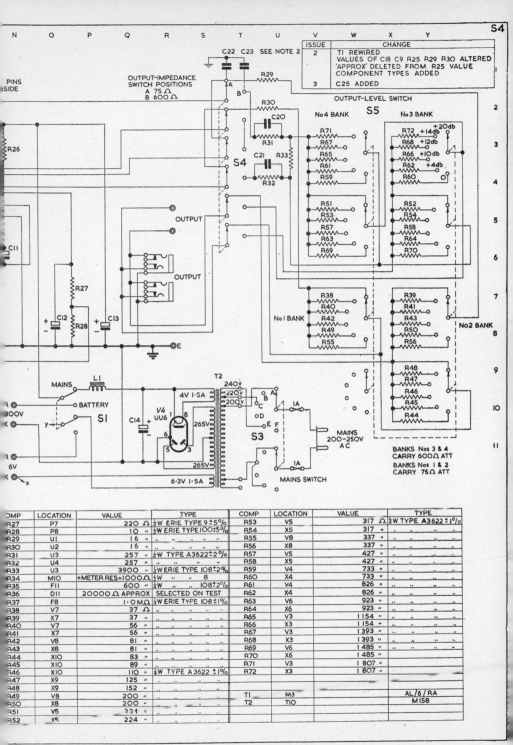

COMP	LOCATION	VALUE	TYPE
R27	P7	220 Ω	½W ERIE TYPE 9 ±5%
R28	P8	10 "	½W ERIE TYPE 100 ±5%
R29	U1	16 "	
R30	U2	16 "	
R31	U3	257 "	½W TYPE A3622±2%
R32	U4	257 "	
R33	U3	3900 "	½W ERIE TYPE 108±2%
R34	M10	+METER RES=1000Ω	½W " 8
R35	F11	600 "	½W " 108±2%
R36	D11	20000Ω APPROX	SELECTED ON TEST
R37	F8	1·0 MΩ	½W ERIE TYPE 108±1%
R38	V7	37 Ω	
R39	X7	37 "	
R40	V7	56 "	
R41	X7	56 "	
R42	V8	81 "	
R43	X8	81 "	
R44	X10	83 "	
R45	X10	89 "	
R46	X10	110 "	½W TYPE A3622 ±1%
R47	X9	125 "	
R48	X9	152 "	
R49	V8	200 "	
R50	X8	200 "	
R51	V5	221 "	
R52	X5	224 "	

COMP	LOCATION	VALUE	TYPE
R53	V5	317 Ω	½W TYPE A3622 ±1%
R54	X5	317 "	
R55	V8	337 "	
R56	X8	337 "	
R57	V5	427 "	
R58	X5	427 "	
R59	V4	733 "	
R60	X4	733 "	
R61	V4	826 "	
R62	X4	826 "	
R63	V6	923 "	
R64	X6	923 "	
R65	V3	1154 "	
R66	X3	1154 "	
R67	V3	1393 "	
R68	X3	1393 "	
R69	V6	1485 "	
R70	X6	1485 "	
R71	V3	1807 "	
R72	X3	1807 "	
T1	M3		AL/6/RA
T2	T10		M158

nent list and all relevant information added.

Corporation)

Between pages 152–153.

Construction of Circuit Diagrams

Much work has been done in recent years to improve the technique of circuit drawing, particularly by the late L. H. Bainbridge-Bell; many of his recommendations are incorporated in B.S. 530 : 1948. *Graphical Symbols for Telecommunications.*

Some of these recommendations are of far-reaching importance ; for example the method of representing a junction or crossing of two lines. For many years this was shown as in Fig. 4.46a, where the wires were joined and as in Fig. 4.46b, where they crossed without joining. Later, the crossover loop was dispensed with, and wires crossing without joining were indicated as in (a). The junction was indicated by a dot (Fig. 4.46c).

FIG. 4.46. *Methods of indicating the junction and crossing of two wires (a) is now obsolete for indicating a junction.*

In this arrangement there is the possibility of the dot being omitted, with the risk of serious consequences from wrong wiring. To avoid this, Bainbridge-Bell suggested that all junctions should be staggered, as in Fig. 4.46d, making the junction obvious whether the dot was omitted or included.

It is important that when a circuit has a definite input and output the sequence should be from left to right as in block schematics.

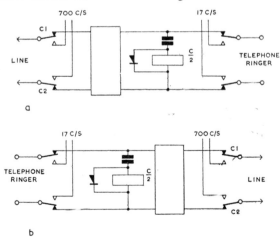

FIG. 4.47. *A circuit diagram drawn with right-to-left sequence (a) and left-to-right sequence (b).*

153

Fig. 4.47a was submitted for publication with a right-to-left sequence. The text implied that the ringing signal from a telephone operated a relay C/2, the contacts C1 and C2 connecting a 700 c/s signal to an outgoing telephone line.

In Fig. 4.47b the sequence is reversed and the reader can judge for himself which is the easier to follow.

The Detached Contact System

In relay circuits, the circuit controlling the operation of the relay coil is usually unrelated to the contact circuits. The purpose of the ' detached contact ' system is to relate the relay to its contacts, and at the same time segregate the control circuit from the contact circuit. The contacts can then be drawn in at the part where they most conveniently show their function.

The relay is coded in the form of a fraction, the numerator being the component reference number or letter, and the denominator the number of contact units *in use* on the circuit. The separated contact units are coded in numerical sequence as in Fig. 4.47b, retaining the reference code letter.

Wiring Diagrams

The primary purpose of wiring diagrams is to give precise information to a wireman on how to connect up the terminals of an electrical device or installation. Its secondary purpose is to aid the service engineer in tracing faults.

At one time, when most electrical circuits were relatively simple, wiring was arranged in neat geometrical patterns and the wiring diagram often consisted of an array of parallel lines.

The complexity of modern electrical circuits and the rapidly increasing application of electronic devices has had drastic repercussions on the layout of wiring diagrams. For example, in a television receiver hundreds of components are crammed into a space of not more than one or two cubic feet. This has necessitated a new technique in wiring, known as ' point-to-point ', in which connexions from one point to another are made by the shortest possible route, and crossing each other in all directions.

It is not an easy matter to lay out a wiring diagram of this type and it is well-nigh impossible to arrange components in their relative positions, especially when a chassis has several sections, and components are mounted on both sides of panels. The best that can be done is to lay out each part of the chassis separately and arrange the components on the diagram as nearly as possible to their physical positions. Fig. 4.48 shows a section of a wiring diagram illustrating this method. It will be noted that on this diagram, the wireman's job is greatly simplified by the numbering of components, the

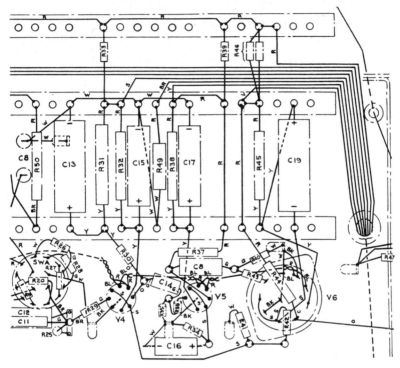

FIG. 4.48. *A wiring diagram arranged according to the layout of the components.*

numbers being painted on the actual components, and conforming to the component references on the related circuit diagram. This practice is also of great use to the service engineer when tracing faults with the aid of a circuit diagram. He does not waste time in tracing R42; it is marked on the component.

Functional Representation on Circuit Diagrams

The function of certain sections of many electronic circuits can

155

often be made clear by the adoption of suitable conventions. A familiar example is a Wheatstone Bridge circuit (Fig. 4.49). It so happens that this figure provides a theoretical explanation of the corresponding valve circuits of Fig. 4.45. It is clear that the complete component array in Fig. 4.45 could not very well be drawn in the form of Fig. 4.49, but the technical writer can often help his readers by reconstructing the diagram, using conventional circuits of this kind in the text.

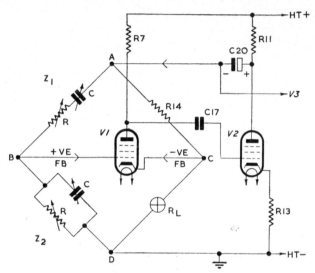

FIG. 4.49. *A conventional method of drawing a bridge circuit.*

Another example of functional layout is the push-pull valve circuit (Fig. 4.50a). By placing the valves one above the other, and connecting them as shown, the nature of the circuit becomes immediately obvious to an electronic engineer.

A multivibrator circuit is drawn as in Fig. 4.50b. Fig. 4.50c shows the same circuit in which the interaction between the valves is less clear.

When the two valves of Fig. 4.50d are included in one envelope or tube, the envelope is drawn in two halves as indicated in Fig. 4.50e. Since there is only one component, the same component reference number is used for both valves.

A cathode bias resistor in a valve circuit is drawn on the left of the symbol as in Fig. 4.50f. If, however, the resistor provides a voltage into a subsequent circuit, as with the *cathode-follower*, the resistor is drawn on the right of the symbol (Fig. 4.50g).

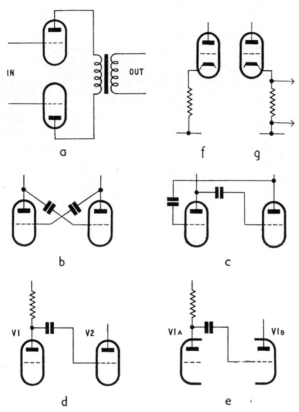

FIG. 4.50. *Examples of the functional arrangement of components in a diagram :*
(a) *two valves in push-pull,* (b) *a cross-over connexion in a multivibrator circuit,*
(c) *the same connexion clumsily drawn,* (d) *two separate valves, and* (e) *two valves in the same envelope.* (f) *a cathode bias resistor, and* (g) *the resistor arranged on the right-hand side for taking the output leads from it, as in the cathode-follower.*

Component Stencils

Attempts are continually being made to simplify the work of circuit drawing, and various devices designed to this end have appeared both in Europe and America. The reader will be well advised to treat with caution some of the claims made with regard to time saved. Nevertheless there is no doubt that certain devices may be adopted with confidence, and first among these is the component stencil. The specimen used for constructing Fig. 4.45 is shown in Fig. 4.51. Stencils of this kind can be made to order; the example shown is intended for half-scale reduction and the illustration has been reduced by this factor. The time saved by using the stencils is considerable: an illustrator took 4 minutes to draw the symbols with a stencil and 39 minutes without. A draughtsman unfamiliar with stencils would probably take only 20 minutes to draw without them, but the time would be saved by

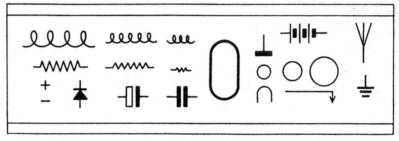

Fig. 4.51. *Drawing of a typical UNO stencil made to specification.*

using them. An important advantage is that complete uniformity can be obtained among several illustrators engaged on the same project.

Letter Guides

For illustrators who are not expert at lettering by hand, the letter guides are indispensable for ensuring uniformity and neatness although they may not save as much time as would be expected. The most satisfactory form of letter guide is the UNO stencil, which is made in a variety of type sizes based on the Gill sans letter (see p. 256). Equivalents of these guides in America are the Wrico and the Leroy lettering outfits. A more elaborate instrument is the Varigraph, in which letters may be drawn from a single master alphabet in a wide range of sizes and shapes.

In using stencils of the UNO type it is important to keep the letters free from ink, which clogs the outlines and spoils the finished work. The best effect is obtained by making the letters close together (Fig. 4.52) and if a specially neat effect is required for larger letters the ends may be 'squared off' with a brush dipped in Process White ink.

For lettering to be easily readable on a finished reproduction, the minimum height should be about $\frac{1}{16}$ in., and the stencil must be selected to produce this size *after reducing in scale*. It is convenient to remember that a No. 2 stencil is suitable for a 2 : 1 reduction and No. 4 for a 4 : 1 reduction.

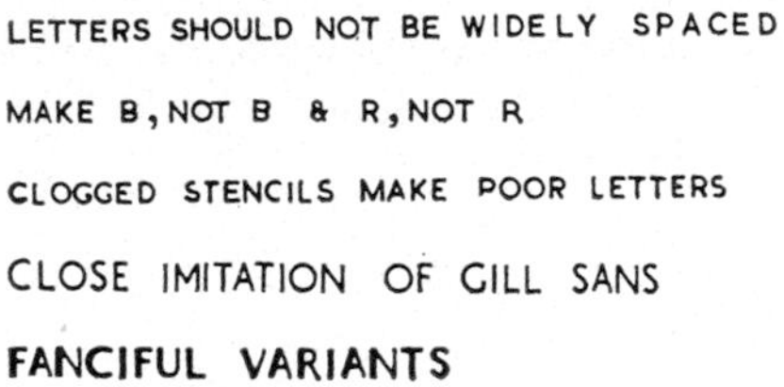

LETTERS SHOULD NOT BE WIDELY SPACED

MAKE B, NOT B & R, NOT R

CLOGGED STENCILS MAKE POOR LETTERS

CLOSE IMITATION OF GILL SANS

FANCIFUL VARIANTS

FIG. 4.52. *Lettering done with UNO stencils.*

Adhesive Symbols and Letters

In recent years many advantages have been claimed for the use of circuit symbols printed on adhesive paper or transparent plastic film. Theoretically, untrained office personnel can lay out a circuit by placing the cut out symbols in place on the drawing and joining up with straight lines, but in practice the original illustration must be laid out by the draughtsman and the fitting of the symbols to the layout is a finicky job requiring patience and a steady hand. With a trained draughtsman, the method has little advantage over the component stencil, and it must be remembered that if an adhesive symbol is stuck on a tracing the dyeline prints may not be satisfactory. On the other hand, the 'Artype' letters printed on a translucent adhesive background give a neat print-like finish to drawings. These have already been mentioned (p. 113) and can be obtained in a wide variety of styles and type sizes.

Opaque " Pasters "

Certain information which is common to all drawings may be pre-printed on gummed paper and stuck on the drawing area. The gummed paper labels, or " pasters ", are prepared from a block made from an original drawing or letterpress and can be used to cover such items as valveholders (Fig. 4.45), switch contact diagrams, or manufacturing instructions.

159

Large areas of lettering can be prepared on a Vari-Typer and photographically reduced. The complete lettering of circuits by this means is hardly practicable, but other engineering drawings containing no component references can be lettered entirely on a Vari-Typer. The principle can be applied to tracings provided that a firm impression can be assured. A process ribbon must be used, and a process-carbon sheet placed behind the transparency is a distinct advantage.

However experienced the draughtsman it is possible that he may not be familiar with the requirements of drawing for reproduction from line blocks. The principles of block-making are described in Chapter 5, p. 208, and in addition to understanding the technique of the process the draughtsman should be aware of the method of costing in order to produce the most economical drawings for the work in hand.

The cost of the block is calculated on an area basis, with a minimum charge* for a block not exceeding 14 square inches. It follows that two line drawings can be economically processed on the same sheet if their combined area does not exceed the minimum. A small charge is made by the blockmaker for cutting the blocks and mounting them separately, but even with this charge it is possible to keep the cost of the two small blocks below that of two separate blocks which would each be charged at the minimum rate. Drawings on the same sheet should be separated by at least $\frac{3}{4}''$ and the blockmaker should be instructed to make separate blocks by drawing a blue pencil line to separate the drawings and marking in the margin " Separates ".†

To keep the cost of the block as low as possible, the area should be as small as possible, and this implies that lettering should not be allowed to wander far from the main drawing. A series of badly-placed descriptive letters may increase the cost of the block by 25%.

It is convenient both for the blockmaker and the estimator to prepare all drawings for a standard reduction throughout—either 2 : 1 or 3 : 1. In drawing the details, it is often overlooked that the thickness of the lines is reduced in the same proportion as the overall dimensions of the drawing.

---

* At present from 13s. to 21s.

† The majority of illustrations for this book were drawn in pairs on sheets of thin board 10 in. by 7 in. and reduced to half scale.

Thin construction lines, when reduced to half their thickness, will tend to break up or blur on the block, and the reproduction will suffer after a printing of several thousand copies. In preparing a series of similar drawings (such as circuit diagrams) the uniform thickness of lines is of great importance, and it is more convenient and accurate to ink them in with a stylo pen of the type used for UNO or Leroy stencils.*

In general, the accuracy and neatness of drawing requires a higher standard if the work is intended for reproduction by line blocks. Imperfections which pass unnoticed in dye-line or photostat prints are noted by a reader in the printed page; it is possible that the machine-like accuracy of printer's type emphasizes any irregularities in hand-drawn illustrations. For this reason, each drawing should be scrutinized carefully before sending it to the blockmaker and any flaws should be corrected.

These corrections can be made by painting over the lines with white ink. The photographic plate used in block making will not distinguish between the white paper background and the white ink, provided that " Process White " is used. It is very important the corrections should *not* be made in Chinese White, as this ink absorbs the ultra-violet light used in photography and appears grey on the negative.

" Process White " ink, in addition to its use as a correcting medium, can be used as a time-saver in breaking up lines or black areas. Broken or chain-dotted lines can be more easily made by drawing a uniform line and marking the breaks with a brush charged with " Process White ", and, by a combination of " blacking-in " and " whiting-out " any part of a drawing may be altered without the necessity of starting over again. The broken lines of Fig. 4.43 were produced in this way.

It is no exaggeration to say that any drawing, however well produced, is improved by judicious touching-up with white ink.

Use of Mechanical Tints

The tedious work of drawing section lines by hand, or of dotting in areas can be avoided by using the so-called mechanical tints.†

---

* The No. 0 pen is very suitable for a 2 : 1 reduction in line thickness.

† The word " tint " in printing is applied to shading of various types and does not imply colour.

They consist of a series of lines, dots, or other patterns printed with mechanical accuracy on sheets of transparent material which is coated with adhesive on the back.   The patterns which are of most use to technical draughtsmen are the line tint and the dot tint, examples of which are shown in Fig. 4.53.   Similar tints are marketed in Great Britain under the name " Zipatone " by Hunter-Penrose Ltd. of Farringdon Rd., London, or under the name " Plastitone " by West & Partners, of Broadway, London, S.W.1.   In use, the tint is pressed down over the area to be covered and rubbed lightly to make it adhere to the paper.   The unwanted portion is then cut away with a sharp knife.   A wide variety of patterns is available, and additional patterns can be made by superimposing one tint on another (see centre pattern of Fig. 4.53).

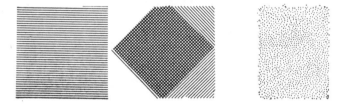

Fig. 4.53.   *Typical line and dot tints for sectioning or shading.   The central cross-hatching is obtained by crossing two line tints.*

If the draughtsman does not wish to lay the tint himself on the drawing it can be done by the blockmaker on the negative.   For this, the outline of the area should be marked in *blue pencil,* and the specification of the desired tint given on the drawing near the marked area.   As these tints are transparent, they are equally suitable for shading tracings which are to be reproduced by dye-line, and it is surprising that they are not more widely known and used.

Patent Drawings

Drawings which are satisfactory for illustrated descriptions are not necessarily acceptable for accompanying patent specifications. The following special requirements are listed in the official leaflet issued by the Patent Office, Southampton Buildings, London, W.C.2 (free on request).

Drawings shall be on sheets 13 × 8 in. or 13 × 16 in. with a half-inch margin all round.   They must not be folded.

Section lines and shading must be kept to a minimum and should not be closely drawn. Solid black or wash shading is not acceptable.

No dimensions may be marked on the drawings, and a scale should be drawn, not stated in words.

Letters and numerals must not be less than $\frac{1}{8}$ in.

Thin lines (constructional or indicating) should not be used: they should be as thick as the drawing lines.

Suitable drawing paper is smooth surface 70–90 lb per 500 sheets, Imperial size.

The Use of Colour

It is unfortunate that the economics of reproducing colour prevent the wider use of coloured illustrations in technical literature, since they would undoubtedly help the reader in grasping some of the more complex descriptions of apparatus or its working. The high cost of even one additional colour is inevitable because, whatever the process used in duplicating a line illustration, the processing time is doubled and the equipment is more costly and troublesome to use. Nevertheless, the value of an additional colour in helping out an explanation, or in rendering dry material more attractive, should make the writer consider whether the extra cost is not justified more often.

Except in certain offset reproduction methods, the use of a second colour involves preparing a separate master (stencil or plate) and changing the inking arrangements. The paper, already printed in black, is then run through the machine again to receive the colour impression. It is obviously of importance that the colour impression should fall exactly in the required place, that is, it should 'register' with the black impression and keep this registration throughout the running-off. The drawing for the colour work should therefore be prepared at the same time as the original black-and-white drawing, and if any photographic process is involved the camera adjustments should not be altered. For any but the simplest colour additions it is convenient to prepare a master drawing to show the finished result and then produce the colour portion by tracing from the master. An example of the improvement made by the addition of a single colour to a diagram is shown in Fig. 5.26, which explains the action of the Rotaprint machine.

The inking unit is clearly distinguished from the printing cylinders and the path of the paper through the rollers is shown.

Apart from its use in clarifying diagrams, colour may also be used as a background to charts or graphs and even to distinguish one curve from another in a closely-drawn series. It is, however, not possible to rely on the registration of the colour overprint to the extent of taking accurate readings, as slight changes in the quality of the paper, the tension, or even the humidity may alter the position of the lines by a fraction of a millimetre. Colour as an ornament to the printed text may be used as a background (see Tints, p. 161) or to reproduce a line diagram either in colour lines on a white ground, or white lines on a coloured background— the so-called ' reverse ' block (see p. 123 and Fig. 4.15)—and with blue ink a successful imitation of a blue-print can be produced. For further notes on printing in full colour see p. 213.

A good example of the use of full colour in technical illustrating is shown in Fig. 4.37. The sectional drawing was prepared by the draughtsman-artist from the original and photographed by a tri-colour camera.

CHAPTER 5

PRINTING PROCESSES

Production Costs

ONE of the problems many technical writers have to face is how to produce a sufficient number of copies of their work at a reasonable cost. No difficulty exists if the writer has a contract with a publisher, because the printing and publication costs are borne by the publisher, whether the writer's work appears in a technical journal or a textbook. The majority of technical writers are, however, employed by scientific or industrial organizations, public corporations, or government departments and in all these there is a constant need for the circulation of technical information in the form of reports, specifications, or handbooks.

As a general rule the number of copies to be circulated is inversely proportional to the technical level of the work; for example, a research report may be restricted to 50 copies whereas an operating handbook may have a circulation of several thousand. With some methods of reproduction the cost rises in direct proportion to the number of copies; with others, the cost falls steeply as the number of copies is increased.

The difference in cost between the various methods of reproduction depends mainly on how much of the work can be done by machine and how fast the machine can deliver copies. For example, a dye-line printer, taking a minute or more to produce one copy, compares unfavourably with a rotary duplicator delivering 60 to 100 copies a minute. The reference to dye-line reproduction is not out of place in considering typescript because in certain circumstances the reproduction is a practical and economical method. If a dozen copies of a specification are required, each copy containing four pages of typescript and two drawings, it is convenient to type the related material on tracing cloth and allow the print-room operator to produce type and drawings in one job.

In considering where any system ceases to be economical, allowance must be made for the facilities available: although a particular system may not be the cheapest for a given job, it may be expedient to use it if other methods are not equally to hand. Often a compromise must be made between relative costs and urgency of requirement, and the choice of the system may be governed by the time available.

There is a marked difference between reproduction by letterpress printing and the usual forms of office duplication, the difference

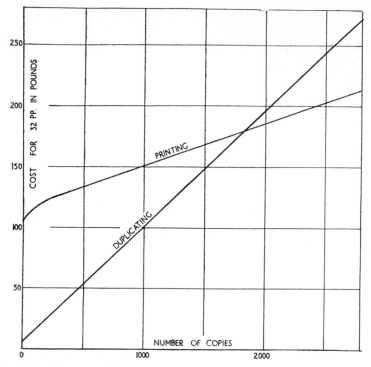

FIG. 5.1. *Comparison between printing and duplicating costs ; the figures are only indicative.*

being in the cost of labour involved in typesetting. The graphs of Fig. 5.1 illustrate the relative costs of duplicated and printed copies of a handbook of, say, 32 pages. The initial cost of the duplication is that of the stencils or litho plates, and thereafter the cost increases linearly with the number of copies at a rate determined by the cost of paper and operator's time. It is, of course, only possible to print one sheet at a time. If the material is set in type, there is a

166

heavy initial cost of composing and preparing the pages for the machine; this cost is incurred whether one or a thousand copies are run off. Since the machining of the printed sheets can produce 32 pages in one operation, the cost per thousand increases at a slower rate. The two curves intersect at a point between 1000 and 2000 copies, indicating the number at which the printing by letterpress becomes economical. Curves of this type can be plotted for a particular duplicating system and are a useful guide, but owing to the rapidly changing costs of paper, typesetting, and machining they will require frequent revision. For this reason approximate figures only are given on the scales. This economic consideration takes no account of the aesthetic value of typeset matter—a few hundred copies of a report intended for the firm's customers would be preferably reproduced by letterpress for good appearance.

LETTERPRESS PRINTING

The principal operations in letterpress printing are:

Composing	*Printing*
Typesetting	Making ready
Make-up	Running off
Imposing	

Typesetting

In these days it is general practice for printing houses to set normal straightforward subject matter by mechanical means. However, when larger letters are required for titles, chapter headings, and the so-called displayed matter, they are usually set by hand. Hand setting may also be necessary for complicated mathematical expressions, as will be shown later.

The method of hand setting used by the early printers has changed little in some hundreds of years. Stocks of individual letters or characters are arranged in partitioned trays or 'cases' and the compositor selects them and arranges them in a 'stick' or hand tray to form the lines of type. The stock contains a wide range of sizes and styles of letter, with numerals, special characters, and capital letters in two sizes (the larger called 'capitals' and the smaller ' small capitals '). In the early printing shops, both sizes of capital letters were kept in an upper case, and the small letters in a lower case nearer the compositor's hand. The terms ' upper case ' for capitals and ' lower case ' for the ordinary small letters have persisted to this day, and are still used for type which is no longer set by hand.*

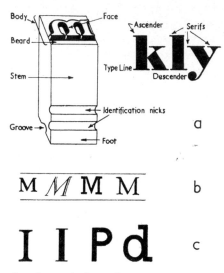

FIG. 5.2. *Illustrating the terminology of typesetting.* FIG. 5.2a *shows the character ' m ' cast on its stem. The portions of a letter projecting above or below the type line are known as ascender and descender respectively (right). Below (b) are shown four Ms cast on the same size of body. The difference in style shows a marked difference in the size of the type face. Four main varieties of type are shown in the lowermost row (c) : Old Style I, Modern I (with straight serifs), Sans-serif P (" Gill sans ") and a slab-serif* d *(known as Egyptian style).*

Characteristics of Type

The terms relating to a piece of type are illustrated in Fig. 5.2a. Each character is cast in relief on a body with an accuracy that ensures almost perfect alignment between the letters. Depending on the design of the type face, a letter may occupy nearly the whole depth of the body or a certain proportion : the difference between

* The term ' lower case ' deserves to be more widely used in referring to the small letters of the alphabet to avoid confusion with letters of small size, which may be capital letters.

the sizes of face is shown in Fig. 5.2b in which the four ' M 's are all cast on the same size of body (shown by the parallel lines).

For this reason, measurements relating to type are applied to the *body* and not to the face. The unit of measurement used by printers is the *point*, which is approximately equal to $\frac{1}{72}$ in., and the type size is expressed in so many points. The pages of this book are printed in 10 point (abbreviated to pt.). It is possible to cast the same size of letter on a larger size of body in order to allow more white space between lines : for example, 10-pt. type can be cast on a 12-pt. body. If occasional extra white space is required between lines (as in the headings to these paragraphs) it is introduced by inserting strips of lead to separate the lines—a method known as ' leading out ' (*ledding* out).

Although the size of the character is expressed in points, the width of a line is measured in terms of the number of characters which

FIG. 5.3. *A scale marked in point sizes for estimating type area.*

will fill it. The characters, however, differ in width, and accordingly a standard width is taken to be that of the letter ' m ', which has a square body. A further complication is that the width of the ' m ' varies with the size of type used, the 12-pt. ' m ' being $1\frac{1}{2}$ times as wide as the 8-pt. ' m '. Accordingly the standard unit of measurement is taken as that of the 12-pt. ' m ', and the width of the line is given in so many ' ems ', the 12-pt. size being understood irrespective of the size of type actually used.* Since the 12-pt. em measures $\frac{12}{72}$ or $\frac{1}{6}$ in. the measurement in ems is obtained by multiplying the column width in inches by 6: a $4\frac{1}{2}$-in. column width is 27 ems.

Another unit used in spacing is the ' en ', the width of the letter ' n ', which is half that of the em.

Special scales divided into point and em measurements are obtainable, and a specimen scale is shown in Fig. 5.3. This is useful for estimating the space occupied by letterpress, although much of the information required can be obtained from tables (p. 303).

* The 12-pt. type size was formerly called ' Pica ', and this term persists in speaking of the column width, which some printers will call so many picas.

Mechanical Typesetting

The principal machines for setting straightforward subject matter are known as *Monotype*, *Linotype* and the *Intertype*. The Linotype, as its name implies, produces a complete line of characters in one casting (the ' slug ') (Fig. 5.4). The Intertype produces a similar line, whereas the Monotype imitates hand composition by casting each character as a separate unit and assembling them automatically to form the line. In all three machines the characters are selected by operating a keyboard similar to that of a typewriter but containing many more characters.

In the Linotype machine (Fig. 5.5) the matrices from which the type is cast are stored in channels in a magazine at the top of the machine behind the keyboard. Before the setting is commenced, the type metal is melted and the matrix holder is adjusted for the width of column required. When the appropriate key is depressed, a selected matrix is released from the magazine and passes down the guides to an assembly box where it is joined by the succeeding matrix until the whole word is formed. At the completion of the word a ' space-band ' key is operated, causing a wedge-shaped space-band to fall into the assembly box. When the line is nearing completion a bell warns the operator, who then decides where to stop setting and, if necessary, where to hyphenate the last word in the line. A lever at the side of the keyboard then causes the complete line of matrices to pass to a position where a ' justification block ' pushes up the space-bands into place between the words, expanding each spacer until the line of matrices is packed out to the full width of the line. The molten type metal is then forced into the matrices, casting the line of type as a complete unit. After casting is completed, the matrices are carried by a distributing mechanism back to the storage magazine for further use. The operation of the machine is continuous, for while the operator is setting one line the previous one is being cast, and the matrices of the one before it are being distributed. The speed of setting by the Linotype machine is approximately 6000 characters an hour, but this figure depends on the skill of the operator and the complexity of the type matter. It is possible for the operator to read the line in the form of the assembled matrices before casting and thus correct errors of setting, but if the finished line contains a typographical error (termed a ' literal ') the whole line must be re-cast.

170

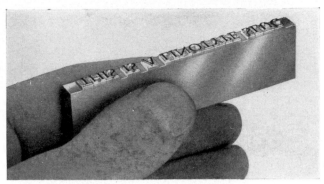

FIG. 5.4. *A Linotype ' slug '.*
(By courtesy of Linotype and Machinery Ltd.)

FIG. 5.5. *A modern Linotype setting and casting machine with multiple
matrix storage trays.*
(By courtesy of Linotype and Machinery Ltd.)

In the Monotype machine the keyboard and type casting units are separate, and are housed in separate rooms. The operation of the keyboard on the setter produces perforations in a roll of paper which is moved on by means of sprocket holes each time a key is depressed (Fig. 5.6). The paper resembles the perforated roll of an automatic player-piano and performs a similar function in releasing compressed air to operate the casting mechanism. The completed roll contains the coded instructions for casting the letters and also for varying the width of the type body (see below) to give a uniform length to each line as it is cast. The matrix box on the casting machine contains 255 characters, each one being individually cast and assembled to form the finished line of type. This feature distinguishes the Monotype machine from the Linotype, and it gives the advantage that a misplaced or wrong character can be corrected by the compositor without having to reset a whole line. A further advantage is that the perforated roll can be stored until required for setting and does not take up space in the composing room, nor does it tie up capital in the form of type metal kept in store.

The Galley. The finished lines of type, whether assembled by hand or by machine, are stored in trays, or galleys, which hold one or more columns.

It is seldom possible at this stage to make up the type into the form it will occupy on the final page as it requires to be checked carefully, first by the printer's reader and then by the author. A proof is taken from the galley on a simple hand press and the obvious errors of setting are rectified by the compositor (Fig. 5.7) before a second proof is taken and copies sent to the author. The procedure in checking and marking proofs is described in Chapter 7.

Making Up Pages (Make-up)

The amount of work involved in making up pages from the galleys varies with the subject matter; if there are no illustrations or tables, all the compositor has to do is allow adequate space for margins at the head and foot of the page, and measure off from the galley the required amount of type. For example, suitable margins for a page 9 in. deep by 6 in. wide are 1 in. at the top and $1\frac{1}{2}$ in. at the bottom.

This leaves 38 picas for the depth of the printed page, and the compositor separates the corresponding number of lines from the

172

FIG. 5.6. *Setting keyboard for the Monotype machine.*
(*By courtesy of the Monotype Corporation.*)

galley and ties them up in preparation for imposing with other pages (see on).

If the work contains illustrations, make-up is more complicated. The compositor can, however, complete his work much more

FIG. 5.7. *A compositor correcting the type in a galley.*

quickly if the pages have been made up in pasted form by the author or by editorial staff. *It cannot be over-emphasized that if the author wants text and illustrations to appear in the form most convenient for his purpose, he should supervise the page make-up himself, or place the work with an experienced sub-editor.* Hints on sub-editing will be found in Chapter 7.

Imposing

In multi-page work, it is customary to print 4, 8, 16 or 32 pages at once, on one large sheet of paper. The art of arranging the pages in the correct order for folding and slitting the printed sheet is called *imposing*. To do this, the compositor makes up the requisite number of pages and locks them in the ' chase ' or frame

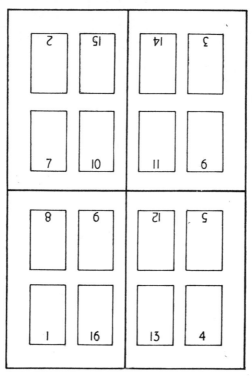

FIG. 5.8. *One method of making up 16 pages in the forme. The sheet will be printed on the reverse side to give two sets of 16 pages (folios).*

in correct order. Fig. 5.8 shows one of the many arrangements for printing a set of 16 folios. After one side of the sheet has been printed it is turned end for end and the back of the sheet is printed in the same order of folios, so that p. 2 is on the back of p. 1. The sheet is then divided to make two sheets each of 16 folios. The complete set of pages, locked in the chase, is called a *forme*.

Make-ready

The next stage is to mount the forme on the printing machine and make final adjustments to ensure uniformity of printing over the whole area of the forme. This ' make-ready ' requires considerable experience and skill, because the slightest maladjustment may cause the print to appear lighter or heavier in one part of the page than on another. It is therefore essential that the type height is adjusted and that there is equal pressure on the paper over the whole contact area of the printing rollers. There are many other details to be attended to in the make-ready stage: these are, however, the business of the machine minder, who is responsible for seeing that all is in order before the run-off is begun. Not only must the machine be in perfect working order, but paper and ink must be of the right quality for the job in hand. Moreover, if over-printing is wanted, as in multi-colour work, the greatest care must be taken to ensure that the separate printings are in perfect *register*, that is to say, each printing must be in its precise position on the page.

Machining

The final stage in letterpress printing is running off the copies. Theoretically, it might seem that, given a perfect make-ready, all that remains is to set the machine in motion and watch the copies being delivered. In practice, the paper may crease or crinkle; the ink may become too dry; the ink may dry too slowly on the paper, causing the print on one page to appear on the back of the following one (this is called ' set-off '). These and a host of other faults may arise during the run-off and call for constant vigilance on the part of the machine minder.

Types of Printing Machine

Machines for large-scale printing are either of the flat-bed or rotary type, the flat-bed machine being used for ordinary letterpress and bookwork and the rotary press for high-speed newspaper and periodical printing. The principle of the flat-bed machine is shown in Fig. 5.9a. The forme moves to and fro in a horizontal plane, passing under the inking rollers on its travel towards the left. A sheet of paper is wrapped round the rotary cylinder and is pressed on to the type as the forme returns to its position under the cylinder.

176

As the cylinder continues to revolve, the paper is lifted off and passes down the guides to the stack at the end of the bed and the forme moves back again for a fresh inking from the slab (shown shaded). In some types of machine the cylinder revolves only during the forward movement of the type bed, but in the so-called two-revolution machines the cylinder completes one revolution on the forward movement of the forme and one on the return movement.

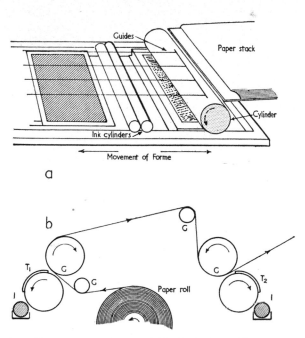

FIG. 5.9. *Diagrammatic layout of* (a) *flat-bed and* (b) *rotary presses.*

In small machines the forme is mounted vertically (Fig. 5.10) and the inking roller passes over it from the top.

The characteristic of the rotary press is that the type impression is applied from a curved plate on the surface of a revolving cylinder. The process is shown diagrammatically in Fig. 5.9b. Paper from a roll (or sheets from a stack) passes over the guide cylinders G,G and is printed on one side from the type cylinder T_1, which receives ink from the reservoir I,I. After passing to the rollers on the right, the paper is then printed on the reverse side by the type cylinder T_2.

177

FIG. 5.10. *A vertical flat-bed press.*
(*Holmes & Co. (Printers' Engineers) Ltd.*)

The Multigraph Duplicating Machine

The Multigraph duplicating machine is a simplified letterpress printer for use in business offices. It is the letterpress counterpart of the office-type offset machines such as the " Multilith "(p. 190).

The three-bank type case (Fig. 5.11) carries special sorts, capitals and lower case characters. The compositor's stick is replaced by a composing fork, and as each line of type is completed it is transferred to a semi-cylindrical segment which accommodates up to 68 lines (Fig. 5.12). When the setting is completed the segment is attached to the cylinder of the printing machine (Fig. 5.13).

178

FIG. 5.11. *Type case for Multigraph printing machine.*

FIG. 5.12. *The type segment for the machine.*

Half-tone or line illustrations may be mixed with the type by fixing flexible electros or zincos (p. 209) to the segment.   As the segment is locked to the cylinder, no make-ready is required.

A range of type faces is available, but it should be noted that the horizontal spacing is related to the groove spacing in the cylinder. For this reason, complicated mathematical setting can only be done

FIG. 5.13.   *The complete Multigraph printing machine.*
(*This photograph and the preceding two are by the courtesy of Addressograph-Multigraph Ltd.*)

with difficulty. On the machine illustrated in Fig. 5.13, the maximum paper size is 11 by 16 in., and paper stock may vary between 13-lb bond to 3-sheet card.

PHOTO-TYPESETTING

For many years the printing industry has been alive to the need for a method of typesetting and printing which does not involve the use of heavy and costly metal type and the casting machines that are required for setting it. This need has resulted in the development of a method of typesetting by which the characters are produced photographically on film and are transferred after composing to a lithographic plate. From this stage the printing is done by lithography, as explained later in this chapter.

Many different firms are developing or have developed phototype-setting equipment, and the principles involved can be explained by quoting from information given by the Monotype Corporation and the Linotype Corporation.

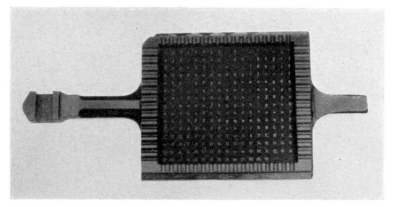

FIG. 5.14. *Monophoto machine : Master Negative Assembly.*

" Monophoto " Filmsetting Machine

The Monophoto machine is the film-setting counterpart of the Monotype composition caster, but it produces exposed film or paper, either positive or negative, ready for subsequent processing. The type composing mechanism is similar in principle to the Monotype Caster described on p. 172, and the perforated ribbon can be prepared with suitable equipment on an existing Monotype keyboard.

Master Negative Assembly. This is shown in Fig. 5.14 and is similar in appearance to the matrix case for casting solid type. The steel frame houses 255 characters and spaces, each occupying a square of 0·2 in. side.

The master negative assembly is positioned by pneumatic control actuated by the ribbon from the caster so as to bring the required character into a light beam, where it is held while the exposure ($\frac{1}{50}$th sec) is made. An auxiliary cut-off blade is provided if a line of copy is to be omitted.

The Optical System. The character is reproduced as an image on a film or paper wrapped round a drum. The optical system includes a projection lens, two reflecting prisms and a pair of front-surface

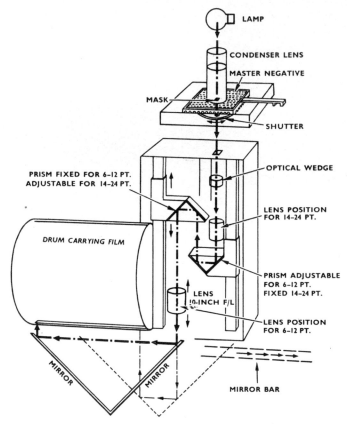

FIG. 5.15. *Optical system of the Monophoto machine.*

mirrors (Fig. 5.15). By means of a set of focusing bars the lens and prisms are located to produce an image of any required point size from 6 to 24 point; the two mirrors travel laterally to focus the image of each succeeding character in the type line on to the drum.

182

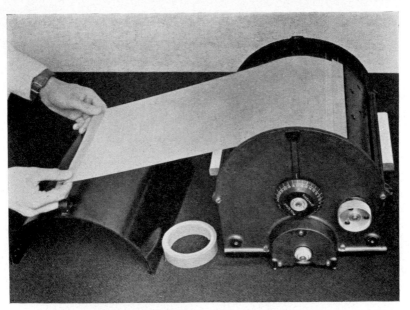

FIG. 5.16. *Monophoto machine : Drum Unit.*

FIG. 5.17. *Outfit for making corrections.*

Two drum units are used, enabling the machine to work continuously; while one is in operation the other can be unloaded or loaded (Fig. 5.16). The film can be of any width up to $11\frac{1}{4}$ inches, and the maximum length is 24 inches. Extreme accuracy is required in machining the drum and gear, so that the film can be accurately

FIG. 5.18. *The complete Monophoto machine.*
(*Figs. 5.14–5.18 by courtesy of the Monotype Corporation.*)

located and returned to the same point if additional matter is to be inserted.

Corrections. The equipment for making corrections to the type matter is shown in Fig. 5.17. The lines containing errors are stripped out from the film and the replacement line is freshly set on the keyboard and set on special stripping film, from which it can be transferred to the main film.

The complete typesetter is shown in Fig. 5.18.

The Linofilm Photocomposing System

The Linofilm photocomposing system is an electronically controlled

Fig. 5.19. *The Linofilm keyboard unit, comprising an electric typewriter, control panel (left) and fount selection panel (right).*
(By courtesy of Linotype and Machinery Ltd.)

185

equipment in which the characters are coded on tape before being interpreted by the photographic composition unit. The complete equipment consists of a keyboard unit and a photographic unit. Composition is done by the operator at the keyboard of the electric typewriter which produces simultaneously a typewritten copy and a perforated tape (Fig. 5.19). The tape is then fed to the photographic unit which reads the coded perforations and builds up the lines of

FIG. 5.20. *Turret containing 18 fount plates, giving a choice of 1584 characters.*
(*By courtesy of Linotype and Machinery Ltd.*)

type by projecting the characters photographically on to a film. Corrections can be made on the tape before the characters are photographed, as the operator can detect the error on his typed copy and punch a code signal on to the tape to erase the line in which it appears. Alternatively the tape can be altered by cutting and splicing.

At the keyboard the operator determines the line length, type size, type face, and leading by means of push-button controls, and these instructions are coded on the tape to set the adjustments of the photographic unit before the characters are decoded.

The photographic unit contains 18 grids, or glass negatives, each containing 88 characters in a particular type face (Fig. 5.20); the correct grid is selected by the coding signal interpreted by the reading device. A novel feature of the photographic system is that the images of all 88 characters are projected together on to the film, and an individual character is selected by interposing a shutter to blot out all images except that of the desired character. The position of the character in the line is determined by a mirror which moves along the optical axis of the system and reflects the image on to the plane of the film. When the character is selected and located in the line, an automatic light flash makes the exposure. The photographic unit operates continuously without attention after the tape and film have been inserted. The completed film may be used directly to make the litho plate or it may be made up with other film in a composing unit to form a composite layout for a page. The composing unit, which also forms part of the system, can enlarge or reduce the copy on the film and place it at any part of the layout. The output from the composer is a finished film or paper ready for plate making.

A detailed account of the Linofilm system, from which this is an abstract, is given in the *Penrose Annual*, Vol. 57 (1957) p. 94 (L. Rosetto).

LITHOGRAPHY

General Principles

Almost all the basic principles applying to modern lithography have resulted from experiments made in the latter part of the eighteenth century by a Bohemian named Senefelder who lived in Munich. The object of these experiments was to discover practical methods for printing from a flat surface in contrast to the embossed or engraved surfaces used in letterpress printing. It was obvious that planographic printing would greatly reduce the number of mechanical processes that had hitherto been indispensable. The essential requirement was a surface that would be suitable both for a drawing medium and a printing plate.

The medium originally used was limestone, on which the image to be printed was drawn direct; hence the word 'lithography', (Greek *lithos* = stone, *graphos* = a writing). Since this obviously called for unusual artistic ability, Senefelder developed a system of drawing the image on cartridge paper and transferring it to the stone. Towards the middle of the nineteenth century experiments were made in the use of zinc plates instead of stone, and these or their aluminium counterparts have now almost entirely replaced stone as a medium for modern lithography. It is interesting to note that Senefelder also produced paper plates surfaced with a powdered-stone compound.

Whatever medium is used, the basic principle depends on the natural law that grease and water are mutually repellent. To understand the application of this principle, suppose that the plate has an image drawn on its surface in greasy ink or pencil (Fig. 5.21), and the whole surface area is damped with water. The parts of the

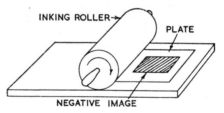

FIG. 5.21. *Principle of operation of the lithographic process.*

surface covered by the image will not accept the damping. If a roller with ink distributed evenly over its surface is moved over the plate, the ink, because of its grease content, will adhere to that portion of the plate which rejects the water (i.e. the image area) but no ink will adhere to the remainder of the plate surface where water is present. If a sheet of paper is now applied under pressure to the inked-up plate, the image will be transferred to the paper.

Printing by lithography, whether direct or offset, is based on this principle, although the preparation of plate surfaces and other materials involves more complicated processes.

Offset Lithography

The example given above, where the plate was inked by a roller and a copy of the image pulled is called *direct* lithography. It must be noted, however, that the transferred image will be the reverse of the plate image, the reversal corresponding to a photographic negative and positive. If therefore, positive prints are wanted, the image on the plate must be drawn as a negative. This presented difficulties to early lithographers who lacked artistic ability. As a result of this, methods were evolved by which the image could be

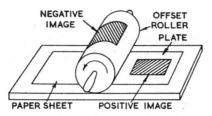

FIG. 5.22. *Principle of offset lithography.*

drawn on the litho plate in positive form and transferred to a rubber-surfaced roller; the image on the roller then became negative and the copies positive.

A development of this idea forms the basis of all modern *offset* lithography. The principle is illustrated in Fig. 5.22, which shows a lithographic plate at one end of a long table and a sheet of paper at the other. The plate with a positive image is inked up and a rubber-covered roller moved over the plate surface; the image is transferred to the rubber roller in negative form. If the movement of the roller is continued over the table, the image is transferred from roller to paper.

The explanation need be carried only one stage further to illustrate the principle of modern offset lithography as practised on small office-type machines or on the largest multi-colour lithographic presses.

Suppose the plate in Fig. 5.22 to be flexible, and capable of being fixed to the

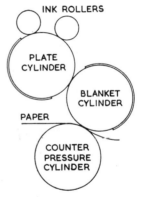

FIG. 5.23. *Diagram illustrating the rotary offset machine.*

surface of a cylinder (Fig. 5.23). Now imagine a second cylinder, around which a rubber mat or 'blanket' is fixed. If the plate is inked up by a system of inking rollers, and the two cylinders rotated in contact, the image is transferred to the blanket. A third cylinder, called the *counter-pressure cylinder*, is now rotated

189

in close proximity to the rotating blanket. A sheet of paper is passed between pressure cylinder and blanket, making firm contact at the point of pressure, and the negative image on the blanket is transferred to the paper in positive form.

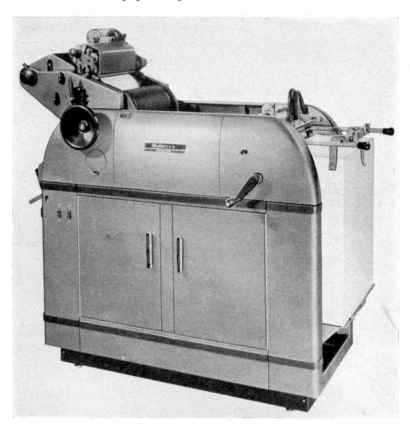

FIG. 5.24.   *Multilith offset litho machine Type 1250.*
(*By courtesy of Addressograph-Multigraph Ltd.*)

Office-type Offset Lithographic Machines

Two different types of small offset litho machines are illustrated in Fig. 5.24 and 5.25.   The primary consideration is image area, as defined in the manufacturer's specification.   This must be large enough to accommodate illustrations up to the maximum size envisaged for the publications.   Other considerations are accuracy in register (particularly if multi-colour work is wanted), ease of operation, and mechanical reliability. Another machine is shown in diagrammatic form in Fig. 5.26. Ink is transferred to the plate

FIG. 5.25. *Rotaprint offset litho machine Type R30/90.*
(*By courtesy of Rotaprint Ltd.*)

by a carefully designed system of rollers which ensure even distribution of a fine film of ink over the plate surface, the ink adhering to the image area only. Instead of the more orthodox water

191

damping, with this machine an ink-conditioning fluid is fed to the inking rollers from a reservoir or *fount*. The effect of the fluid is to supply the non-image area of the plate with an ink repellent.

When the machine is revolving, the image on the plate is transferred to a rubber blanket by virtue of contact between plate and blanket cylinders.

Sheets of paper are fed from the stack by a pawl-wheel mechanism, each sheet in turn passing between the blanket and counter-pressure cylinders and, after printing, is flicked into the delivery tray by a 'shoo-fly' bar. The machine is driven by an electric motor and delivers about 60 copies per minute. Provision is made for rotating the machine by hand during the preliminary set-up.

The plate size for this machine is $14\frac{1}{2} \times 8\frac{7}{8}$ in., which permits a maximum printed sheet of 13×8 in. Larger machines of similar type are available, taking sheets up to 20×14 in.

It has been said on page 165 that the method used for producing copies of technical reports, papers or instructions must depend very largely upon the number of copies to be issued, and the extent to which the material is illustrated. The outstanding advantage of offset lithographic machines is their versatility. They can be used for producing a considerable number of copies from typescript on paper or metal plates, for line and half-tone illustrations from metal plates or for reproduction by photo-litho of existing books, papers or reports.

Both paper and metal plates are sufficiently flexible to be used on a standard typewriter; methods of preparation are discussed later.

Theoretically, line illustrations can be drawn direct on paper or metal plates, but the technique is not without limitations particularly if fine detail or lettering is wanted.

Photo-lithography

The alternative is to make use of photo-lithography, which implies the combining of the photographic and lithographic arts. The original illustration is photographed and the negative developed and printed on to a metal plate, the image on the plate being positive as explained on page 189. By using this method, the draughtsman is not restricted to a given size of drawing, although, as stated on page 160, he must pay attention to proportions and to size of

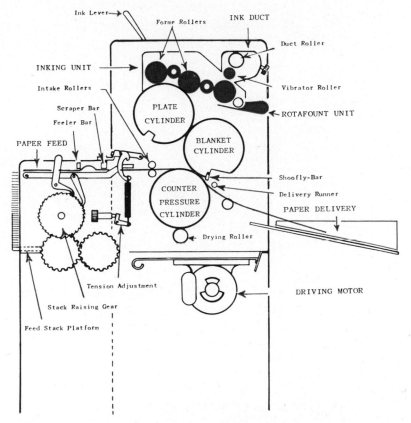

Ink Lever
Forme Rollers
INK DUCT
Duct Roller
INKING UNIT
Intake Rollers
Vibrator Roller
Scraper Bar
PLATE
CYLINDER
Feeler Bar
ROTAFOUNT UNIT
PAPER FEED
BLANKET
CYLINDER
COUNTER
PRESSURE
CYLINDER
Shoofly-Bar
Delivery Runner
PAPER DELIVERY
Drying Roller
Tension Adjustment
DRIVING MOTOR
Stack Raising Gear
Feed Stack Platform

FIG. 5.26. *Schematic drawing of the Rotaprint machine*

[*Facing p. 192*

lettering. Such an illustration will be reduced in the photographic process to suit the format of the publication.

Half-tone illustrations can be reproduced in a similar way. Both line and half-tone illustrations can be reproduced in any colour or combination of colours.*

The preparation of plates for both half-tone monochrome and colour work is a highly-specialized art, which depends not only on first-class photographic equipment but on skilled photographers and re-touchers. The smaller office-type offset machines are quite suitable for half-tone monochrome printing, but for high-class colour work, larger machines such as the Rotaprint R30/90 are more suitable because of their accurate register.

An important application of photo-lithography is the reproduction of technical papers or books when the original letterpress type has been broken down. Printers will keep type standing indefinitely if the customer is prepared to pay a rental charge, but this is usually uneconomic and the printer breaks down or *distributes* the type and melts down the metal for further use.

When this is done, additional copies wanted at a later date can be produced more cheaply by photo-litho than by re-setting the type.

The Process Camera

The rapid extension in the use of small offset machines throughout the world has led to the introduction of various methods to simplify the making of printing plates.

' Making plates ' does not here imply the mass manufacture of the printing surfaces, but the transfer of the original ' copy ' to the printing surface.

The long-established practice of using a process camera to prepare photographic negatives is still widely used and where high quality reproduction is essential, it remains unequalled in reliability.

With a process camera (Fig. 5.27), a negative of the original is made to the required size, the camera being capable of reducing or enlarging. This in itself is a most important facility which must be taken into consideration when installation of plate-making equipment is contemplated; the same-size reproduction of detailed

---

* In some circumstances satisfactory results may be obtained by regarding the half-tone print as a line illustration, omitting the screen from the camera. The method is often referred to as the ' dot-for-dot ' process.

technical illustrations is often impracticable because it is impossible for the illustrator to lay out a complicated drawing on a sheet not bigger than a small offset plate, the largest of which is approximately 20 by 14 in.

When the negative is completed, the next stage is to sensitize the printing plate so that the image can be transferred from the negative

FIG. 5.27. *Minilith Process camera.*
(*J. J. Huber Ltd.*)

by exposure to a light source. This is done by pouring a sensitizing solution on the plate which is held on a metal table called a Whirler (Fig. 5.28). The Whirler is rotated, either manually or by an electric motor, to ensure even distribution of the solution over the entire surface of the plate. The plate is then dried off and is ready to receive a photographic image.

Next, the photographic negative and the plate are inserted in a printing-down frame (Fig. 5.29) and exposed to intense light from

FIG. 5.28. *Whirler for use in sensitizing plates for small offset machines.*
(*J. J. Huber Ltd.*)

FIG. 5.29. *Printing-down frame with arc light.*
(*J. J. Huber Ltd.*)

an arc lamp, or other suitable light source. The process camera shown in Fig. 5.27 incorporates printing-down facilities.

After exposure, developing ink is distributed evenly over the image area on the plate, and the image becomes apparent. The sensitizer on the unexposed part of the plate is then removed by washing with running water. A second washing follows, with an ammonia solution.

The next step is to etch the image on the plate by sponging an etching solution over the surface. After a further washing, a pre-serving solution is applied and the plate is ready for storage or immediate printing.

Pre-sensitized Plates

All the operations described above are essential when the printing plates are of non-sensitized material. In recent years, pre-sensitized plates have become available in plasticized paper and in metal. The object is to save processing time by omitting the whirling operation. The plates are sold under various trade names and are obtainable from most lithographic suppliers.

Recently, Kodak Ltd. have introduced a special film (Autoscreen film) for making half-tone negatives without the use of a screen. The film itself contains a pattern which breaks up the image into a dot formation, and has a particular application in plate-making for small offset machines.

Plate Making without a Camera

Various methods of preparing plates without using a process camera have been developed, and the two methods outlined below are typical of modern developments. There is no intention of assigning any specific merit to one or other method, and it must not be assumed that other equally satisfactory processes are not available.

" Azoflex " Transfer Foil

This foil enables opaque originals to be copied and a positive image to be transferred to unsensitized opaque paper, translucent paper, or lithographic plates as used on offset machines. As the image obtained from the foil is in carbon black, it will provide a copy as permanent as if produced by conventional printing ink.

Azoflex foil is a ' diazo ' type material, and can be exposed on any photo-printing machine which has a light source rich in ultra-violet.

It requires no chemical development, and the image is produced by passing the exposed transfer foil and the material on which the reproduction is required through a bath of water and then through a pair of 'nip' rollers.

These rollers press the materials tightly together and dry them. As they emerge from the rollers they are separated, and the act of separation transfers the image from the foil to the material (the 'image support'). The final product will be a support bearing an intensely black image of the original, and a foil which will be photographically negative.

When only one copy is required from the original, the image from the foil is transferred to opaque receiving paper, but if a number of copies is required the image is produced on translucent receiving paper or an unsensitized offset litho plate. A selection of Azoflex products is obtainable from Ilford Ltd, Ilford, Essex.

Xerography

Xerography* is not primarily a plate-making process but a system of document copying that is readily adaptable to making lithographic plates without the use of normal photography and without wet processing of any kind. This may be difficult to understand at the outset because the equipment does incorporate a camera, a processor and a fuser, but the camera does not use photographic film or plate, the processor requires no light source and the fuser (or fixer) no water or chemicals.

The whole process depends on electric charge and discharge and is therefore a completely dry process, hence the name 'xerography' (from the Greek *xeros* = dry, and *graphos* = a writing).

The first operation is to prepare a xerographic plate which takes the place of a negative in the photo-litho method. The plate is a metal sheet coated with a photo-conductive material such as selenium which will act as an electric conductor only when exposed to light. To distinguish this plate from the offset-litho plate, it will be referred to as the *master*.

The master is inserted into the processor where it is placed under a system of wires charged to a potential of the order of 6000 volts. This causes the selenium surface to be 'sprayed' with electrons over its entire area.

* Pronounced *zero*graphy.

Before removing the master from the processor a dark slide or shutter is placed over it to preserve the electrostatic charge. (Remember the plate is light sensitive.)

The master and the original copy are now inserted in the camera and exposed to a light source. From all light areas on the copy, that is to say where there is no image, light is reflected on to the master causing the electrostatic charge at the corresponding points to be discharged into the backing material of the master.

Conversely no light is reflected from the dark areas of the image, so that the charged areas on the master now take the form of an invisible image of the copy. The shutter is now replaced and the master taken from the camera and placed in the developing section of the processor, and the shutter removed. Developing is done by deposition. A suitable powder is deposited all over the surface and adheres to the charged areas only. There is now a visible negative image of the copy on the master.

This image can be transferred to a lithographic plate by placing the master and the plate in contact and inserting them into the charging compartment of the processor. The high-voltage charge causes powder particles to be attracted from the master to the plate, which has the effect of forming the required image on the plate.

When the plate is separated from the master, the image on the plate is made permanent either by heat treatment or by the vapour fuser supplied with the equipment.

The above description applies to the copying of line illustrations, typescript or other matter not containing tone gradation. For half-tone work additional steps in the process are necessary. Dot formation is obtained by exposing the master to a sheet of paper ruled up to form a suitable screen. This exposure precedes the exposure of the master to the copy.

The applications of xerography are not confined to making offset litho plates; in particular the process is likely to be widely used for making microfilms.

For this and other purposes the Rank-Xerox Copying Service has been recently introduced into Great Britain.

Reproduction of Typescript

There are many different ways of preparing typescript for repro-duction on an offset machine, but whatever form is used, a master lithographic plate must be produced. Photo-litho produces the best results.

By far the simplest method is direct typing on a paper plate, which then forms the printing image. Lithographic ribbons, in fabric or carbon-paper, must be used on the typewriter. Corrections can be made by using special erasers, and provided that materials of uniform quality can be obtained without difficulty, this method has the advantage of simplicity in operation and economy in cost.

Flexible metal plates can be used instead of paper plates and there is no difficulty in obtaining uniform supplies. Before using these plates for direct typing, users will do well to satisfy themselves that erasures can be made without difficulty and that corrections typed over the erased areas will print satisfactorily.

It is important to note that the direct-typing method involves the use of no additional machinery or equipment.

Diapositive Stencils

With this method, reproduction is by normal photo-litho process but instead of a film negative a black or yellow stencil is used for printing down. Typescript is prepared in exactly the same way as for the familiar Roneo and Gestetner duplicators and corrections can be made to a diapositive stencil just as easily.

This method of preparing typescript has much to commend it, for it gives photo-litho results without having to use a process camera. Moreover, photographic negatives of illustrations can be let into the stencil and the whole page containing typescript and illustrations printed down to an offset plate in one operation.

The Photo-litho Method

This method of reproducing typescript needs no special explanation, since it is an application of the principles of photo-lithography discussed on page 192. The typescript is prepared on plain white paper, and a photographic negative prepared. From this, a printing plate is obtained in the way described on p. 193.

The advantage of this method is that no special materials are needed in the typing stage, but it is essential for the typing to be bold and clear. A new ribbon should be used in the typewriter and, if thin or transparent paper is used, improved results are obtained by backing up with a sheet of carbon paper so as to produce a denser image. This trick is often useful when typing data sheets for dyeline reproduction.

METHODS OF REPRODUCING ILLUSTRATIONS

The methods used for reproducing technical illustrations vary considerably and depend upon a number of related factors, such as the number of copies required, size of original, original medium (for example, opaque or translucent material), production cost and facilities available.

Blue-prints

For many years, blue-prints were used extensively for reproducing line illustrations by all industrial drawing offices. The method is also known as the *ferroprussiate* or *cyanotype* process. It depends on the principle that a ferric salt when exposed to light becomes a ferrous salt, that is to say its combining power is reduced to a suitable value for combining with water. If a sheet of paper sensitized in this way is placed in contact with an original tracing, and exposed to a concentrated light source, the whole area of the paper will be partially de-sensitized except where the drawn lines intercept the light.

If the paper is now developed in a water bath, the whole of the exposed area becomes blue by virtue of the combining action of the the ferrous salt with water. The unexposed areas, where the lines occur, are unaffected and remain white. The advantages of the process are simplicity in operation, and good wearing properties; the latter implies a durable surface rather than textile strength. The blue surface can be handled extensively under workshop conditions, where a white background would become soiled. Its disadvantage is that the blue background is a bad medium for writing purposes; hence blue-prints do not lend themselves to correction or annotation. As a result of this, the use of blue-prints is now mostly confined to workshops and factories. Designers and architects prefer dyelines which have a light background.

It is possible to add lines to a blue-print by using a thin nib dipped in a weak solution of sodium carbonate. This bleaches the background but, owing to the absorbent nature of the paper, the result is seldom neat, and great care must be taken if an unsightly blob is not to appear. White lines can be obliterated by ordinary ultramarine water colour.

Dyeline Prints

Dyeline or ' diazo ' prints are produced in much the same way as blue-prints, the translucent original being placed in contact with

FIG. 5.30. *Continuous dyeline copier and developer.*
(*Lawes, Rabjohns Ltd.*)

sensitized paper and exposed to a light source, the image then being developed in ammonia solution or vapour. With this process the light action has the opposite effect on the sensitized paper : a colour change occurs on the unexposed parts of the paper, i.e. where lines are drawn, the exposed parts remain white. Theoretically, this produces black lines on a white background, but in practice the contrast is less sharply defined. The degree of contrast depends very largely on exposure time. Since most modern dyeline printers operate on a moving-belt principle, the contrast can be controlled by adjusting the speed of the machine. Machines of this type are called *continuous copiers* ; such printers have a further advantage over static machines, in that there need be no limit to one dimension

FIG. 5.31. *Dyeline copier* (*table model*).
(*Lawes, Rabjohns Ltd.*)

of the original and once the machine is in motion, a number of tracings can be printed in quick succession. After printing, the sensitized paper is developed either by a solution or by vaporized ammonia. The vapour developer involves the use of more elaborate equipment but has the great advantage of producing copies more quickly because they are dry and ready to handle immediately after leaving the developer, whereas with the solution, they must be left to dry for several minutes. When using the dry developing process, the copying paper must be of the dry-developer type. Typical modern machines are shown in Figs. 5.30 and 5.31.

Since the dyeline process depends on the direct transmission of light through the original, on to the sensitized paper, it follows that its use is limited to drawings finished on transparent material such as tracing linen, tracing paper or semi-transparent detail paper.

Typewritten matter such as specifications, tables or data sheets typed on tracing paper or on double-dull pencil cloth (i.e. tracing cloth having a matt surface on both sides) can be copied effectively by the dyeline process provided that a photo-process ribbon is used when typing. Clearer prints are obtained by placing a black carbon paper or a yellow-process carbon paper behind the tracing material, carbon side in contact with the back of the tracing and backed by a sheet of plain paper. The point of this is that it strengthens the opacity of the typed image on the transparency and thus produces a print with improved contrast values.

Reflex Copying

Reflex copying machines can be used with both opaque and transparent originals, but the reflex principle only applies to the opaque. The copies can be printed on either opaque or transparent material, but each copy has to be developed by a wet process. If a large number of copies is required, a transparency can be prepared on the reflex machine, and copies printed off by continuous dyeline. Where these combined facilities are available, this method of reproduction saves considerable time.

A reflex copier, Fig. 5.32 consists essentially of a light box containing a number of lamps so disposed as to give uniform light distribution over the printing area, a glass exposure frame (usually formed by the lid of the box), and a pressure or suction device to ensure air-free contact between the original and the sensitized paper.

If the original is printed on one side only and is translucent, or is a photographic negative, the transmitted-light method may be used. The original is placed face upwards on the glass frame, and the sensitized side of the copying material placed in contact with the original. On exposure, light is transmitted through the original direct to the sensitized paper, but is of course interrupted where the image occurs.

For opaque originals, the process is by reflected light. The sensitized material is placed on the frame face upwards, and the original on top of it, face downwards. On exposure, light is transmitted through the sensitized paper and reflected back to its surface from the original. The intensity of reflected light will vary as the density of the image on the original varies; it will be at a maximum where there is no image, and at a minimum where the density of the image is greatest. If the original is a half-tone illustration, the copies produced will have the same tone gradations as the original. Exposure time will depend on the composition of the original and on the speed of the printing material. Correct exposure is a matter of experience.

The print produced by either direct or reflex method is a negative;

Fig. 5.32. *Reflex copier.*
(*Copycat Ltd.*)

to obtain positive copies, the process is repeated, using the negative as an original. On completion of exposure each copy has to be subjected to a full photographic developing process. It is for this reason that it is often cheaper and quicker to produce the final prints by the dyeline process from a transparent reflex positive.

It will thus be seen that by using the dyeline and reflex systems in conjunction, dyelines can be readily obtained from all types of originals. It is important to realize, however, that with both dyeline and reflex methods, whether used individually or conjointly, the size of the copies is always the same as the original; there is no provision

204

for enlargement or reduction. There are many different makes of reflex machines available, for example ' Copycat ' or ' Rutherstat '.* There are also many different models of small document copiers available, using reflex principles. With some of these, operation is extremely simple, and prints can be produced without dark-room facilities. They are obtainable from firms specializing in the sale of drawing-office equipment and supplies.

The Gelatine Process

This process of copying is generally referred to as True-to-scale or ' Ordoverax ' and is particularly useful when accuracy in dimension is wanted on the copies. With this process, originals should preferably be drawn in waterproof ink on tracing cloth or tracing paper ; pencil tracings are not satisfactory unless drawn with strong black lines. The copies produced by this process may be on any material normally used in drawing offices, whether transparent or opaque.

The principles of operation are as follows : a table is covered by a sheet of suitable lino, coated with a chemically-treated gelatine which is allowed to set. A dyeline or reflex print is prepared from the original on sensitized paper, and pressed on to the gelatine. Chemical action takes place between the sensitized paper and the gelatine leaving an impression of the drawing on the gelatine surface. The transfer is now removed from the gelatine table and the impression on the gelatine is inked up with printer's ink by a hand roller, the ink adhering only to the drawing areas. The copying paper is now pressed on the table and the impression transferred to the copying material which, as previously explained may be tracing linen, tracing paper, cartridge paper or Bristol board. This method of copying has a particular application to drawing-office work, since during the printing stage, portions of a tracing which may not be wanted, or which need modification, can be completely obliterated ; thus the copy returned to the drawing-office may serve as a new original for immediate use, or for correction as required. This application can often save the complete re-drawing of an original.

* Most of these derive from the original ' Typon ' box introduced into Britain by J. J. Huber in the early 1920s.

205

Photostats

Photostat is a proprietary name and is used to denote photographic copies made with photographic paper supplied by the owner of the name. A Photostat copy is made by means of a photographic camera, and may be smaller or larger than the original, but when used for document copying, is usually the same size.

A peculiarity of the Photostat process is that although negatives have reversed colour tones, i.e. white lines on black background, the image can be either positive or negative in form; a positive print is not essential if a single copy only is wanted.

Photostat copies are often useful to the technical writer, when a very small number of prints from original line drawings or photographs are required for attaching to drafts before checking. If reduced to publication size, such copies are also useful in the make-up stage of a printed book or article (see Make-up). There is a further use which is less obvious : if it is decided to reproduce work by photo-litho from typescript pages, and this work contains inset illustrations, photostat copies of appropriate size can be prepared and pasted on the typescript sheets in their relevant positions before the sheets are photographed on lithographic plates. With this method of production, the writer can exercise complete control over presentation ; its success depends upon the quality of the photostat positives and should be used only when high-class facilities are available.

Offset-litho Copying

The reproduction of illustrations by the offset process is a highly-developed art and its general application is beyond the scope of this book. The process has, however, many advantages in its application to reproduction of technical illustrations and office-type offset machines are particularly suited to this purpose. If these machines are not directly available to the writer, the work can be put out to printers specializing in offset-litho reproduction. The methods of preparing illustrations for reproduction by this process are set out below, and are applicable whether local services are available, or whether the work has to be contracted out.

Extravagant claims are sometimes made that line drawings for reproduction by office-type offset machines can be easily prepared on paper, plastic or metal plates ; such claims are rarely justified in practice and the reader is warned to treat them with reserve.

In the first place, unless suitable drawing media are used, failure will be inevitable; some success may be achieved by using pencils or crayons with a high grease content. Ink drawing is possible provided that lithographic and not ordinary indian ink is used. A special ink is prepared for this purpose and sold under various trade names. Another difficulty likely to arise is that if erasures are necessary, the surface of the plate may be damaged and become useless, or break down before the run is completed. Very recent developments in this field have done much to solve this problem; a Duplimat ball-point pen has been introduced by Addressograph-Multigraph, and a re-fill type pencil by Rotaprint. Both of these have been used with satisfactory results.

Line Illustrations by Photo-litho

The alternative and much safer method, is to produce or have produced photographic negatives and reproduce the drawings by the photo-litho process. Such reproductions are of a very high quality and can of course, be printed in any desired colour or combination of colours.

If two or more colours are wanted, it is usually unnecessary to make separate drawings for each colour; the photographer can make separate negatives, masking the unwanted portions for each colour, according to directions given by the writer. It must be remembered, however, that the use of two colours doubles production costs, because separate negatives and plates are necessary for each colour, and the copies must be printed twice, which involves considerable time in cleaning down the machine each time the ink is changed. For these reasons, the writer should consider carefully whether the effects produced by multichrome will justify the expense incurred. Quite often, adequate distinction between different parts of a drawing can be made by judicious variation in line formation, shading or cross-hatching. Shading to produce variation in tone must be avoided, because it turns the line drawing into a half-tone. For the same reason, very fine scales on a graph must not be used.

Half-tone Illustrations by Photo-litho

Half-tone illustrations can be reproduced successfully by photo-litho on office-type offset machines, provided that plates are carefully prepared and that suitable paper is used for the run-off. The making of the half-tone plate is an expert job, and should be left to the professional, as it has much in common with the production of half-tone blocks by photo-engraving.

Nevertheless, good results can be obtained by using the Auto-screen film mentioned on p. 196.

The choice of paper is largely a matter of experience : art paper may present drying problems, but a good lithographic paper (such as G.B. Litho) will be satisfactory and will not introduce set-off or difficulties in drying.

PROCESS ENGRAVING

The term process engraving is applied to the making of printing surfaces from which copies of illustrations can be produced by letterpress. The printing surface is usually of zinc or copper, which is etched to produce a relief image of the illustration. The first step in the process is to produce a photographic negative of the original drawing; it is for this reason that the process is often called *photo-engraving*. The negative is then printed on to the surface of the metal, which has been previously coated with an emulsion of albumen and ammonium bichromate. Where the light passes through the transparent parts of the negative the bichromate emulsion becomes insoluble, and subsequent washing will remove the soluble part which was under the opaque portions of the negative. It should be noted that for printing from a metal the image is a mirror image of the original (as in an ordinary rubber stamp), and it is necessary to reverse the negative during the process of obtaining the printing surface. After the image is printed on the coated metal the surface is covered with etching ink. During the washing, the soluble sensitized material is washed away together with the ink coating, leaving the outline of the drawing on the metal. To prepare the plate for etching it is dusted over with bituminous powder which adheres to the ink, and on heating forms a protective coating over the whole outline of the image. When placed in the acid bath the metal is etched away in all areas except those under the resistive coating, so that the image eventually stands out in relief. Large areas of surplus metal are removed from the plate by a routing machine, which is also applied to the edges to trim the plate. A proof is then taken, and if the image is clearly defined the plate is fixed to a wood block so that it is ' type-high ' when the block is imposed in the forme with the type matter.

Some printers prefer to mount the blocks themselves, and specify the block to be unmounted.

Line Blocks

If the illustration is composed of lines or areas of black and white with no intermediate tones, the block is referred to as a *line block* or *zinco* (from the metal usually used).   If an intermediate positive print is made from the negative and used to print on to the metal, the tones on the block will be reversed, i.e. black will be white on the finished print.   This type of block is known as a *reversed* block (see Fig. 4.15) ; it should be noted that the reversal relates to the *colour* and not to the *image*.

It is important to remember that, once made, a block cannot be altered except with extreme difficulty.   It is sometimes possible to make a minor alteration or erase a line on a line block, depending on its position, but any appreciable alteration requires a completely new block, with added expense and extra time wasted.

Every drawing should be checked before the block is made, and proofs of blocks cannot be treated as rough proofs for further correction.

Half-tone Blocks

In the line block there are no intermediate tones between black and white such as appear in a photographic print.   The tones of a photograph can be simulated by breaking up the whole area of the print into a regular pattern of dots, the proportion of black dot area to white paper giving the appearance of the grey tone. The dot pattern is produced by interposing a ruled mesh screen between the camera lens and the negative (Fig. 5.33).   The fineness of the screen determines the amount of detail that can be reproduced and is governed by the grade of paper used for the reproduction. Soft absorbent paper or ' newsprint ' will cause the ink to spread round the dots and will also clog the spaces between them on the metal.   For this reason it is seldom possible to use a screen finer than 50–85 lines per inch.   On imitation art paper a screen of 120 per inch may be used, and with special coated or ' art ' paper,

o   209

133–200 per inch.   It follows that if fine detail of photomicrographs is to be reproduced a special paper must be used and inserted separately in the printed book.   Blocks with screens finer than 150 are more expensive both to make and to print, as they require frequent cleaning and extra care in the make-ready.

Fig. 5.33.   Left :   *Portion of half-tone screen* (65 *mesh*).   Right : *Portion of half-tone print, showing variation in dot size between black and white areas.*

Combination Blocks

It sometimes happens that an illustration requires both line and tone for its reproduction, as in Fig. 4.6.   This involves making separate negatives for the line and the half-tone and combining them on the block—an expensive process which should only be used if the results justify it.   It is also possible to introduce lettering on the block in the form of a title or description by having the letters set in type and photographed separately; the negative is then combined with the half-tone negative to make the printing image. This method was used in reproducing Fig. 4.6.

Duplicate Blocks

Duplicates of line or half-tone blocks can be made by moulding, at a cheaper rate than by producing two or more originals. Moulded duplicates are known as electrotypes (electros) or stereo-types (stereos).   Electros are suitable when fine detail is a feature of the original block, for example a 150-screen block.   For line and coarse-screen work, stereos, which are less costly, are adequate. When ordering duplicate blocks, the word *duplicate* should not be used, because the engraver may take this as meaning two original blocks, and the charge will be nearly doubled. The order should specify *Electro* or *Stereo*. If a large number of duplicate blocks is needed, for example an illustration to be published in a number of different journals, they can be produced by a plastic process. Plastic plates are a comparatively recent development, and because of their small weight, are particularly suitable for mailing overseas.

When making a drawing for block making it is important to specify whether the reduction is to be made in the *width* or in the *depth*. If no definite instruction is given the blockmaker will reduce the *depth* dimension. Drawings marked ' $\frac{1}{2}$-scale ' will have their linear dimensions halved. See also p. 160.

Electronic Process Engraving

During recent years the principle of photo-electric scanning which is employed in sending pictures by photo-telegraphy has been adapted to the production of half-tone blocks directly from the original print. Three types of electronic engraving machines have been developed: the Fairchild " Scan-a-Graver " (U.S.A.), the " Klischograph " (Germany) and the " Elgrama " (Switzerland). The Scan-a-Graver, which is marketed in Great Britain by J. F. Crossfield Ltd., can produce half-tone plates with screens of 65, 85, 100, or 120 up to a maximum of 10 in. × 8 in. The photograph to be reproduced is fastened on the circumference of a cylinder and a scanning system consisting of a light source, lens, and photo-electric cell traverses the picture. The output from the cell is applied through suitable amplifiers and correcting circuits to an engraving stylus which burns an image on to a plastic plate corresponding accurately to the tone gradations of the original. After the plate has been produced no further processing is required apart from washing and mounting. As many as 200,000 impressions have been taken from a Scan-a-Graver plate, and the saving in cost of production is considerable. A disadvantage of the original system is that it will only reproduce pictures of the same size as the original, but a later development, the " Scan-a-Sizer ", will give a choice of two screens on the same machine and also reduce the picture by $4\frac{1}{2}$: 1 if required. Among the advantages claimed for the electronic method of block production is the speed and the convenience of producing half-tone plates by a self-contained machine on the users' premises. The plates are produced in Britain by Wace & Co., Eyre St. Hill, London, E.C.1, and the cost of a 12 sq. in. plate (minimum size) is 38*s*. for 100 screen and 42*s*. for 120 screen.

COLOUR PRINTING

In the process of colour printing all the colours of the spectrum can be simulated by the combination of the three primary colours red, yellow and blue. A line or half-tone block prepared for monochrome reproduction can of course be printed in any single colour, but when an illustration contains several different colours the art is in relating tone and colour values of the finished work to the original illustration. Successful colour printing is dependent upon the combined skills of the photographer, the engraver and the printer.

Colour Line Blocks

For simple two- or three-colour line drawings such as Fig. 5.26, colour separation introduces no difficulty and the use of colour in technical illustrations very often takes this form. The drawings may be prepared in two different ways. Blockmakers prefer the complete key drawing in black; where coloured areas are to join black lines, very thin lines are shown on the key and erased at a later stage by the blockmaker. The colour scheme should be shown on a separate tracing.

An alternative method is to prepare a separate black-line drawing for each colour and one for the black outlines. When this method is used the tracing paper must be dimensionally stable. In technical manuals coloured illustrations are usually limited to well-defined separate areas produced by solid colour which do not overlap. A number of hues can be obtained by overlapping and this number can be considerably increased by the use of tints (Fig. 4.53). It is of course possible to obtain similar effects by using printing inks of various hues.

Colour Half-tones

The Three-colour Process. In the three-colour process the only colours used are yellow, red and blue; black is obtained by combining all three. The precise hues in these colours are laid down in British Standard 1480 : 1949.

The Four-colour Process. With the four-colour process black is treated as a separate colour; the hues for the coloured inks are laid down in the Standard quoted above.

For the reproduction of half-tone illustrations from a full-coloured original, much skill in colour separation and colour matching is called for. The initial colour separation is obtained by making three monochrome negatives of the original, using a different filter for each negative; the filters used are blue for yellow printing, green for red and red for blue. Screens are used as for monochrome half-tones, but the grid angle must be different for each exposure, otherwise the dot formation of the three blocks would coincide. These mechanical processes are inadequate for perfect colour matching, and some hand retouching has to be done to the plates during the etching stage to ensure correct tone values. In half-tone colour printing either the three-colour or four-colour process is used, according to quality of the work; since black is usually needed for the text printing, the difference in cost is not so great as it would seem to be.

Cost of Colour Printing

It is not an easy matter to compare the cost of colour printing with that of monochrome and many factors must be considered. In the simple case of a line illustration in two colours one of which is black, the additional cost would be assessed on two items, one for making an extra block, and the other for dual printing. For the page concerned, the increase in total charges might be about 30% if the illustration filled only part of a text page, or 100% for a full-page illustration. This difference is accounted for by the fact that when a page contains type matter, the major portion of the printing charge is for type-setting. The figures quoted are indicative only and should not be used for purposes of estimating.

It is safe to assume that for each colour used in addition to black, the cost per page will be increased to roughly the percentages quoted. Thus a full-page line illustration printed in three colours will cost three times that of a monochrome. This applies to both letterpress and offset litho.

The difference between the costs of monochrome and coloured half-tones may be even greater than for line work because of the considerable amount of re-touching usually needed. There is no doubt that the use of colour can be an asset to technical illustrating but production costs will be greatly increased. The table on p. 215 shows the cost of monochrome and colour blocks at the time this book was printed.

Colour Illustration by Offset-litho

The reproduction of illustrations in colour lithography involves much the same processes and problems as those discussed in the previous section. Separate plates are made for each colour, and relative costs are the same as for colour in letterpress.

Where office-type offset machines such as Multilith and Rotaprint are used for the production of technical reports and instructions, the use of coloured illustrations may be practicable provided that accurate registration is possible. The disadvantage of using colour with these machines is loss of time; for two colours, each sheet must be run off twice, and the general rate of production is slowed down.

A process for colour printing by offset machines of the Rotaprint or Multilith type has recently been evolved by the Eastman Kodak Co. which is suitable for short runs of 1000 to 5000 copies. Three separation negatives are made and printed down on to " Lithofoil " pre-sensitized plates. Colour correction is made by automatic masking, and the process has been made as simple as possible to eliminate skilled handwork. As quick-setting inks are used which, would thicken on the ordinary rollers of the machine, special buna rubber rollers and offset blankets have to be fitted. The only further modification needed is the attachment of a drying spray of powdered starch to prevent the copies 'setting-off' (see p. 176) as they come from the machine. The inks used are high gloss, and the paper recommended is Kromekote, a proprietary type of heavy coated paper. Full particulars of the process are given in a booklet issued by Kodak Ltd.

Colour Printing on Spirit Duplicators

Spirit duplicators such as the Banda and Fordigraph can be used for printing line illustrations but not for half-tones. With these duplicators, a master is made on art paper by drawing on a carbon transfer sheet, the business side of which is in contact with the paper. Since the transfers are made in several different colours, multi-coloured illustrations can be prepared on a single master, and only one printing is required. Copies are reproduced by contact printing on a rotary cylinder, the printing paper being damped with spirit as it passes through the machine. This method appears to offer a solution to certain problems in technical illustrating, but it has its limitations. The drawings cannot be reduced or enlarged in size; the number of copies obtainable from one master does not exceed three hundred; the quality is inferior to normal printing standards.

Cost of Blocks

Type of Block (mounted)	Cost	Note
	£ s. d.	
Open Line 14 sq. in.	19 0	
Fine Line ,,	1 2 9	1
Colour Line ,, (per colour)	2 8 7	
Half-tone squared-up	1 14 6	
Half-tone simple cut out	2 10 0	see p. 246
Half-tone deep etch	3 9 0	
Half-tone 3-colour	25 1 3	2
Half-tone 4-colour	31 8 7	
Half-tone from transparency	42 8 2	3

Notes : The charges are for single mounted blocks, line blocks on zinc or magnesium and ½-tones on copper. Unmounted blocks are slightly cheaper. The minimum area for costing on monochrome blocks is 14 sq. in.
1. Fine line work is the reproduction of any fine typematter or drawing which includes tints and lettering below 12 pt. in size.
2. The minimum area for costing colour blocks is 30 sq. in.
3. The costs quoted are for copying flat coloured originals except in this item, which applies to Kodachrome and similar transparencies.

PAPER FOR PRINTING

All paper is made from fibrous pulp such as rag, esparto grass, or wood pulp, and the quality depends on the proportions in which these pulps are mixed together with thickening or loading compounds added during the manufacture. Paper for printing must be opaque, durable and of even texture, but its quality can vary from a pure rag paper, which has an almost perfect finish and shows up print to its best advantage, to ' newsprint ' made almost entirely from wood pulp. Pure rag paper is rarely used for printing on account of the cost, but a high quality paper can be made from a mixture of rag and wood-pulp fibres.

The fibres, after preparation and washing, are interwoven and the interstices between them are filled by a *loading* compound to make the paper opaque. The loading is mainly by means of china clay, and the amount added determines the smoothness of the finished paper; in high quality art papers the loading may account for as much as 30% of the finished weight.

The loading material does not render the paper non-absorbent, and size is added to prevent the ink from spreading on the paper or soaking into the surface. The smooth finish of high quality printing papers is obtained by passing it finally through a set of rollers under pressure; the rollers, or *calenders*, give the surface a varying degree of glaze and a highly-glazed paper is referred to as *super-calendered* (S.C.).

Types of Paper

Laid and Wove. Paper showing parallel lines in one direction along its texture is known as ' laid ' paper. The pattern is impressed, together with the watermark, by passing the wet fibres under a ' dandy roll ' which compresses them into a homogeneous sheet before the calendering process. Wove paper is equally homogeneous but has no line texture.

Antique Wove Paper is characterized by a rough surface and fairly good bulk. Featherweight A.W. is used for book production if a good bulk is required with a small number of pages. The surface makes it unsuitable for half-tone illustrations or large areas of solid colour.

Machine-finished (M.F.) Papers. Machine-finished wove papers are suitable for all types of printing and can be obtained in a variety of finishes according to requirements. They bulk less than antique papers and have a smoother surface. Super-calendered paper also comes under the general heading of M.F. paper, but is more highly finished.

Art Paper. This is an important class of paper which has a highly glazed or enamelled surface imparted to it by coating the base with china clay. A paper with exceptionally heavy coating is known as ' chromo-art ' paper. This paper is particularly suited to fine detail printing and will reproduce half-tones to the best advantage. Its reflectivity is high, and under certain conditions the glitter from the surface may prove irritating; for this reason it is not the best medium for letterpress. *Imitation Art* paper has a polished surface, but is not enamelled, and the finish is obtained by concentrating the loading on the surface. It is often used instead of art paper on grounds of economy. Comparative costs (1957) are (for making not less than one ton)

Art paper 1*s*. 7⅝*d*. lb.   Imitation art paper 1*s*. 2⅞*d*. lb.

Miscellaneous Types of paper not primarily used for printing purposes include *Bank* and *Bond* writing papers—strong durable papers with a slightly roughened surface, bank being lighter in weight than bond. Both papers may be obtained in various pastel colours (tints) and may be either laid or wove. *Cartridge* paper resembles antique wove paper, and is used extensively for drawing office work and artist's work. It has the merit of being exceedingly hard and tough. *Tracing* paper is a form of toughened paper treated with turpentine or a similar oil to render it translucent.

Boards

The term board, as applied to paper, may mean a single sheet of heavyweight paper or a number of sheets pressed together to obtain greater thickness and toughness. It is important to note that the printer may speak of a board cover when he means a cover of extra thick paper and not necessarily a sheet of cardboard. *Bristol Board* is a finely finished smooth white paper which is particularly suitable for black-and-white drawings. It can be obtained in various thick-nesses, which are designated 1-sheet, 2-sheet . . . depending on the number of sheets compressed together. *Ivory Board* is a thin and slightly cheaper form of Bristol Board. *Fashion Plate* is made by mounting a single sheet of Bristol Board (or its equivalent) on to a thicker backing of paper, totalling about $\frac{3}{32}''$ in thickness. *Scraperboard* is a thick board with a heavy coating of chalk, giving the surface a smooth finish. It is used for producing black-and-white drawings by means of an engraving technique. The surface

217

is blackened over by the artist, who then cuts away the black areas with an engraving tool to expose the white under-surface where required. This method of drawing enables fine detail to be preserved in photographic reduction, as there is no tendency for the fine lines to spread, and it enables fine cross-hatching to be done without the ink tending to run.

Cover Paper

Cover papers for 'paper-bound' booklets can be obtained in many weights and colours; the finish is usually antique. For a glazed cover paper, suitable for half-tone reproduction, a grade of thick art paper can be used. A serviceable cover paper for small manuals is 'index paper' which can be obtained in flat sheets in various shades of pastel colour. It should be noted that a coloured ink on a pastel coloured paper may appear of a different shade from that on the sample card.

Paper Sizes

Apart from newsprint and paper intended for rotary printing presses, most printing paper is sold in sheets of various standard dimensions. The size of sheet as obtained direct from the maker is termed the *broadside*. The following list of standard sizes is based on British Standard 730 : 1951 :

Writing and Printing Paper Broadsides

Name	Size (inches)	Name	Size (inches)
Foolscap	$13\frac{1}{2} \times 17$	Double Demy	$22\frac{1}{2} \times 35$
Double Foolscap	17×27	Quad Demy	35×45
Oblong Dble. F'cap	$13\frac{1}{2} \times 24$	Medium	18×23
Quad Foolscap	27×34	Double Medium	23×36
Pinched Post (W)	$14\frac{1}{2} \times 18\frac{1}{2}$	Royal	20×25
Post (W)	$15\frac{1}{2} \times 19$	Double Royal	25×40
Double Post (W)	$19 \times 30\frac{1}{2}$	Double Crown	20×30
Large Post	$16\frac{1}{2} \times 21$	Quad Crown	30×40
Double Large Post	21×33	Imperial	22×30
Demy*	$17\frac{1}{2} \times 22\frac{1}{2}$	Double Imperial	30×44

* Pronounced 'demy'. (W) indicates writing paper sizes.

218

For special purposes, papers may be made to sizes not given in the above list, but it is obvious that standard sizes should be used wherever possible to reduce cost.

Board Sizes

(*inches*)

Index (Board) Royal	$20\frac{1}{2} \times 25\frac{1}{2}$
Index Royal and a Half	$25\frac{1}{2} \times 30\frac{1}{2}$
Paste (Board) Royal	$20\frac{1}{2} \times 25$
Postal	$22\frac{1}{2} \times 28\frac{1}{2}$
Paste Imperial	$22\frac{1}{2} \times 30$

Broadside Sub-divisions

In Fig. 5.34 a broadside sheet is shown divided into two equal

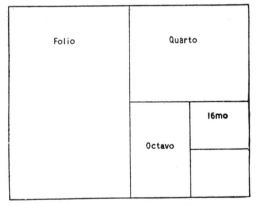

FIG. 5.34. *Sub-divisions of a broadside sheet of paper.*

parts, each of which is termed a *folio*. A folio divided into two is termed a *quarto* (4to), and a quarto divided into two is an *octavo* (8vo).

It will be clear from this that the terms quarto, octavo, are *not actual paper sizes* but are sub-divisions of the broadside. The size of the broadside determines their dimensions. Nevertheless, by custom, the term quarto is usually understood to refer to a sheet of paper approximately 8×10 in., and an octavo sheet is approximately 5×8 in.

The page size chosen for a book should bear a relation to one or

219

other broadside standard sizes if the wastage is to be kept to a minimum. For example, a quarto sheet measuring approximately 8 × 10 in. can be cut from Large Post (21 × 16 in.). A slightly larger sheet is often preferred for technical publications, and a sheet 8½ × 11 in. can be cut from Demy 17½ × 22½ in.

Paper Measures

Weight. Some indication of the relative thickness of papers in any grade can be obtained from the weight per ream. In general, this weight refers to a ream of broadside sheets, e.g. Double Royal 80 lb. means a ream of approximately 500 sheets 25 × 40 in., weighing 80 lb.

Quantity. The standard ream contains 500 sheets, and the standard quire 24 sheets. Paper may be packed in reams or half-reams according to size and weight. Variations in the number of sheets to the ream are commonly found : in stationery, a ream of 20 quires will contain 480 sheets. In printing it is usual to allow an extra number of sheets for printing or binding spoilage, and reams of 504 or 516 sheets are usually supplied. This extra allowance on the standard figure of 500 ensures that if 1000 copies are ordered the buyer will receive 1000 finished copies from the printer.

CHAPTER 6

SETTING OUT THE TEXT

Typewriting Technical Material

THE successful reproduction of technical material depends ultimately on the skill of the typist and the quality of the typewriter. Whatever the method used for reproducing the copies, a neat layout will add to the impression produced on the reader.

Any typed matter is made more readable by the use of ample white space, and double-line spacing should be used unless circumstances prevent it. For the same reason, wide margins are desirable and $1\frac{1}{2}$ in. can be allowed on standard quarto paper; if the type matter is to be bound, the left-hand margin should be wider than the right-hand by $\frac{1}{4}$ to $\frac{1}{2}$ in. It is seldom possible to ' justify ' the right-hand edge of the lines without taking extra time and trouble (see p. 222), but it is possible to avoid clumsy breaks in the words by careful note of the approaching end of the line. If it is necessary to break the word at the end of a line, the following compositors' rules should be followed:

(a) Do not separate a group of letters forming a single sound.
(b) Divide the word so that each part of the division retains its normal sound.
(c) Divide after the vowel, and between two consonants, unless the previous rules are disobeyed.
Examples : starv-ation (retaining the normal sound), not star-vation. haemor-rhage, not haemo-rrhage.

In general, the first part of the word division should suggest the conclusion of the word, but awkward breaks, like camel-lia, do occasionally occur.

The Typewriter

Compared with letterpress printing, the typewriter is an inflexible machine. The normal keyboard is limited to capitals and lower case in one style of letter (which is not particularly elegant) and there is only one size of numeral. These limitations lead to a uniform and dull presentation which can only be relieved by alterations in spacing and occasional display.

Even in expert hands a badly-kept or badly worn machine will produce indifferent results which will be shown in a stencil or litho plate used for reproduction. Faults in duplicated copies are more often caused by bad typing than by bad duplicating, and the best equipment cannot produce good copies from poorly cut stencils or plates.

The type size of normal commercial typewriters is either " Pica " (10 letters to the inch) or " Elite " (12 letters to the inch). The elite size has become more popular in recent years because of its neater appearance and the ability to put more words on a page. This asset is useful if the typescript is to be reproduced by photo-litho, since it reduces the costs on multi-page work—an important point with the present high cost of paper.

In estimating the amount of space occupied by typescript it is convenient to assume the length of line as 6 inches and the average number of characters per word, including space, as 6. The words per line are then the same as the number of characters per inch for pica and elite types. The words per page are then calculated for a given number of lines per page, as for example :

	Lines per page		Words per page	
	Quarto	F'cap	Quarto	F'cap
Elite	24	32	288	384
Pica	24	32	240	320

Although necessarily approximate, these figures will be sufficiently accurate for estimating the quantity of paper required for typing manuscripts.

Justification of Typed Lines

One of the characteristics of typewritten matter is the irregular right-hand margin, and the appearance of the typed pages is con-siderably improved if trouble is taken to *justify* the right-hand edge of the text, i.e. to make all lines of equal length. This justification is easily done by a compositor in setting type, as he has a variety of space units available which can be inserted between words or even letters to spread them out to occupy the correct length of line. To imitate this variable spacing on the typewriter involves some time and trouble, as it is only possible to increase the spaces by a fixed amount, and a preliminary draft will have to be typed. The procedure is explained in the accompanying illustrations (Figs. 6.1 and 6.2), which are reproduced by courtesy of the publishers of *Office Magazine.** (See also p. 229.)

Typewriters for Technical Symbols

In technical typing, the lack of special symbols compels the writer to insert them by hand on the finished typescript—an unsatisfactory method when stencils or plates are used for reproduction. For extensive mathematical work hand lettering is impracticable and even on single copies it gives an untidy appearance.

There are several ways of overcoming this difficulty, according to the volume of the work involved.

Some writers may need only a limited number of symbols, repeated many times in each article or paper they have to write. If, for example, the symbols are mainly confined to λ, ω, θ, π and μ, they can be fitted to any standard typewriter in place of seldom used characters such as @, * and the fractions $\frac{1}{8}$, $\frac{3}{8}$ etc. It must be admitted that this is rarely a complete solution, but it helps.

A more effective method is to use two separate typewriters, one having a standard and the other a Greek keyboard. The latter should contain the complete Greek alphabet in upper and lower case (50 characters), the remaining keys being fitted with square root, differential and other mathematical signs in normal use. The numerals on this keyboard should be small in size, suitable for indices and suffixes, and for greater adaptability the mechanism should include half-line spacing. The method of operation is as follows: the writer prepares his manuscript and sets out the formula as it is to appear in print. The complete manuscript is checked and passed to the typist, who types the plain language first, leaving the required number of blank lines or spaces, and transfers the sheet to the Greek

* W. H. Hollis: 'Letter Spacing', *Office Magazine*, May 1954, p. 167. This periodical is a source of much useful information on typewriting and general office procedure and equipment.

223

I am afraid that, for the present at least,//
you will have to prepare a draft copy to work on.//
You know your given column-width, and you should///
start by ruling a couple of pencil lines down the
page, the required distance apart. Set your left-
hand margin-stop to the left-hand line, and start/
typing your column, finishing your lines as close/
as possible to the right-hand line. Lines which/
fall slightly short of the required width should be
filled up with an arbitrary sign, e.g.//. If you
have to over-run the line by one or two letters, do
not worry, finish off the word; you can make the/
necessary adjustment on the finished copy.

     Now for 'justification'. If a line is short
by, say, two spaces, you will have to introduce///
these into the line somewhere - and that's where/
your good judgement comes in. You can generally//
add an extra space after a full stop: but it is/
as well to avoid spacing before or after 'spindly'
letters such as 'l' or 'i'; rather select the more
full-bodied characters like 'm' or 'w'.
If you have to insert three spaces, it is better//
to gain this extra width with six half-spaces. The
result almost defies detection.

     If the line is a little too long, you will///
have to take space out. You can always pull a comma
to the left with the back-spacer and follow it with
a half-space; you can spare a space after a full-
stop; you can even type a full line with half a//
space between each word.

Will. H. Hollis.

FIG. 6.1. *Draft for justifying typewritten matter.*
(*By courtesy of ' Office Magazine '.*)

I am afraid that, for the present at least,
you will have to prepare a draft copy to work on.
You know your given column-width, and you should
start by ruling a couple of pencil-lines down the
page, the required distance apart. Set your left-
hand margin-stop to the left-hand line, and start
typing your column, finishing your lines as close
as possible to the right-hand line. Lines which
fall slightly short of the required width should be
filled up with some arbitrary sign, e.g.//. If you
have to over-run the line by one or two letters, do
not worry; finish off the word - you can make the
necessary adjustment on the finished copy.

     Now for 'justification'. If a line is short
by, say, two spaces, you will have to introduce
these into the line somewhere - and that's where
your good judgement comes in. You can generally
add an extra space after a full stop: but it is
as well to avoid spacing before or after 'spindly'
letters such as 'l' or 'i'; rather select the more
full-bodied characters like 'm' or 'w'.
If you have to insert three spaces, it is better
to gain this width by means of six half-spaces. The
result almost defies detection.

     If the line is a little too long, you will
have to take space out. You can always pull a comma
to the left with the back-spacer and follow it with
a half-space; you can spare a space after a full-
stop; you can even type a full line with half a
space between each word.

Will. H. Hollis.

FIG. 6.2. *Finished typescript with varied spacing.*

machine to complete the formulae. With modern machines extreme accuracy of alignment is possible, but the method is laborious, particularly when using duplicating stencils or direct offset litho plates which at all times need careful handling.

The Dual-keyboard Typewriter

An obvious improvement on the method of typing mathematics just described is the combining of a normal and a Greek keyboard on one machine with a simple mechanism for transferring the carriage from one keyboard to the other. At least one firm has put

FIG. 6.3. *Dual keyboard typewriter.* (*Imperial Typewriter Co., Ltd.*)

such a machine into production (Fig. 6.3). It is orthodox in design and has no electrical contrivances. The carriage is moved across to the other keyboard by the operation of a central lever; the machine therefore doubles the range of available typing characters without having to remove the paper and transfer it from one carriage to another.

The choice of characters from either keyboard is with the purchaser; a specimen Greek and mathematical face is shown in Fig. 6.4. The introduction of this machine is an important development in the field of technical and scientific writing, since it removes the difficulty of typing mathematics, chemical formulae or foreign languages in combination with plain English. There is, of course,

P

R	C	L	%	_	(	)	-	/	$	¼	?
1	2	3	4	5	6	7	8	9	=	¾	?
A	Z	E	P	T	Θ	Y	I	O	;	~	
α	ζ	ε	ρ	τ	θ	υ	ι	ο	η	'	
½	Σ	Δ	Φ	Γ	H	Ξ	K	Λ	{	}	
ς	σ	δ	φ	γ	η	ξ	κ	λ	[	]	
X	Ψ	Ω	B	N	M	Π	•	.	..		
χ	ψ	ω	β	ν	μ	π	,	ϛ	ˋ		

Fig. 6.4. *Specimen of Greek keyboard with mathematical signs.*

a limit to its versatility, set by the number of characters that can be accommodated on the two keyboards; it would not be possible to provide a full range of mathematical symbols and chemical formulae, and at the same time retain a complete English alphabet in upper and lower case.

Electrical Typewriters

The development of electrically-operated typewriters in this country has been slow, but some are now in production. It can be claimed that these machines introduce no difficulties for the typist, since the operation involves no special technique; indeed, the typist's work is simplified because ' touch ' has no significance. The striking mechanism is driven by a small electric motor; the pressure on the platen is therefore independent of the typist's touch. Provision is made for adjusting the striking pressure, and at maximum setting of the control, ten or more carbon copies may be produced simultaneously. The machines are particularly suitable for preparing plain text on duplicating stencils or offset-litho plates, but for the offset work slight modifications are usually necessary.

226

The Vari-Typer*

This machine combines the function of a typewriter and letterpress typesetter, and when used in conjunction with an office-type offset litho machine offers the technical writer most of the facilities provided by letterpress printing. The two outstanding features of the machine are that most of the type faces normally used in letterpress printing are available, and right-hand margins can be ' justified '.

The significance of choice in type faces, as far as the technical writer is concerned, is that one of the faces may comprise the Greek alphabet plus a range of mathematical symbols. The justified margin has two advantages : first, it permits the setting of a page in two or more columns; second, it enhances appearance for single or multi-column pages.

The type faces are carried on a semi-circular plate (Fig. 6.5) approximately $2\frac{1}{2}''$ in diameter, and two faces each carrying 90 characters are loaded into the machine before use ; the loading presents no greater difficulty than placing a ribbon spool on an ordinary typewriter.

Justification of the right-hand margin is conditional upon the copy being in its final typed state; if the copy contains heavy corrections in manuscript it must first be typed in the normal way and then re-typed for justification. The procedure is simple in operation : suppose the measure (i.e. line width) required is 6 inches ; a lever on the machine is set for this measurement and typing is stopped at the end of a word or syllable just before the limit is reached. When re-typing for justification the operator counts the spaces needed to fill the line and sets a dial to this number before commencing to type the line. The machine then spaces the lines automatically to the correct length.

An unusual feature of this machine is that typing paper is inserted at the side of the machine; this means that the size of sheet is not limited by the length of the carriage. This is of considerable advantage to the technical writer, because lettering on many illustrations can be printed by machine, saving much time on the drawing board. A special model can be obtained to extend this facility to large engineering drawings.

* Manufactured in U.S.A. by the Ralph C. Coxhead Corporation. Distributors : Vari-Typer Ltd., 11 Southampton Row, London, W.C.1.

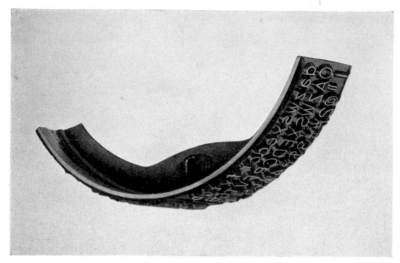

FIG. 6.5. *Type plate used in the Vari-Typer.*

FIG. 6.6. *Coxhead D.S.J. typewriter.*
(*Both photographs by courtesy of Vari-Typer Ltd.*)

Two types of machine are available, one being the standard Vari-Typer; the other, known as the Coxhead D.S.J. (differential space justification) is illustrated in Fig. 6.6. The essential difference between the two is shown by Fig. 6.7: with the Vari-Typer, as in ordinary typewriters, each letter occupies the same amount of space regardless of its width and the result is an irregular spacing between individual letters. In the D.S.J. machine the spacing is proportional to the width of the letter, in conformity with typographical practice. Necessarily the design of the machine is more complex, and it is therefore more costly.

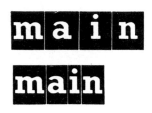

Fig. 6.7. *Illustrating the effect of differential spacing.*

The Vari-Typer Headliner

The introduction of a new machine for setting display has just been announced (June 1958). This is the Headliner, Model 400, which produces complete headlines by photo-composition. A very large range of type faces from 12 to 72 point is available. Copy leaves the machine ready printed on 35-mm paper strip which can be immediately pasted up for photo-litho reproduction. Operation requires no more skill than a Vari-Typer.

It has been claimed that the Vari-Typer gives a 40% saving in printing costs for mathematical setting, using offset litho reproduction, but this does not include overhead charges nor capital cost. It is probable that a 15–20% saving might be realized with everything taken into account.

The Olivetti " Graphika "

A manually operated typewriter giving proportional letter spacing (as in Fig. 6.7) is the Olivetti " Graphika ", marketed in 1957. The letters and symbols on the keyboard are divided into four groups, each group being a multiple of the basic unit of $\frac{1}{04}$ in. (0 8 mm). The space bar is divided to give two- or three-unit spacing between

229

words, and an expander key will add an extra unit to each letter to give the effect of ' letter-spaced ' words. By operating the expander key and back-spacing key it is possible to select six different spacings ; right-hand margin justification is thus made possible with the minimum of trouble.

THE PRINTING OF MATHEMATICS

The setting of mathematical expression in letterpress type presents little difficulty to those printers (not many) who are equipped with the special characters or matrices to cover the symbols used, and who also have a compositor who is experienced in the setting of mathematical expressions. Many printers, however, do not consider the initial cost of the special matrices to be justified,* especially if they only handle occasional mathematical setting, and they sometimes subcontract mathematical work to specialist typesetters.

To avoid delay it is better to deal with a printer who has the necessary type and who understands the art of displaying equations. It is always desirable to ask for samples of typesetting from an unknown printer before placing an order.

All complicated mathematical expressions involve a certain amount of hand setting. This slows down the rate of production and increases the cost per page of typeset matter. If the work is almost wholly mathematical the cost of typesetting may be doubled or even trebled, and it is also customary to make a small extra charge for any line of type in which formulae or special symbols occur.

In order to keep the cost and time to a minimum, a writer should be particularly careful in setting out any mathematical expressions, and should give clear instructions to the compositor on the type face and style required for the setting. Certain conventions have been recommended by the Royal Society and by the British Standards Institution for mathematical setting, and these are summarized in the following pages.

Before undertaking the marking up of mathematical copy or

* The Monotype Corporation lists over 240 special mathematical signs in their catalogue of matrices.

setting out mathematical expressions, the writer should consult the following textbooks for full details of accepted practice:

CHAUNDY, T. W., BARRETT, P. R., and BATEY, C. *The Printing of Mathematics* (Oxford: Clarendon Press, 1954).
Notes on the Preparation of Mathematical Papers (C. F. Hodgson & Son for the London Mathematical Society, 1954).
PHILLIPS, A. *Setting Mathematics* (The Monotype Corporation, 1956) (*The Monotype Recorder*, Vol. 40, No. 4).
THE ROYAL SOCIETY : *Symbols, Signs and Abbreviations.*

General Recommendations

Unless specially directed, all symbols used in mathematical expressions are set in italic type.

Exceptions to italic type are:

> Operators and constants, e.g. the operator ' j '*
> Trigonometrical symbols : sin, cos, tan . . .
> Vector quantities

Symbols requiring a special type face (e.g. $\mathscr{J}$) should be ringed in the copy and a list of such special symbols should be supplied to the printer.

Underlining should not be used as part of a symbol, but should always be retained to indicate italic type.

Particular care should be taken to distinguish between symbols which may be confused. The following symbols should be clearly differentiated:

a (italic)	α (alpha) $\propto$ (varies as)
δ (delta)	∂ (partial differential)
κ (kappa)	k (lower case) K (capital)
v (italic)	u (italic) ν (nu) μ (mu)
p (italic)	ρ (rho)
x (italic)	χ (chi) $\times$ (multiply sign)
w (italic)	ω (omega)
1 (numeral)	l (italic) l (roman letter)

Common Errors in Setting

The book by A. Phillips, referred to above, gives a list of the

---

* The differential ' d ' should be set in roman, but many authors prefer to keep to italic, and it is doubtful whether this rule will be observed.

most common mistakes made by inexperienced compositors in setting mathematical expressions. These are :

1. Inferior and superior sorts are set in wrong size and face, and are positioned incorrectly (see p. 236).
2. Brackets are the wrong size and weight.
3. Fractions are not placed correctly in the formulae and are set in the wrong size.
4. Vertical spacing is badly arranged.
5. Horizontal spacing is incorrect, the compositor being unaware of the rules of spacing peculiar to setting mathematics.
6. The correct signs and symbols are not recognized by the compositor.
7. Roman is used instead of italic, and the compositor does not recognize the correct Greek letters.
8. Some printers not possessing the correct sorts endeavour to make them by mutilating other characters.

While this list may appear to show the shortcomings of an inexperienced compositor, it serves equally well to guide the writer of mathematical text to the details that he must look for in correcting proofs and which also require clear instructions in the original text. A compositor is a highly-skilled craftsman, but not a mathematician, and if the original copy is obscure he may be excused from making a bad guess at the author's intentions.

There are other agreed recommendations which will save time and trouble if they are followed, and a summary of these is given below :

Root Signs

If the writer insists on a vinculum or bar over each expression following the root sign, e.g. $\sqrt{a + x}$, the bar will have to be cut by hand from a metal strip and fitted in place by the compositor. This hand work can be eliminated by the method recommended by the London Mathematical Society, which treats a square-root expression in the same way as a ' squared ' expression and places the whole of the term following the root sign in brackets, thus :

$$\sqrt{(x + y)} \quad \text{or} \quad (x + y)^{\frac{1}{2}}$$

This method is not only less troublesome for the printer but avoids any inaccuracy arising from careless setting. For example, $\sqrt{\dfrac{x + 1}{1 - x}}$ might be printed as $\dfrac{\sqrt{x + 1}}{1 - x}$ or $\dfrac{x + 1}{\sqrt{1 - x}}$.

An even more awkward setting is required in an expression such

232

as $\dfrac{x+1}{\sqrt{1-x}}$ where the compositor would have to fit two short rules in the centre of the fraction. The bracketed form of expression eliminates this trouble also.

Fractions

The setting of fractions is simplified by using a solidus (/) instead of the fraction bar : $1/x$ instead of $\dfrac{1}{x}$. This setting avoids an inelegant white space between the lines where the printer has to space the preceding and succeeding lines to clear the fraction. Care must be taken in setting multi-term expressions ; for example $a/x - y/b$ may be misread, and should be clarified by adding brackets : $(a/x) - (y/b)$.

The solidus should not be too heavy or too long, or it may detract from the neatness of the text, but strokes of a different thickness may be used to distinguish the parts of a fraction : $(a/x)/(y/b)$. It may be preferable in some expressions to display the fraction in full with a horizontal bar :

$$\frac{x-1}{1-b} + \frac{y-2}{1-a}$$

care being taken to centre the expressions on the bars and make them the same length as the longer term in the fraction :

$$\frac{x-1}{(x-2)(y-1)}$$

Numerical fractions of common order, such as $\frac{1}{2}$, $\frac{3}{4}$ . . . are usually cast on a single body of type and involve no extra setting. For this reason, the fraction $x/2$ may sometimes be set more conveniently as $\frac{1}{2}x$.

Irregular fractions such as $\dfrac{5}{32}$ can be set in small numerals by means of so-called ' split fractions ', e.g. $\frac{5}{32}$.

Indices and Suffixes

These figures are referred to by the printer as *superior* and *inferior* numerals respectively, and they are usually cast on the same size as the text type but above or below the x-height (see Appendix III). For this reason it is not ordinarily possible to set an index and a suffix in the same vertical line, and the combination usually appears as $U_3{}^2$. The requirements of modern physics, however, have led to the making of special matrices which will produce aligned figures, but these are not always available and will have to be specified. Before criticizing the typesetting of an ordinary printer the writer should bear in mind that each character occupies a rectangle, and there is a limit to the closeness with which the characters can be packed. This feature is often seen in integral expressions, where the integral sign occupies a space which prevents the limits from being set close to it: $\int_0^\pi$. The modern tendency is to use vertical integral signs which overcome this defect: $\int_0^\pi$

The exponential ' e ' always presents a problem, especially if the index is a complex expression. It is almost impossible to make a neat setting of $e^{-\frac{t}{CR}}$ which involves two lines of small type, and the alternative $e^{-t/CR}$ is neater, but still involves trouble in setting the superior type.

The recommendation of the London Mathematical Society is that the abbreviation ' exp.' should be used with the index figures set in the line following: $\exp(-t/CR)$, and this saves the compositor time and trouble.

An awkward position sometimes arises in writing electrical engineering formulae where e is also used for instantaneous values of electromotive force. If the writer does not wish to use the ' exp ' abbreviation, the Greek ε can be used for the exponential, with an explanatory footnote.

Brackets

The symbols ( ) which are commonly called brackets are known as *parentheses* by the printer, who uses the word brackets for the square brackets [ ]. The ' curly bracket ' { } is known as the *brace*.

The general order in which these symbols are used is { [( )] }, but it is sometimes convenient to arrange them differently, depending on the size and shape of the expression. In some type founts the brackets are of disproportional thickness [ ] and make the expressions look clumsy.

234

In general, the use of heavy signs should be avoided, and there are several founts of mathematical type which are designed to match the symbols with the letters and numerals.

Decimal Points

The correct setting of the decimal point is a dot in the centre of the figures: 89·8 ; most printers however will place the dot on the line unless instructed otherwise. It should be noted that in European literature the decimal point is a comma (36,345) which leads to confusion in translating. Writers of English who have been accustomed to the European comma should be particularly careful in using the · in its correct place, as the printer will not always make the necessary modification, nor may he know that it is necessary.

The use of the · to indicate multiplication is deprecated as it leads to ambiguity.*

The comma which is used to point off thousands (4,560) is now being superseded by a small space equal in width to the comma (4 500) which is not liable to confuse and looks neater in tabular figure setting. If this style is used the printer should be notified by the instruction ‘Leave comma space between groups of 3 figures.’ Some writers prefer to apply this rule to numerals exceeding 10 000, thus: 4560 but 45 600.

Equations

If a number of equations are set out in a single article they should be numbered in sequence. In books, many authors prefer to number the equations according to the chapter (e.g. Equation 3.1 . . .) instead of allowing the numbers to run serially through the book. If a system of numbering is adopted it is preferable to give a number to each equation regardless of its importance, although sometimes it may look pretentious to write

$$x = 2b \qquad \ldots \qquad \ldots \qquad \ldots \qquad (3.23)$$

and the author should use discretion in setting out the text.

The successful display of equations both in typescript and letterpress lies in adequate spacing between lines and between separate

* An extreme case occurred in a book in which the central dot was used to denote multiplication and not the decimal point ! This gave rise to the odd-looking expression 94·88 = 82·88 + 12·88, which implied that the author could not add.

expressions. If ample white space is left, the expressions stand out and catch the reader's eye.

In the stages of resolving an expression, care must be taken to align the equals signs vertically and also to align them in the centre of a fraction bar.

It frequently happens that an expression contains more terms than can be accommodated on a single line of type, especially when narrow columns are used. Occasionally the expression can be allowed to run into two columns in width and be separated from the text by a thin rule or dotted line, but with experience it is possible to break the expression at a convenient point. If the break occurs at a sign such as $+$, $-$, $\times$, or $\div$, the sign should end the line at the break and be repeated at the beginning of the continued line below.

It should be remembered that a compositor who is not a mathematician will break an equation automatically at the end of the measure, unless instructed where to separate the terms.

Examples of Setting Equations

The following examples of good and bad setting of an equation are reproduced from *Setting Mathematics*,* with the explanation that accompanies them:

$$L = 2\kappa \mathrm{d}\left\{\pi/2 - \frac{a}{r}(e\,\pi/2 - \pi/_2)\right\} ; \quad \frac{r}{a} \geqslant e^{\pi}/_2 \qquad . \qquad (1)$$

$$L = 2\kappa d\left\{\tfrac{1}{2}\pi - \frac{a}{r}(e^{\frac{1}{2}\pi} - \tfrac{1}{2}\pi)\right\} ; \quad \frac{r}{a} \geqslant e^{\frac{1}{2}\pi}. \qquad . \qquad (2)$$

$$L = 2\kappa d\{\tfrac{1}{2}\pi - ar^{-1}(e^{\frac{1}{2}\pi} - \tfrac{1}{2}\pi)\} ; \quad r/a \geqslant e^{\frac{1}{2}\pi} \qquad . \qquad (3)$$

There are a number of errors in (1); the second and fourth $\pi/2$ are indices, the first and third are not. A compositor who is used to mathematical setting would recognize that the $\pi/2$ which follows the exponential function (e) is an index value. In every case where the numerical value is in the denominator the fraction should be set as $\tfrac{1}{2}\pi$, $\tfrac{1}{4}\pi$, etc. rather than $\pi/2$, $\pi/4$. It is not easy to bring (1) into a single line by the use of a solidus; $r/a \geqslant e^{\frac{1}{2}\pi}$ is satisfactory, but $a/r(e^{\frac{1}{2}\pi} - \tfrac{1}{2}\pi)$ would be wrong, for it puts the brackets into the denominator. The alternative is $a(e^{\frac{1}{2}\pi} - \tfrac{1}{2}\pi)/r$, but the best solution in a single line is (3) in which a/r becomes ar^{-1}.

This example has been elaborated to show that an author could often write an expression in one line with no loss to the reader if he realized that it would assist the printer.

* By permission of the Monotype Corporation and Mr. A. Phillips.

Other faults in composition will be seen in Equation (1): the symbols are set in roman instead of italics, and there is too much space between numerator and denominator in the fractions—a common example of careless setting.

TABULAR MATTER

The setting out of tabular matter on the typewriter is more difficult than setting out in letterpress for the reasons that have been given previously. It is not possible to distinguish between headings or symbols by using heavier type* or italics, and therefore greater care has to be taken to make the tables easily readable by orderly arrangement and well-defined spacing. The following general rules apply to all kinds of tabular matter:

(a) Words or phrases in the left-hand column should be aligned on the left.

(b) Figures should be aligned on the right hand or on the decimal point, as:

$$
\begin{array}{lll}
1 & 1 & \quad 1{\cdot}2 \quad\quad 1{\cdot}2 \\
10 \quad \text{not} \quad 10 \quad \text{and} & \quad 2{\cdot}36 \quad \text{not} \quad 2{\cdot}36 \\
120 \quad\quad\quad 120 & \quad 12{\cdot}44 \quad\quad 12{\cdot}44
\end{array}
$$

Equations should be aligned on the $=$ sign, irrespective of the length of the expressions on each side of it.

(c) Lines of uneven length followed by a figure should be linked to it by .... or ... ...

(d) The use of ditto marks („) should be avoided.

Ruled Tables

A fault sometimes found in the layout of small tables is excessive use of ruled lines (termed ' rules ' by the printer); this applies both to typewriting and typesetting. It is often possible to avoid using rules by grouping the items in the column and separating them by white space. If a table contains two short columns, no rules are needed:

TABLE 1. MAXIMUM SPEEDS

First Gear	.	.	.	.	10 m.p.h.
Second Gear		.	.	.	25 m.p.h.
Third Gear		.	.	.	40 m.p.h.
Fourth Gear		.	.	.	70 m.p.h.

* W. H. Hollis recommends overprinting the characters several times for emphasis. See reference on p. 223.

If the lines are well spaced, horizontal rules can be limited to the separation of headings from the contents, but an additional rule should be put at the bottom of the table to improve the appearance :

TABLE 2. TEST READINGS

Test	Connexions	Volts	Output mA
a	Parallel	24	200
b	Parallel	30	250
c	Series	30	50
d	Parallel	48	400

Table Headings

The column headings in the table must be fully explanatory and unambiguous. For example, a column headed " Dimensions " must specify the units and the specific dimension, height, width, and length.

A common form of ambiguity arises in the use of multiplication or division signs in the headings to indicate that the quantities in the column have to be increased or decreased by a constant factor. The sub-heading ' $\times$ 10 ' may make the reader ask ' Are the figures under this heading actual readings to be multiplied by 10 or have they been already multiplied ? ' The Institution of Electrical Engineers in its *Handbook for Authors* recommends placing the factor at different points in the table to distinguish between the meanings :

x ft	x ft $\times$ 10^4
$\times$ 10^4	
2	2
4	4

the first column indicating that the multiplication has to be performed and the second that it has been performed. This is satisfactory, but wherever possible all ambiguity should be removed by the plain statements ' 10 times Meter Reading ' or ' Weight in hundreds of pounds '. No difficulty will arise in metric units if the correct multiples are used, e.g. ' Length in km '.

Style of Numerals in Tables

There is a belief that tabular work is best set with lining numerals, (1 2 3 4 5 . . .), preferably sans serif. It is true that for open tables, where ample space is available, lining numerals are often desirable, but for closely-packed tables, such as logarithmic tables or railway time charts, old-style numerals with descenders (123456789) are preferable, because their irregular pattern breaks up the solid mass and individual numerals can be readily picked out. This is shown in the example below in which the lining numerals form part of an obsolete time-table. The effect is that ' the trees cannot be seen for the wood ' and this confusion becomes worse when a bold face is used.

```
..........|1144|........|........|1229
11 9|1132| .  |1154|1217| .
1111|1134|....|1156|1219|....
1120| .  |1152|12 5| .  |1237
1124|1139|1156|12 9|1224|1241
1127|1142|1159|1212|1227|1244
1129|1144|12 2|1214|1229|1247
1132|1147|12 5|1217|1232|1250
1135|1150|12 8|1220|1235|1253
1139|1154|1213|1224|1239|1258
1154|12 9|1227|1239|1254|1 12
1159|1214|1232|1244|1259|1 17
..........|....|........|........
```

```
..........|1144|........|........|1229
11 9|1132| .  |1154|1217| .
1111|1134|....|1156|1219|....
1120| .  |1152|12 5| .  |1237
1124|1139|1156|12 9|1224|1241
1127|1142|1159|1212|1227|1244
1129|1144|12 2|1214|1229|1247
1132|1147|12 5|1217|1232|1250
1135|1150|12 8|1220|1235|1253
1139|1154|1213|1224|1239|1258
1154|12 9|1227|1239|1254|1 12
1159|1214|1232|1244|1259|1 17
..........|....|........|........
```

```
..........|1144|........|........|1229
11 9|1132| .  |1154|1217| .
1111|1134|......|1156|1219|......
1120| .  |1152| 2 5| .  |1237
1124|1139|1156|12 9|1224|1241
1127|1142|1159|1212|1227|1244
1129|1144|12 2|1214|1229|1247
1132|1147|12 5|1217|1232|1250
1135|1150|12 8|1220|1235|1253
1139|1154|1213|1224|1239|1258
1154|12 9|1227|1239|1254|1 12
1159|1214|1232|1244|1259|1 17
..........|....|........|........
```

If lining numerals are to be used for comprehensive tables, great care must be exercised in the choice of type face and size. A good example of clear setting is illustrated in the following table:

FIRST 700 ZEROS OF BESSEL FUNCTIONS — $J_l(x)$ AND $J'_l(x)$ 691

TABLE

	Mode*	l_m	Value†		Mode*	l_m	Value†
1	TE	1–1	1.841184	(48	TM	1–4	13.323692
2	TM	0–1	2.404826	(49	TE	0–4	13.323692
3	TE	2–1	3.054237	50	TM	9–1	13.354300
(4	TM	1–1	3.831706	51	TM	6–2	13.589290
(5	TE	0–1	3.831706	52	TE	12–1	13.878843
6	TE	3–1	4.201189	53	TE	5–3	13.987189
7	TM	2–1	5.135622	54	TE	8–2	14.115519
8	TE	4–1	5.317553	55	TM	4–3	14.372537
9	TE	1–2	5.331443	56	TM	10–1	14.475501
10	TM	0–2	5.520078	57	TE	3–4	14.585848
11	TM	3–1	6.380162	58	TM	2–4	14.795952
12	TE	5–1	6.415616	59	TM	7–2	14.821269
13	TE	2–2	6.706133	60	TE	1–5	14.863589
(14	TM	1–2	7.015587	61	TE	13–1	14.928374
(15	TE	0–2	7.015587	62	TM	0–5	14.930918
16	TE	6–1	7.501266	63	TE	6–3	15.268181

239

Illustrated Tables

It is sometimes necessary to include small diagrams, symbols or Isotypes in a numerical table. If separate blocks are used for this purpose, production costs are high because the blocks have to be dropped into their appropriate positions in the imposing stage. It is often more convenient and even cheaper to print the table by stencil on drawing or graph paper together with the illustrations and then produce a single line block from the composite drawing. Graph paper, provided that the lines are of pale grey or blue tint, is convenient and aids correct spacing of the lettering. The table shown in Fig. 6.8 was produced by stencils on pale blue lined

a	Square Wave, Mark/space ratio unity.	$f(\theta) = \dfrac{2A}{\pi} \sum\limits_{k=1}^{k=\infty} \dfrac{\sin(2k-1)\theta}{(2k-1)}$
b	Infinitely short pulse	$f(\theta) = \dfrac{A\phi}{2\pi} + A \sum\limits_{k=1}^{k=\infty} \dfrac{\phi}{\pi} \cos k\theta$ where $\phi \to 0$ but $A\phi$ remains finite
c	Short square wave, duration ϕ	$f(\theta) = \dfrac{A\phi}{2\pi} + \dfrac{2A}{\pi} \sum\limits_{k=1}^{k=\infty} \dfrac{1}{k} \sin\dfrac{k\phi}{2} \cos k\theta$
d	Uniform triangular wave	$f(\theta) = \dfrac{8A}{\pi^2} \sum\limits_{k=1}^{k=\infty} (-1)^{k+1} \dfrac{1}{(2k-1)^2} \sin(2k-1)\theta$
e	Sawtooth wave with infinitely short flyback	$f(\theta) = \dfrac{2A}{\pi} \sum\limits_{k=1}^{k=\infty} (-1)^{k+1} \dfrac{1}{k} \sin k\theta$
f	General sawtooth wave.	$f(\theta) = \dfrac{2A}{\phi(\pi-\phi)} \sum\limits_{k=1}^{k=\infty} (-1)^{k+1} \dfrac{1}{k^2} \sin k\phi . \sin k\theta$

FIG. 6.8. *A composite table with diagrams, prepared with UNO stencils.*

millimetric paper, the lines not appearing in the finished reproduction. If a Vari-Typer is available the letterpress can be typed on thin Bristol board and the illustrations drawn separately and pasted into place.

Typeset Tabular Matter

The size of type for typeset tables and the method of display require careful thought and some experience in typography if a good appearance is to be obtained. Much of the previous discussion applies to typesetting, but there is additional scope for display in the choice of two or three kinds of type and in the grading of sizes to suit the importance of the items. Some tables can be set without rules, but others are improved in appearance by complete ruling. The choice is one of preference rather than necessity. It must be remembered that the cost of a fully ruled table is considerable, as all the lengths of metal used in separating the columns have to be cut and set in by hand. Further, it is difficult for the printer to alter the arrangement of the table or to make additions if the figures are closely surrounded by ruled lines.

CHAPTER 7

EDITORIAL PROCEDURE

I T is not possible to define the functions of an editor in simple terms because these functions vary considerably in different fields. Many well-established technical journals have at least two editors, one of which may be styled the Managing (or General) Editor and the other the Technical Editor.

The function of the managing editor is largely commercial; he is concerned with general policy and the management of business affairs, whereas the technical editor is responsible for the acceptance or rejection of material submitted for publication. The main qualifications necessary for these two types of editor are therefore distinct; the managing editor must have business acumen and training, whilst the technical editor must have a sound scientific background, with experience in the specific field covered by his journal. Since both editors are directly concerned with the presentation of their journal, it follows that each must have a knowledge of printing procedure.

In some technical journals the editor combines the functions of manager and specialist. There are also certain types of publication, for example the Proceedings of learned societies, which maintain an Editorial Board of specialists, to control the technical policy and level of the papers published.

The foregoing comments apply mainly to established journalistic practice, but technical writers in industry and the public services are not normally directly concerned with periodicals, and have frequently to adopt their own editorial procedure. The remainder of this chapter is intended to give guidance on this procedure, for unless logical editorial practice is applied to industrial publications their presentation may be decidedly below standard.

In Chapter 9 the special case of a large organization employing a technical writing unit is discussed in detail.

Technical Editing

There is always a risk of confusion between technical editing and the editing of technical writing. Technical editing implies the testing

242

of manuscript for accuracy, relevance and level, whereas the editing of technical writing is concerned with matters of style and presentation, coupled with the preparation of the manuscript for the printer.

In most large business or service organizations the range of specialized subjects is formidable, and the centralization of purely technical editing in one person is sometimes difficult. A common procedure is to submit each writer's output to a specialist in the subject, and employ a general editor to supervise production.

The duties of such an editor may be summarized as follows:
(i) To maintain an acceptable standard of writing.

This implies above all else that the technical level of the written work is suitable for the readers to whom it is addressed. The natural tendency of most technical writers is to place on record the full extent of their own knowledge. The editor must curb this exuberance and ensure that writers keep their feet on the readers' ground.

(ii) To ensure adherence to recognized standards in terminology, symbols and abbreviations.*

This is best achieved by compiling and circulating a set of ' house rules ' (see p. 59), and by insisting on uniformity in symbols and nomenclature.

(iii) To exercise over-riding supervision in all matters affecting presentation.

In this work, the editor must apply a sound knowledge of technical printing, as well as a mastery of style in writing. Technical printing standards must be based on an authoritative reference book, such as *The Printing of Mathematics* (p. 231), *Words into Type* (p. 324), or the books cited in Appendix II (p. 307).

An editor must avoid trying to mould the writing of different authors to a common pattern or to his own style—a more usual offence. To deny freedom of expression is to destroy individuality.

The editor must be thoroughly versed in the elements of typography; this implies ability to discriminate between suitable and unsuitable type faces, coupled with a knowledge of pictorial presentation and the layout of pages. Much of this know-how can be learned from textbooks on typography (p. 327), but its successful application is a matter of experience.

* The first requirement is to obtain and use the relevant standards Many professional editors and publishers are still ignorant of the agreed standards of terminology and symbols.

243

Sub-editing

It is not easy to draw a line between editing and sub-editing in the field of writing with which this book is concerned. Quite often the editor will have to do his own sub-editing, which implies the steering of the final drafts into print. A sub-editor would check the illustrations and scale them down for blockmaking, order the blocks, and mark the manuscript with instructions for the printer.

Proof Correction

At least three sets of galley proofs should be called for from the printer, one of which should include corrections by the printer's reader and be labelled ' Marked Proof '. This set of galleys should be read through carefully by the sub-editor and errors marked in a colour different from that of the printer's reader's corrections. At the same time, a second set should be checked by the writer. Changes in the order of paragraphs are quite permissible at this stage, but any changes likely to disturb the type space should be discouraged. Words or sentences needing revision should be replaced by matter occupying the same space as the existing text. Additions to a paragraph are permissible, or new paragraphs may be added provided there are adequate grounds for their inclusion.

When the writer's marked galleys are returned to the sub-editor the printer's set must be re-marked and additional matter included.

It is customary for printers to set all display matter, such as main titles, running headlines* and captions, separately and proof them on a separate sheet. This sheet must be checked as carefully as the text ; there is often a tendency for errors to be overlooked in headings and sub-headings. The bigger the type, the more it is taken for granted. It would save much time and trouble to everybody concerned if authors would understand and use the standard proof correction marks. Although over 70 different markings are recognized, it is generally sufficient to learn about 12 of the more commonly used ones, such as are shown in Appendix II. Above all, authors should be warned not to make arbitrary markings which might confuse the printer : for example, a correction printed in capitals (for legibility) may be set as a capital letter by the printer.

A method of correction sometimes used by inexperienced authors

---

* In book work these are usually set after making up the page.

is to make a separate list of the corrections, numbering them to match the line in the galley proofs. This is an unnecessary and tedious procedure for the author and is exasperating to an editor or printer, who would be quite justified in returning the proofs with a request for more orthodox marking.

Additional matter should not be written on the back of a galley (where it might be overlooked), nor should additions be pinned to the galley proof. It is always safer to identify the extra matter with the galley or page reference number and gum it into place at the edge of the paper.

In making corrections on the sheet, the column of type is mentally divided into equal portions on each side of the centre line and the corrections to the portion on the left are made on the left-hand side of the sheet, those to the right being on the right-hand side. When there is more than one correction in the margin, the marks are made in order of occurrence in the text line, and are separated by a / to show that the correction is completed.

Make-up

The next step is to make-up the galleys into pages, and insert illustrations and captions. (If the work contains no illustrations, make-up can sometimes be left to the printer.) It is assumed that block pulls of all illustrations are available, and the first step is to mark the first reference to each illustration in numerical order on the spare set of galleys, at the same time inserting the figure numbers on the block pulls. If this is not done, there is a risk of an illustration being missed out of the make-up, and the whole job may have to be done again.

It is convenient to rule up a number of paper sheets to page depth; an *em* rule should be used for this purpose in preference to an inch rule.* (A common depth for quarto-size formats is 48 ems.)

The layout of the preliminary pages, i.e. title, contents, list of illustrations, etc., should conform to good typographical practice; some guidance is given in Chapter 8, but a successful layout depends on experience, and ingenuity, and a study of first-class publications.

When laying out text pages, the space required for additional

* A printer will supply a ream of paper ready ruled to specified column or text size at a reasonable cost.

matter must be taken into account and suitable cross reference made, e.g. *take in ' A ', ' B ' or ' C '*, the matter being marked to correspond.

Position of Illustrations

In a good layout illustrations should not be placed at the extreme top or bottom of the page; a few lines of text above and below each illustration improves page balance. If the page is set in single column it may be necessary to run the text round the smaller illustrations. The area required must be carefully measured and the same area calculated from the galley. For example, suppose the measure to be 6 in. and the illustration to be $3\frac{1}{2}$ in. wide, and $2\frac{1}{2}$ in. deep, including the caption. The run-round will occupy a space roughly 2 in. wide and $2\frac{3}{4}$ in. deep. Since the galley is set in 6-inch measure, just under one inch of galley must be cut out for the run-round.

This problem rarely arises when the page is set in two or more columns, and for this reason alone a multi-column format is preferable for larger technical publications.

All illustrations should be placed as closely as possible to related text; in particular, they should be placed in their appropriate section; a fresh heading separating an illustration from its context is highly undesirable. It sometimes happens that an illustration cannot be contained on the same page as the reference to it. Where this occurs the illustration should follow and not precede the reference.

It often has to be decided whether an illustration should be placed to the right or left of the page. Rectangular or *squared-up* illustrations are displayed to best advantage on the free edge of the page, avoiding the binding margin. A squared-up illustration implies one prepared in the form of a rectangle; with line blocks, this can be done by drawing a rectangular frame around the illustration, and in the case of half-tone blocks, the block containing the illustration and background is cut out in the form of a rectangle. Irregular illustrations, including cut-outs,* should be centred on the page or column wherever possible.

---

* The term cut-out refers to a half-tone block on which the background is cut completely away, leaving the firm outline of the illustration. See p. 208 and Fig. 5.31.

Full-page *landscape* illustrations should be placed with the head at the left on both right- and left-hand pages. The captions are set in landscape at the foot of the illustration, reading in the same direction as the illustration.

In many technical publications, references to the larger illustrations occur throughout the length of the text. Here it may be preferable to place all the illustrations in numerical order at the end of the book. Most readers prefer such illustrations to be printed on fold-out sheets, but this greatly increases production costs and wastes a considerable amount of paper. In certain circumstances, particularly on small runs, the problem can be solved by placing illustrations in a separate pocket at the back of the publication, but there is a risk of their being lost, and the binding costs are increased.

Page Proofs

When the printer receives the corrected galleys and make-up sheets, he first corrects all the type whilst in galley form, and then proceeds to impose the type in page form and insert illustrations and captions as indicated by the make-up. This done, fresh proofs are taken and submitted to the editor for approval.

In technical work it is desirable for authors to see page proofs, even if they have already seen and corrected the galleys. It is of paramount importance that at this stage the author should be warned that any corrections or additions must be of a minor nature. The deletion of a single word from a line may quite easily necessitate the re-setting of a whole paragraph. The addition of a paragraph on an early page may upset the make-up for the whole work. *In the page-proof stage, corrections to a line must be arranged so as to retain the same number of characters in that line ; a replaced sentence or paragraph must contain the same number of words as in the original sentence or paragraph.* An example will make this clear :

Suppose the original line is :

Written permission need not be obtained as it is

and the author wishes to alter this to :

Written permission must be obtained . . .

The replacement of ' need ' by ' must ' involves the same number of letters and can be made easily, but the omission of ' not ' leaves a blank space in the line. To compensate for this, the author must try to re-word the line so that the extra space is taken up by letters. Such an alteration may read :

Written permission must be obtained since it is

and the rest of the text is unaffected.

Carefully planned corrections of this nature will ensure that the printer has no trouble in altering the final proofs and will not delay publication.

As in the galley-proof stage, the printer's marked copy should be used for entering up final corrections, and the page proofs must be checked most carefully against the corrected galley sheets which will accompany the page proofs. Before passing page proofs for press, a final check should be made of preliminary pages, running headlines and captions to illustrations.

Second page proofs (' revises ') should be called for only if changes have been made to vitally important matter ; it is not so much the volume of correction that matters; the alteration of a single line may be of sufficient importance to warrant a further proof of that particular page.

A few warnings may not be out of place before concluding this section :

First, in either galley- or page-proof stage, the printer often finds it quicker to re-set a sentence than to correct the existing type ; therefore, in checking the revised proof, read through the *whole* sentence and not merely the corrected words.

Second, the printer's attention should be called to any misplacement of a character at either end of a line ; there is a risk that it will fall out of position and be missed altogether on the run-off.

Third, do not over-estimate the time needed by the printer to correct proofs. A complete page of type can be re-set within an hour, unless it involves considerable hand-set display or formulae. The printer of technical work cannot be expected to work at this speed, but time for correction may be assessed in days, not weeks.

Summary of Procedure in Checking Page Proofs

This stage in the production of technical publications is so important that a summary in Dos and Don'ts is worth setting down :

DO

Check the proofs page by page against the corrected galley proofs.
Read through the whole proofs as a final check against printer's errors.
Read through all the captions to illustrations.
Read through all the running headlines.
Check the index page by page.
Check all references and quotations.
Check all preliminary pages and see that they are presented in the right order.
Check the names and qualifications of authors.
Check the names of all firms mentioned anywhere in the publication.
Check all references to illustrations.

DON'T

Don't try to do all the operations listed above simultaneously.
Don't make any alteration to text that will affect existing space.
Don't refuse additional matter that can be inserted easily without re-paging.
Don't embark on large-scale alterations to punctuation; the transposing of a single comma may cost half-a-crown or half a dollar.
Don't invent printer's marks.
Don't make corrections in illegible handwriting.
Don't add corrections on blank sheets of paper without adequate reference to where they are to be inserted.
Don't be too critical of half-tone blocks if the blockmaker's pulls were satisfactory. Page proofs do not indicate printing quality.
Don't pass any illustration that is not set square on the page.

Reprints

It is not always possible to estimate beforehand the number of copies needed to meet the full and final demand. It is the general custom for a printer to keep type standing for six months free of rental charge if requested. After this period he is entitled to make a charge based on the total area of type.

Until the type is broken down, or *distributed,* reprints are obtainable at a reasonable cost. Once instructions have been given to distribute the type, a reprint in letterpress will cost precisely as much as the original. To reduce the cost of reprinting in such circumstances, consideration should be given to reproduction by photolitho. In offices where an offset machine is available, such as Multilith or Rotaprint, reprints from most normal formats can be produced at about one third the cost of letterpress. Where no such machine is available it will still be cheaper to give the work to a competent photo-litho printer than to have it re-set in letterpress. The disadvantage of reprinting by photo-litho is that no corrections are possible without extra trouble and cost. If these are necessary, the corrections are set in type and patched into the affected pages. If corrections on the majority of pages are essential, a straightforward letterpress printing may be more economical.

Casting-off

The estimation of the number of printed pages that will be occupied by a given amount of copy is known as *casting-off*, and is done by calculating the number of characters in the copy. Casting-off can be done with accuracy on typed matter : an estimate from handwritten matter, unless it is very regular, will be approximate.

The total number of characters in the copy is found by multiplying together :

Number of pages × Number of lines per page × Line length in inches and the number of characters per inch—10 for pica type and 12 for elite. (See also p. 222.)

The simplest method of casting-off from typescript is to measure the average width of a line ; short lines at the end of paragraphs are counted as full lines, since they will occupy the space of a full line in the typeset page. The accuracy of this method depends on the regularity of the typing, unless each line is measured separately. On this basis, a page containing 40 lines averaging 6 inches in width would contain 40 × 6 × 10 characters = 2400 in pica type and 2880 in elite type.

If greater accuracy is required, a vertical line is drawn on the right-hand side of the typescript through the majority of the shorter lines (excluding paragraph endings). For ease of calculation, this line should be a round number of inches from the left-hand margin —say 4, 5 or 6. The characters to the left of the line can be calculated as described above and those on the right counted individually.

If the whole work is evenly typed with the same number of lines to each page, it is only necessary to calculate for one page; typists should be trained to maintain this uniformity, but it is usually desirable to cast off each page separately, especially if there are mathematical formulae inserted in the text.

Having found the number of characters in the copy, the number of pages of letterpress type required for the whole matter can be found from the tables of type given in Appendix I, which give the number of picas per inch for various styles of type face.

For example, suppose the matter is to be set in Caslon Old Face, 9 pt. on a 10-pt. body, and that the measure (page width) is 24 picas. The page depth is then determined, excluding headlines and folio numbers; assume this to be 42 picas. The chart of Appendix I, p. 304, shows that Caslon 9 pt. has 77 characters to 24 picas. Since the body size is 10 pt., the number of lines per page will be $42 \times {}^{12}/_{10}$* or 50·4—say 50. The number of characters per page will therefore be 77×50, or 3850. To obtain the number of folios the total number of characters is divided by this number.

* The figure 12 appears in this fraction because the pica em is 12 points. Note also that this calculation assumes that the type is set solid with no lead between paragraphs.

CHAPTER 8

TYPOGRAPHY FOR TECHNICAL PUBLICATIONS

IN its broadest sense, the term typography means the art of printing, embracing every step in the art from the design of a type face to its impression upon paper and its appearance as a finished work. In the early days of printing no distinction could be drawn between printer and typographer, but in these days of specialization in the printing industry typography has a more specific meaning, and although it would be false to assume that the modern typographer is less skilled in the printing art than his illustrious predecessors, his work is more concerned with planning than with production. This is made clear in the foreword by Beatrice Warde to Vincent Steer's excellent book *Printing Design and Layout*. Indeed, the title of that book aptly describes the function of the modern typographer.

The technical writer would be in a happy position if he could assume that every printer employed a skilled typographer or layout man; he would be happier still if he could be certain that the typographer was highly skilled in the special requirements of technical printing. Unfortunately, neither of these assumptions can be made, and unless the writer can make use of a printer who specializes in this work, it is desirable that he should understand the elements of typography if his work is to be presented in a form conducive to clear understanding by the reader. It is of no use studying the reader in the writing stage if he is forgotten when the work is being prepared for printing.

Choice of Type Face

It is an axiom of typography that different subjects require different treatment as far as type faces are concerned. This applies in a special way to technical subjects because many characters are needed which are not found in type faces designed purely for non-technical printing—for example, mathematical or chemical symbols. It is rare to find a type face which is suitable for all technical needs, and in choosing one it is important to make sure that it will give a

252

reasonable match for the unusual symbols and display faces used in formulae. An example of mis-match would be a Gill Sans* text used with sloping Greek symbols.

The growing importance of technical typesetting led to the setting up of a consultative committee for co-operating with the printing organizations in 1950 by the Royal Society. The Committee recommended the following type faces for technical work involving mathematical setting:

Modern Series 7; Imprint Series 101; Times New Roman Series 327.

It may not be necessary to restrict one's choice to these three faces, but it is certain that with these there will be no difficulty in matching mathematical signs or symbols. A great deal of work has been done by the Monotype Corporation in designing suitable symbols and Greek faces to match the series listed above.

Greek Type Faces

The Greek faces designed to match are:

Modern Series 7:	Greek Series 472
Times New Roman:	Greek Upright Series 565
	Greek Inclined Series 566
	Greek Bold Upright Series 567

No Greek face is cut specifically to match Imprint, but the Porson Greek Series 106 is suitable. Porson Greek is a sloping face and may be used with almost any of the type faces normally used for technical printing; it has a greater range of mathematical sorts than any other Greek face. A Greek alphabet Series 473 has been designed for use with Baskerville.

$ABΓΔEZHΘIKΛMNΞOΠPΣTYΦXΨΩ$ Series
αβγδεζηθικλμνξοπρστυφχψω   106–12

$ΓΔΘΛΞΠΣΦΨΩ$ Series
αβγδεζηθικλμνξοπρστυφχψωϑϖ   473–12

All Greek alphabets are smaller on the body than their Roman† counterparts, and if formulae are used containing both Greek and

* See p. 256 for the explanation of this and other type designations.

† There is sometimes confusion between the printer's use of the word ' roman ' to denote upright letters and Roman lettering, as distinct from Greek or Cyrillic. The printer's roman is best spelt without a capital.

253

Roman characters it may be desirable to use a Greek face one point larger than the Roman.

Much valuable information on Greek and mathematical type faces is given in the *Mathematical Sorts List* issued by the Monotype Corporation, compiled by Arthur Phillips.*

Format and Type Face

The size of format has an important bearing on the suitability of the face used for the text, and some useful statistics are given by Luckiesh and Moss in *Reading as a Visual Task* (D. van Nostrand, N.Y., 1942). If the page is to be printed in single column, a larger face must be used than for double column arrangement, because a long line in a small type face will produce eyestrain on the reader. If the column measure exceeds $4\frac{1}{2}$ inches the size of the face should not be less than 11 pt. for maximum readability; for a 6-inch column measure the face should be 12 pt., although certain type faces will produce strain even in this size.

The two sizes of format frequently used in books and technical publications are the Crown quarto ($9\frac{3}{4} \times 7\frac{1}{4}$ in.) and demy octavo ($8\frac{1}{2} \times 5\frac{1}{2}$ in.). The larger format is convenient when there are several charts or large-scale drawings and can be set in double-column measure $2\frac{1}{2}$ to 3 in. per column. The type width in the smaller format should not exceed $4\frac{1}{8}$ in. A 10-pt. face could be used for both formats.

Table of Book Sizes

Crown Octavo (8vo)	$7\frac{1}{4} \times 4\frac{7}{8}$
Demy Octavo	$8\frac{1}{2} \times 5\frac{1}{2}$
Medium Octavo	$8\frac{3}{4} \times 5\frac{5}{8}$
Royal Octavo	$9\frac{3}{4} \times 6\frac{1}{8}$
Crown Quarto (4to)	$9\frac{3}{4} \times 7\frac{3}{4}$
Royal Quarto	$12\frac{1}{4} \times 9\frac{7}{8}$

The sizes are in inches and refer to the trimmed pages. Allowance for trimming is usually taken as $\frac{1}{8}$ in.

The size of body used for the type is governed by the appearance of the face: for example, Caslon Old Style, which is small on its body, could be set solid, but Times New Roman, which is larger

* The Monotype Corporation, 43 Fetter Lane, London, E.C.4.

on the body should be set on a body which is at least one point larger than the face (10 pt. on 11 pt.).

Before deciding on the type face, the whole range of characters should be examined, as many faces have unsuitable italics or numerals for technical work. Examples are the italic capital *A* of Garamond and the italic capitals *T* and *J* in Baskerville. On the other hand, in Imprint and Plantin the italic capitals are uniform except for the *J*, and in Times all the letters are uniform in character—which explains the popularity of this face for technical work. The Times face is narrow in set, but is large on its body: for this reason it should not be set solid except in narrow columns. This book is set in 10-pt. Times New Roman on a 12-pt. body.

Characteristics of Type Faces

The following summaries of the characteristics and range of some type faces suitable for setting technical matter are intended to serve as a guide. A wider study of the subject should be made by consulting the books listed in the Appendix. Most printers will be pleased to supply specimen alphabets of the type faces that they hold in stock. The specimens below (except the Times Roman) are all set in 10-pt. type on an 11-pt. body.

*Baskerville Series 169.** This well-known type face is clear and easy to read. It is fairly large on its body, and a body size one point larger than the face can be used. It is not particularly suited to mathematical work because of flourishes on the italic symbols *J*, *K*, *N*, *Q*, *T*, and *Y*. The numerals are old style (i.e. non-lining) but lining numerals can also be obtained. The face can be identified by the flourish on the italic *T*, the *J* and the *Y*; in the roman letters the C, J and Q are unusual and the E has uneven lengths of cross-line. There is a matching Greek face in Series 473.

Bodoni Series. A general-purpose face giving a high density of print. It needs great care in treatment to ensure legibility. There is a wide range of styles, ranging from **Bold** (260) Condensed (529) to **Heavy** and **Ultra-Bodoni**, which are used for display. There are other variations such as Bodoni Bold Italic; in fact, this face forms one of the largest groups of modern type. The numerals are lining.

* The numbers of the series refer to the Monotype classification of type founts. There are, of course, corresponding faces in Linotype.

255

Caslon Series 128. This face is small on the body and can be set solid. It is similar to Old Style, but is distinguishable by the flourishes in the Italic face: *ABCDEFGHIJ* . . . Both Caslon and Old Style blend well with Greek characters and are suitable for technical work where density in colour is not required. They are, however, inclined to look anaemic on coated paper. It should be noted that the Italics in this face are light and require careful make-ready by the printer.

Gill Sans-serif. This is one of the most remarkable and versatile type faces ever designed, and as its name implies, is a plain type without serifs : essentially a draughtsman's letter. A feature of the design is that all the letters are clear-cut and well-shaped over the whole range of thicknesses and sizes, from Light (Series 362) to **Extra Heavy (Series 321).**

This line is set in Gill Bold (Series 275). Compare with this line which is set in Gill Bold Condensed (Series 343).

Although an admirable type face for lettering and display work, Gill Sans is not recommended for book printing because of its monotonous appearance, which soon fatigues the reader. The face is large on its body and it is often possible to use a small face (6 pt.) without loss of legibility. Numerals are lining and are almost of the same height as the capitals. This may cause some confusion in reading a mixture of letters and numerals, e.g. TT71. The difficulty of reading the numbers is accentuated when they are used for tabular matter (see p. 239). Note that the UNO stencil lettering is a close approximation to Gill Sans and can be used to imitate the type successfully.

A near American equivalent to this type is Futura, which is cast in several thicknesses.

Gothic. The family of Gothic faces is only suitable for display. A good face for lettering on illustrations is the Series 73, which is approximately equivalent to the Vari-Typer Gothic face. Numerals are lining.

Imprint Series 101. This type face is suitable for most forms of book work. The face is large on the body, with long ascenders, and

256

a body one point larger than the face should be used. The numerals are lining or non-lining and are unusually large on the body. An odd feature of this type face is the italic *J*, which may give trouble in mathematical setting ; it is hard to understand why a single letter should be so out of keeping with the rest of the face.

Modern Series 7. This is one of the most suitable faces for technical publications. It is of medium body size and density and has a full range of mathematical characters. The face has full serifs, but there are no flourishes in either the roman or italic characters. It is one of the few faces for which a Greek alphabet has been specially designed (Series 472).

Recently the Monotype Corporation have produced a Modern Bold (Series 570) (compare Times and Times Bold).

Perpetua Series 239. This most attractive face was designed by Eric Gill for the Monotype Corporation from the original Roman incised letters on monuments. It is quite suitable for some technical work, although there is a long tail on the Q which might cause difficulty with equations. In fact it is not really suited to mathematical setting. The face is small on its body and the 12 pt. is approximately equivalent to 10-pt. lower-case Times. As it is a light-faced type with long descenders (see page 146) it can be set solid for text matter. The figures are non-lining and small on the body.

Perpetua Titling, etc. A separate series of capital letters designed for display work, in sizes ranging from 10-pt. to 72-pt. The numerals are lining and equal in height to the letters. This is an elegant face for headings of articles or for title-pages, and there is also a range of Bold Titling. The series number is 258 ; Bold, 200; Light, 480.

AN EXAMPLE OF PERPETUA TITLING

Plantin Series 110. This type is rather similar in design to Times but is heavier in appearance, and a closer comparison shows several differences, particularly in the capitals. Plantin has a splayed M, the loop of the P does not close, and the W is interlaced. Because of its weight and large size on the body, this type should be set on a body 1 or 2 points larger, i.e. 10 pt. on 12 pt. The numerals are non-lining and equal in size to the lower case.

A thicker face is **Plantin Bold (Series 194).** This is often used for sub-heads, and stands out well against the ordinary book face. The smaller size (410–6) is used for captions under illustrations.

Times New Roman Series 327. This modern face was designed specifically for *The Times* newspaper and first appeared in that journal in 1925. Since then its popularity has steadily increased and it has been used in many technical journals. It is an exceedingly clear and well-proportioned face and can be recommended for all technical publication work. The letters are large on the body and of heavy weight; a minimum of 2 points leading between lines is desirable. A feature of the Times range which is shared by several others is the Bold Face, which can be mixed with the ordinary face when extra emphasis is required. The bold type also makes good headings and sub-headings, although Bodoni can be mixed with Times if desired.

Times Roman Wide Series 427. As its name implies, this face is wider than the standard Times face, and is possibly more pleasing in appearance and easier to read. The wider set affects the space required, and 3% should be added to the figures for Times New Roman when casting-off.

`Typewriter Series 235. This face is mentioned because of its similarity in appearance to that of an Elite typewriter. It has occasional application in office forms, circular letters and notices. The face has the same number of characters as the normal typewriter and is moulded on a 12 pt. body, 11 letters to the inch.`

A similar range of type faces is produced by the Linotype Corporation ; some differ only slightly in appearance from the specimen faces reproduced above. Among the type faces suitable for book work are : Baskerville, Estienne, Georgian, Granjon, Pilgrim, Plantin and Times Roman.

A fine new text face is Juliana, which has been designed for the Linotype Corporation by S. L. Hartz.

Two old-established faces which have been designed for periodical work are Ionic and Paragon. The characters are large on the body and of uniform thickness, making them legible under high-speed printing conditions on paper of ordinary quality. A newer face, Jubilee, is, however, deservedly increasing in popularity with newspapers and periodicals.

Among the type faces suitable for display work are Metro, Memphis, and Gothic. Metro is a sans-serif face designed by W. A. Dwiggins; it has some resemblance to Gill Bold but differs notably in the ' a ' and in the sharpened ends to the ' M ' and ' W '. It is cast in three thicknesses: Metrolite, Metromedium and Metroblack.

Memphis is an example of a type face known as ' slab-serif ' from the thickness of the serifs. It has a wide range of thicknesses, as in Gill Sans, and is favoured by American printers for display work and titles.

Further information on the matching of typefaces is given in *The Use of Type*, J. R. Biggs (London, Blandford Press, 1954). Examples of 67 typefaces are given in *The Studio Book of Alphabets* (London, Studio Publications, 1953).

LAYOUT FOR AN INSTRUCTION MANUAL

Format

In planning an Instruction Manual, the format is usually determined by the number and size of the illustrations. A manual which contains several circuit diagrams cannot be made small, or the reduction of the diagrams to a size which will fit on a page may make them almost illegible. It is possible to print them on a larger sheet and insert this sheet folded into the manual, but this method adds considerably to the cost. If possible, the page should be large enough to take a diagram or chart measuring about 7 × 9 inches. Larger charts can be folded once lengthways and inserted separately; the fold should never be made across the width of the paper, as the lower part is liable to become torn.

The most satisfactory size to accommodate diagrams of all proportions is crown quarto—$9\frac{3}{4} \times 7\frac{1}{4}$—which approximates to the quarto sheet of 10×8 in. It is usually more economical to use a standard size of paper (see p. 218), but this need not be a restriction if the quantity used will warrant ordering sheets to be made and cut specially.

Columns

A sheet of 10×8 in. paper should be printed in double columns, as the eye is easily fatigued in travelling across the whole width of a single-column page. A suitable width of column is 16–18 picas (approximately 3 in. maximum) and the depth of the column 48 picas (8 in.).

In printed books it is usual to leave less margin at the head of the page than on either the side or the bottom. A conventional proportion for the three margins is

$$\text{Head} : \text{Side} : \text{Foot} = 2 : 3 : 4$$

but this rule need not be followed in technical manuals where economy is a prime consideration.

Headings

The headings are intended to guide the reader quickly to the section in which he is interested, and should be carefully chosen and displayed. The book may require three or even four types of heading, depending on the division of the type matter, and these, in descending order of importance are:

Section Heading
Main Heading
Sub-heading
Sub-sub-heading

Section and Main Headings. These can be set in capitals and distinguished by the size of the face:

SECTION 1: CHASSIS
GENERAL DESCRIPTION

Alternatively, main headings could be set in 10-pt. upper and lower case, either centred in the column or set on the side. A 12-pt. lead should separate the heading from the text matter.

Sub-headings. There is sometimes a temptation to set the sub-headings in italics regardless of their importance, but if the text matter has italics inserted at intervals there may be insufficient contrast between headings and text. Sub-headings may be arranged in one of two ways : as part of the text matter, with the text running on after a space, as in the examples on this page, or set flush with the edge of the margin, with a space separating it from the text. This is called a " shoulder head ". There are also " hanging shoulder heads " in which the heading is set entirely in the right or left hand margin, clear of the text, but this type of heading is too expensive for ordinary bookwork. *Example of hanging shoulder head.*

If all four types of heading are used, the sub-sub-headings may be in italic or in a smaller point than the sub-heading. They can also be set in the same type as the face of the text matter, in small capitals or in capitals and lower case with adequate spacing to make them stand out from the line of the text.

Other Display Headings

It is usual to identify the pages of the text by running headlines which indicate the contents of the chapter or even the page. These are set over the right-hand page, the left-hand page carrying the title of the handbook, but it is permissible to use both pages for running headlines if the reader is helped. They are usually set in small capitals, but bold face can be used. The running headline is usually omitted from the page which begins a fresh chapter or section.

Captions. The titles or captions to the illustrations can be set in 8-pt. capitals and small capitals under the illustration, leaving ample space between the foot of the illustration and the text. The caption should be placed between the illustration and the succeeding text matter and there should be no doubt in the reader's mind as to the illustration to which it refers. Sub-captions can be set in 8-pt. upper and lower case.

Numbering Folios

Each folio (page) should be numbered, beginning with the first right-hand text page. The sequence of odd numbers on the right and even numbers on the left must be rigidly followed, although it may sometimes necessitate a blank verso (left-hand page) numbered in the sequence.

The best position for numbering is debatable, but a convenient place is in the centre of the bottom margin; the numbers should be set in the text face without embellishments. If it is necessary to folio each section separately it is better to dispense with the running heads and insert the folio numbers in the top corner of the sheet. Books which have section numbers in addition to the folio numbers usually have the section number set at the head of the page on the inner margin, preceded by '§' or 'Section'.

Chapters or fresh sections should begin on a right-hand page for good appearance; this arrangement also simplifies reissuing pages.

Illustrations

With a 3-inch column measure, small illustrations can be fitted in the text without the necessity of running the type round them:* others can generally be limited to $4\frac{1}{2}$ inches or 6 inches in width, centred on the page. The positioning of illustrations is all-important and the artistic placing should be sacrificed to functional use. The guiding principle is to place the illustration as near as possible to the text reference, but a certain amount of grouping is permissible with small illustrations occurring close together in the text matter.

Unframed illustrations should not be placed at the extreme top or bottom of the page, unless a line in the drawing forms a natural boundary (as sometimes occurs in circuit diagrams).

The placing of fold-out sheets is sometimes dictated by convention: in Service manuals it is the practice to place them at the end of the text matter, but a single folding sheet may be inserted at the appropriate place in the text. Folding circuit diagrams, which are consulted at various stages in reading through the book, can be printed so that they are fully displayed when the sheet is unfolded at the side of the text. This means leaving a blank area on the sheet equivalent to the page area, sacrificing economy for the reader's convenience.

---

* It should be noted that 'run-rounds' are expensive, as they cannot be arranged in the galley stage and must be fitted to the blocks.

Footnotes and References

Footnotes should be separated from the last line of the text by a thin rule, and in making up the page sufficient space must be left at the end of the column to prevent the footnote overhanging. The text can be set in roman, two points smaller than the text type: for the method of displaying the reference, see p. 95.

References to other books are usually unnecessary in instruction manuals, but if they are included they can be set in the text or as footnotes. An instruction manual may have data and illustrations collated at the end, and it is unwise to follow textbook practice and add the references at the end of the text.

Preliminary Pages ('Prelims')

In textbook production a number of preliminary pages are inserted before the main text, arranged in a conventional order and usually numbered in a distinctive style—lower case roman letters, or numerals which differ from those in the text. The order of arrangement of the 'prelims', as they are called, is usually :

Half-title. A right-hand page containing the title only, generally printed in capitals to match the title page.

On the verso of this page a list of books by the same author is sometimes printed, together with any special publisher's notice.

Title Page. The next right-hand page, containing the title of the book displayed with the name of the author, the edition, and the publisher's name and address.

The *Frontispiece*, if any, is inserted between the half-title and the title-page.

Other particulars of the publication may be printed on the verso of the title page, e.g. the printer's name and address, the type face used, the number of reprintings, and the copyright notice (see p. 295).

Foreword. If a Foreword has been written for the book, it is usually placed before the Preface.

Preface. It is usual for an author to write a preface for each edition of a book, and these are all included in the edition.

Contents. The Contents pages give a list of the chapter headings, and sometimes the section headings in the chapters.

List of Illustrations. This and other lists of plates, symbols, and acknowledgements follows the Contents List.

While the foregoing list is typical of the arrangement of prelims in a book, it may be altered at the discretion of the publisher and is usually affected by the number of pages available. A simpler form of book, such as the instruction manual under discussion, will not require a complete set of preliminary pages and a title page and list of contents may be sufficient.

INSTRUCTION MANUAL

for the

OPERATION, INSTALLATION & MAINTENANCE

of

E.M.I. PROFESSIONAL TAPE RECORDER

MODEL BTR/2

ELECTRIC & MUSICAL INDUSTRIES LIMITED

HAYES . MIDDLESEX . ENGLAND

FIG. 8.1. *Example of a well-displayed Title Page, but note that one line is off-centre.*

Title Page

The layout of the title page will reflect the standard of the book as a whole. The keynote of good layout is simplicity, and a mixture of type faces and sizes should be avoided. Particular care in layout is required when the title exceeds one line : the turnover should not be made after a preposition or conjunction, for example, and it is frequently neater to set these words in a separate line in smaller type. The title should be separated from any other matter on the page by ample white space. A specimen title page for a handbook is shown in Fig. 8.1. This title page was originally set in 12-pt. and 10-pt. bold capitals with 10-pt. italic lower case, Old Style, and has been reproduced from the original format which measured 10 × 8 in. The reproduction of the illustration speaks well for modern printing processes, since it has passed through the following stages :

   i. Type set in letterpress and proofed.
   ii. Proof reproduced on lithographic plate.
   iii. Copies printed on an office litho machine.
   iv. Line block prepared from the offset copy by photo reduction to fit these pages.
   v. Printing by letterpress on the page.

The title page of the present book is set in Times New Roman, Series 327, and the following is the type specification :

Title : 36-pt. upper and lower case.
Sub-title : 12-pt. level small capitals letterspaced.
Authors' Names : 14-pt. capitals letterspaced with qualifications in 8-pt. upper and lower case.
Imprint : C. & H. colophon. 10-pt. capitals letterspaced.
36 ems deep overall.

Contents Page

An index to an instruction manual is rarely necessary, and its place can be taken by a contents list which is more detailed than in an ordinary book. The contents page should contain all the headings and sub-headings, with the related page numbers. If the list is long, the type face must be chosen so that the page does not look too heavy and the following arrangement is suggested :

Section headings in 10-pt. capitals, either aligned on the left-hand margin or centred according to taste.
Sub-headings in 10-pt. capitals and lower case, set on a 12-pt. body, with ' leaders ' to the page number.

THE TECHNICAL WRITER

Specimen Contents Page

CONTENTS

The sub-headings should be indented 2 ems or more, and the page numbers should align on the right hand margin.

The top margin of the contents column should conform to the text pages, although the list may not occupy the full depth of the page.

A list of illustrations can follow the contents page : this will be useful in instruction books containing many circuit diagrams or detail drawings.

Folders for Instruction Manuals

The chief consideration in selecting the form of binding for an instruction manual is durability and adaptability. If the manual is complete and permanent there is little difficulty, since ordinary book binding methods are quite satisfactory and books are now bound to open flat at any page and remain flat. The majority of instruction manuals, however, have to be bound with an eye to possible alterations and additions and some form of loose-leaf binder is more often required.

For thin manuals a serviceable folder can be made from 'index board', folded as shown in Fig. 8.2, with stout paper fasteners or "Tower" binders (d), a special form of fastener with a metal collar.

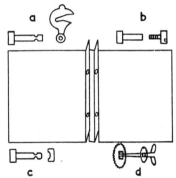

FIG. 8.2. *Loose-leaf binder with various types of fastener.*

With folders of this type the front and spine can be printed with an office printing machine before folding, and the whole arrangement is economical. A disadvantage of the simple folder is that replacement of the pages is laborious and the fasteners may be lost in the process.

For many purposes, a 'window' folder is all that is needed. This consists of a simple folder having a rectangle cut out of the front cover to expose the title page to view.

The title, serial number and date of the report are typed on the title page so as to be completely visible through the window of the cover.

A better form of binder uses fittings that are fixed to the folder : either a stud and clip, (a) or press-stud and pillar (Fig. 8.2c). The extra cost of these is offset by the time saved in replacing pages, and the fitting is more robust than the plain fastener. It is important to estimate the capacity required before ordering the folder, and a dummy set of pages should be collated to check the thickness. If there are several folded diagrams in addition to the text pages it may be necessary to pack the binding margin with extra pieces of board to bring the covers level at each margin and prevent bulging.

For a bulky manual a more durable folder is necessary with a substantial board cover. Various proprietary types of binder are available, e.g. the " Twinlock " binder, which holds all the sheets in place while one is being extracted. A more economical though not so satisfactory form of board binder is the familiar ring binder. This enables the sheets to lie flat, but there is grave risk of their tearing away at the punched holes and some reinforcement is necessary. A small machine can be obtained to perform the punching and reinforcing of the holes in one operation.*

Standards for Technical Literature

British Standard 1311 : 1955 specifies the sizes of trade and technical literature, including brochures, operating instructions, data sheets and books containing technical information. The standard page size is either $11 \times 8\frac{1}{4}$ in. (approximately 4to) or $8\frac{1}{2} \times 5\frac{1}{4}$ in. (8vo) both of which can be cut from standard sizes of paper sheet and fitted in standard envelopes.

The following items are recommended for inclusion in a comprehensive catalogue :

Date and publication identification number
Subject of publication
Purpose and performance of the item described (e.g. scope, qualities, official standards and tests)
Form of the item (e.g. size, weight, finish)
Installation or erection (space required, fixing needed)
Ancillary requirements (fitments)
How to ensure satisfaction (spare parts list, transport and storage instructions)
Method of use (including safety precautions)
Obtaining the item (conditions of sale, delivery, firm's local address . . .)

* The " Ofrex ", distributed by Ofrex Ltd., Stephen St., London, W.1.

It may be considered that a list of essential items of this type would be unnecessary to a competent writer of technical catalogues, but the frequent omission of important information from current sales literature shows that some form of schedule is always helpful, and B.S. 1311 supplies the need.

CHAPTER 9

SET-UP OF A TECHNICAL
PUBLICATIONS UNIT

THE set-up of a technical publications unit depends for its size and scope on the ramifications of the organization; for example, a firm that specializes in manufacturing a single product of relatively simple design may only issue a brief specification to the constructor and an operating leaflet to the user, whereas an instruction on a modern aeroplane may fill many volumes; the parts list alone may cover more than a thousand pages.

It will often be found that the simple instruction is badly written and presented, whilst the more comprehensive instruction bears the stamp of careful preparation and production. This is because, on the one hand the employment of special writing staff by a small firm would be uneconomic, and on the other, a multiplicity of departments concerned in the production or operation of an aircraft may justify or even necessitate having a technical publications unit, independent in function, but co-operating with other sections or departments when collecting and checking information.

Staffing

The staffing of such a unit depends upon the scope of its activities. In some instances, it may be concerned solely with production; instructions will be written by specialists in various departments and passed to the unit for printing and distribution. The number of staff will be proportional to the volume of work and will consist mainly of shorthand-typists and print operators; very large organizations may also employ lithographic and photographic operatives. The head of this unit must have knowledge of duplicating or printing methods or both, and of copying systems used for production of illustrations.

Other units may have to write the instructions as well as produce them. This involves employment of fully-trained and experienced technical writers whose job is to convey information from specialist to user.

270

The Technical Writer in Industry

A technical writer of this kind has considerable responsibility. Above everything else he must have the power of assimilation; in a single day's discussion with a specialist, he may be expected to absorb information that has taken the specialist months to accumulate.

His next qualification must be accuracy in interpretation. If there is one unforgivable sin in technical writing, it is inaccuracy of statement. It is not sufficient for the writer to interpret accurately the information given him; he must be satisfied that the information itself is beyond dispute. In this respect, even specialists sometimes err and freely admit it. It is because of this paramount need for accuracy that it is so important for instruction writers to have technical training and experience related to their sphere of interest.

When submitting the draft to the specialist, the writer must be prepared to accept and to offer criticism without reserve on any point where technical accuracy is in doubt; he must not allow the specialist to dominate in matters of presentation. Successful co-operation with specialists requires tactfulness and restraint, and to some extent depends on the writer's status. If a writer fails at collaboration, he will not last long on the job.

Co-ordination in a Writing Unit

So far, only the individual writer has been considered. Where several writers are employed in one unit, co-ordination is essential in the interests of uniformity in presentation and production. Uniformity in presentation does not imply that the work of different writers can be moulded to a common style. Any such attempt would damp the enthusiasm of the writers and seriously delay publication. It is however important that there should be uniformity in terminology, spelling, abbreviations and symbols. Often a specialist will refer to the same device as a thingammy in one sentence and a thingmebob in the next, even though each has a separate definition in a glossary or dictionary. Technical symbols are frequently invented on the spur of the moment and may bear no relation to national or international standards. Provided that each is apposite and that a list is given in an individual work, this may not have serious repercussions; if however it is permitted where numbers of instructions are issued from a central source, confusion

271

is certain to arise. In these circumstances, some standard must be set, and what is more important, adhered to. There can be little doubt that the recommendations of the British Standards Institution form the most practical references for this purpose.* They are drawn up by committees representing authoritative bodies; they are widely circulated for comment before being published; they are accepted by most scientific, industrial, and educational institutions. The application of these standards to instruction manuals written by different authors is an exacting business and can only be effective if responsibility is centred on one person. Such a person will function as an editor and there is some advantage in his being so styled because it strengthens his status within his own business organization, gives him undisputed control of his unit and saves a good deal of argument with outside contacts.

The person in charge of a technical writing unit, whether he is called an editor or something else, should have technical training and experience in the type of work which his organization undertakes. He should be a good technical writer and have a critical faculty to enable him to discriminate between good and bad functional English. He should be a good collaborator, organizer and staff manager. He should have knowledge of printing, duplicating and copying methods; this is important because the extent of this knowledge will materially affect the financial commitments of the unit. In his dealings with business associates, he must be the antithesis of a sycophant; if he panders too much to his critics, he will be constantly chasing around in circles, his staff will become cogs in a rusty machine and his output will lag hopelessly behind schedule.

Junior Staff

The junior staff in a technical publications unit includes typists, draughtsmen and machine operators, with perhaps semi-skilled help for collating, folding, binding and packing. The keynote of such a staff is versatility. Typists must be familiar with the jargon of the industry, capable of typing formulae and proficient in preparing duplicating plates. Draughtsmen must be good illustrators rather than competent designers; they must understand perspective and isometric drawing and be familiar with the preparation and

* See p. 33.

reproduction of drawings to be reduced in size to suit the format. Machine operators must be something more than duplicator operators; they must understand the principles of lithography, and if colour work is used to any appreciable extent, they must be trained lithographers.

There are many tricks in effective production and close co-operation amongst junior staff is essential to efficiency. Perhaps the best way to ensure this is to give each member of the staff a specific responsibility in addition to routine duties. By adopting this practice, each individual becomes conscious of the importance of his work to the unit as a whole.

INTER-DEPARTMENTAL LIAISON

The Writer and the Research Worker

The importance of close collaboration between a technical publications unit and other departments has already been stressed. The specialists with whom technical writers must collaborate are usually either research or design personnel. Research workers, however, frequently prepare their own reports, and in general apply the same discrimination and exactness to their writing as they do to their investigations. The technical level of such writing, however, is frequently beyond the comprehension of many people having an active interest in the subject. The technical writer who has to interpret such reports in a style that can be more generally understood has a difficult task. He must set about it by first preparing a draft in a style suited to the readers for whom it is intended. The next step is to take the draft to the research worker and discuss it freely. It is of no use sending it through the post and hoping for a speedy return of the corrected manuscript; the specialist will advance numerous legitimate reasons for delay. In such discussions, the writer must remember that research workers are inclined to be pedantic, and will deplore what to them are loose expressions. For example, a research man will not accept a statement such as ' the maximum speed of the car is seventy miles per hour ' but would insist on stipulating conditions, such as the load carried, the state of the road, and the strength and direction of the wind. The writer can learn much from the research worker, and

S   273

there is no better training in the art of technical writing than collaboration with such departments.

The Writer and the Designer

The designer is much nearer to the production line than the research worker; because of this, his work has often to be completed in a specified time, and the writer will find him less exacting in his demands. That is to say, he will be more concerned with accuracy of statement than with the style of writing. Nevertheless, personal discussions between writer and designer are essential in the drafting stage; the final draft should be corrected by consultation and not by correspondence; if this method is not applied, the writer's work may be seriously delayed.

Theoretically, it should be possible for a writer to complete a technical description as soon as design work is completed. In practice, modifications in design are often necessary before manufacture begins. For this reason, it is highly undesirable to release a technical description of a prototype to the general reader; this is particularly important when heavy printing costs are involved. A temporary instruction, based on a prototype may sometimes be essential, but this should be replaced or revised as soon as production of the final model is completed.

The Writer and the Operator

The collaboration between writer and specialist as outlined in the two preceding paragraphs is essential in the interests of technical accuracy, but very often the fundamental purpose of the writer's work is to instruct operating and maintenance staff. Whilst this purpose should be borne in mind by the writer from the beginning, it is sometimes desirable for the final draft to be checked by senior staff of the operating department. This is of special importance in large organizations having operating staff dispersed over many areas.

The purpose of this check should be to ensure that (a) the subject matter is presented in a style that can be understood by the operator, and (b) that the work covers all operating conditions. It often happens that apparatus is used in different ways, not all of which may have been foreseen by the designer.

The most effective way of satisfying operational requirements is for the writer to take his finished draft and drawings to a site immediately after the apparatus is installed, and check that his written instructions can be correctly interpreted by a local operator, and at the same time ensure that the instructions are adequate and accurate.

Drawing Office Personnel

A well-equipped drawing office is an essential part of a technical publications unit. This is sometimes questioned on the grounds that most technical writers have access to drawings of other departments. Unfortunately, many drawings produced in engineering offices are unsuited for reproduction in large numbers, mainly because of size, line thickness and lettering (Chapter 4). The preparation of illustrations for publication demands a technique quite different from engineering drawing-office practice, and the personnel employed for the purpose should be artistically minded, if not trained artists.

A good knowledge of perspective drawing is essential as well as ability in mechanical and electrical drawing. In addition, publication drawing personnel should understand the rudiments of typography, not only as applied to illustrating, but to printing types. Their work is to prepare illustrations for a given format; they must, therefore, visualize the final size of each illustration and arrange their layouts to suitable dimensions for photographic reductions.

PRODUCTION EQUIPMENT

The amount of production equipment required by a technical publications unit is dictated by the size of the unit and its production policy. If the policy is to place all reproduction work with outside firms, the equipment within the unit will be confined to normal office requirements, including drawing office equipment. If, however, the unit undertakes its own production, a wide range of equipment is indispensable and the initial cost may run into several thousands of pounds. It would, of course, be impossible to stipulate the amount of equipment required in precise terms because it depends so much upon the amount of work involved. An important point to consider is that all equipment needs staff to operate it and before additional equipment is obtained it is essential to establish

275

whether such equipment can be operated by existing staff or whether additional staff will be necessary. This is a vital economic factor which must determine whether or not such proposals are economically sound. The provision of equipment and operating staff can only be justified if it can be shown that it will reduce production cost, or increase output. In practice it may well do both.

Reproduction of Typescript

The equipment required for the reproduction of typescript has been fully discussed in Chapter 5 and may be summarized briefly as follows:

1. *Direct Typing on Lithographic Plates*

(a) Office type offset machines according to requirements.
(b) Chemical cabinet for each machine.
(c) Storage cabinets for plates.
(d) Typewriters suited for technical purposes.

2. *Reproduction of Typescript from Diapositive Stencils*

(a) As above.
(b) Whirling machine for sensitizing plates. Pre-sensitized plates can now be obtained; if these are used exclusively, a whirler is not essential.
(c) Printing-down frame and exposure lamp with timing device for printing the diapositive image to the sensitized plate.

3. *Reproduction by Photo-lithography*

(a) As in 1 and 2 above.
(b) Process camera with half-tone screens and associated lighting equipment.

4. *Collating and Binding*

(a) Collating can be done on a sloping bench on which the batches of printed pages can be laid in numerical order, the collator passing from one end to the other while gathering the pages.
   A more efficient method of collating, which takes up less room, is to use a collating rack (Fig. 9.1) in conjunction with a jogging tray (Fig. 9.2) for arranging the sheets in compact piles. A more elaborate form of collating rack is shown in Fig. 9.3.
(b) Stapling Device. For small jobs (up to 50 sheets) this can very

276

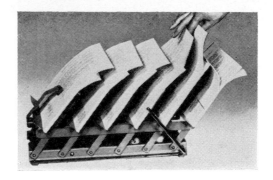

Fig. 9.1. *Collating rack for hand operation.*

Fig. 9.2. *" Metromatic " jogging tray for assembling sheets.*

Fig. 9.3. *Larger collating rack for foot pedal operation.*

(*Photographs by courtesy of the Metro Duplicator Supply Co., Ltd.*)

277

FIG. 9.4. *Pedal-operated wire stitching machine.*
(*British Brehmer Ltd.*)

FIG. 9.5. *Substantial hand-operated guillotine.*
(*Hunter-Penrose Ltd.*)

well be in the form of two office staplers mounted on a wooden base. For heavier work, a wire-stitching machine (Fig. 9.4) is necessary. If the work is bound in loose-leaf folders, a suitable two-hole punch takes the place of the stapler.

(c) Guillotine. For preference this should be a small power-operated machine, but a good hand-operated machine (Fig. 9.5) may be adequate, provided that it is substantially built. The guillotines for photographic trimming are useless for bulky packets of paper.

DRAWING OFFICE

Drawing Office Equipment

1. *Draughtsman's Equipment*

Most of the equipment used in an engineering drawing office is essential to the publication draughtsman or artist and may be listed as follows :

(a) *Drawing Board mounted on Adjustable Stand*

For normal work a Double-Elephant (42 in. × 29 in.) is most suitable ; for very large drawings an Antiquarian (54 in. × 32 in.) may be necessary. Other sizes are : Quarter Imperial (16 in. × 12 in.) ; Half Imperial (23 in. × 16 in.) ; Imperial (31 in. × 23 in.).

(b) *Drafting Machine*

There are several types to choose from but the double-arm machine, with angular adjustment (Fig. 9.6) is probably the most versatile. A simpler device is shown in Fig. 9.7. A machine combining the equipment of Figs. 9.6 and 9.7 is shown in Fig. 9.8.

(c) *Electric Erasing Machine*

Though not strictly essential, these machines save much time, especially when correcting ink drawings (Fig. 9.9).

(d) *Instruments*

Complete set of drawing instruments in case.
Set of French curves.

279

Fig. 9.6. *Double-arm Drafting Machine with angular adjustment.*
(*Lawes, Rabjohns Ltd.*)

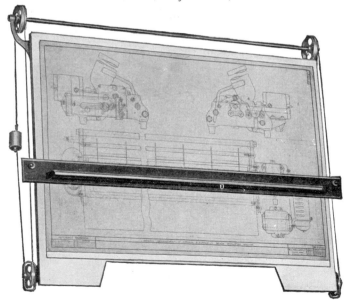

Fig. 9.7. *Parallel motion Drafting Machine.*
(*Hall, Harding Ltd.*)

FIG. 9.8. *Drafting Machine combining parallel motion with angular adjustment.*
(*Hall, Harding Ltd.*)

FIG. 9.9. *Electrically driven erasing machine.*
(*Hall, Harding Ltd.*)

Set of lettering stencils in various sizes with associated reservoir pens, e.g., Uno, Graphos, Standardgraph.

Set of shaped stencils: squares, triangles, circles and radii (obtainable from drawing office suppliers).

2. *Copying Equipment*

The installation of copying equipment to meet all the needs of a technical publications unit is a costly venture and only large business organizations would attempt it. Apart from the cost of the equipment, it involves a large demand on space and operating costs are considerable. For a relatively small unit it is usually preferable to put this work in the hands of competent plan makers. Such firms work at remarkable speed and will deliver normal orders within a day or two, whilst urgent small orders may be ' done while you wait '. When an offset litho machine forms part of the equipment the copying of illustrations within the size limit of such machines presents no difficulty. High-quality reproductions are assured at low cost and in quick time. The various types of copying machine have been described in Chapter 5.

It may be added that a reflex copier of the Copyfix or Duostat type is a useful accessory for taking single copies of drawings or typescript for filing purposes.

CHAPTER 10

TECHNICAL AUTHORSHIP

THE scientist who has gained knowledge and experience in his subject may feel the urge to write a book. The urge is partly philanthropic, as few fortunes have been made by writing technical books, but the publication of a well-written book may help him considerably in his career besides giving him the satisfaction of putting down his knowledge for the benefit of others.

Unfortunately, books, like other commercial articles, are subject to the law of supply and demand. If there is no demand for a book on a particular subject a publisher cannot undertake to invest money in it, and it is perhaps for this reason more than any other that many excellent contributions to technical literature remain unpublished.

The production of books is essentially the result of a partnership between publisher and author. The author produces the work of his brain, the publisher backs his opinion of the author and his work to the extent of several hundreds or thousands of pounds in the expectation that both will profit from the partnership in due course. In addition to the financial backing a publisher is prepared to put his experience at the disposal of the author and advise him on the best way to put down his knowledge. It seems reasonable, therefore, for an author to take as much care in the selection of his publisher as he would in choosing any other professional man to advise him.

A considerable amount of time and trouble would be saved if an author approached a publisher before beginning work on his manuscript.

Most technical publishers specialize in certain branches of science or technology, and from their knowledge of the market can predict with a fair degree of certainty the type of book and contents that may be acceptable. The author's own ideas of how a book should be made up may have to be revised when the economics are discussed. For example, a student's textbook containing coloured plates and folding charts would probably be so expensive to produce that its

283

retail price would be beyond the pocket of the very class of reader that it was designed to suit.

A would-be author who has read the previous chapters will have learnt what is an economic and satisfactory way of presenting his information and will not add to production costs by putting in unnecessary material or by using galley proofs as a basis on which to rewrite the book.

Agreements

If an author submits a synopsis of his projected book with sufficient material for the publisher to form an opinion of its possibilities he can be assured that it will be considered carefully. The belief that publishers return manuscripts or synopses unread is still held by some authors, whose commonsense should tell them that as a publisher lives by issuing books he is not likely to ignore any opportunity of increasing his livelihood.

Assuming that the projected book is well thought out and shows a good prospect of succeeding, the author will be offered a contract or agreement for its publication. Although differing in minor points, the agreements drawn up by reputable publishers are all substantially on these lines:

The publisher agrees to print, publish and use his best efforts to sell the book, and to pay the author a royalty on each copy sold. This royalty is usually a minimum of 10% of the retail price of the book, increasing after a certain number of copies has been sold. Royalties are also paid on overseas sales, translation rights, and (although this seldom affects a technical book) film and broadcasting rights.

The author on his part warrants that the work is his own, that it contains no other unauthorized copyright matter, and that the finished typescript is fit for printing. He undertakes to keep the text up-to-date and revise it for each subsequent edition that may be required. It is usual also for him to give an undertaking that he will not have a book of a similar nature published elsewhere in such a way that the sales of the first may be affected.*

It should be noted that the copyright of the material in a book

* This restriction does not, of course, apply to the publication of articles or papers by the author on his own subject. These would probably assist in making the book known and be correspondingly welcomed by a publisher.

remains the property of the author, who is in effect hiring it to the publisher. If at the end of a number of years the publisher considers that the book has come to the end of its useful life, the rights revert to the author on the termination of the agreement, and he is at liberty to make what use of the material he likes. It is sometimes tempting to an author to sell his rights to a publisher for a lump sum, but this is not desirable. In order to cover his risk the publisher will quite reasonably offer a figure which is below the expectations of the total royalty return, and if the book succeeds beyond the expectations the author will have a permanent grievance that he did not receive enough.

It is usual for royalties to be paid half-yearly, and if the author has been put to some expense in the production of the manuscript he may ask for an advance of royalties, which will be debited to his account. If there is likely to be a delay between the acceptance of the manuscript and its appearance on the market the publisher may not be unsympathetic.

Delivery of Manuscript

Before an author complains of long delay in the publication of his book he must be sure that he himself has not contributed to this delay by defects in the finished manuscript. In the first place the manuscript must be complete before the publisher can get to work on it. 'Complete' means with all the necessary illustrations, bibliography, notes, captions, and list of contents. To deliver a manuscript without these details is equivalent to supplying a piece of equipment to a customer and saying that the nuts and bolts will follow later. No time is saved by sending in a manuscript in a partly finished form, as the publisher must have the whole work for estimating purposes and the risk of mislaying a page or an illustration is appreciable if it is not included with the others in the packet.

The check list given on p. 104 can be usefully applied to checking the complete book manuscript, and a list of the preliminary pages is given on p. 263.

In addition, the following points should be specially checked if a manuscript is to be acceptable:

(a) Each page should be numbered consecutively. If a page is omitted the fact should be noted on the previous page.
(b) Pages added after the numbering is complete should be marked

285

'A', 'B' and so on, with the number of the page that they follow.

(c) Typed pages with a few one-word corrections in handwriting give the printer no difficulty, but if the alterations are extensive the page should be re-typed.

(d) Additions to a page should be numbered to correspond and gummed (not pinned) to the page.

(e) Tables can form part of the made-up typescript, but illustrations and captions are to be kept separate.

(f) Photographs should not be marked on the back. All captions (legends) should be made on separate sheets of paper and listed with the illustration number.

(g) A short summary should accompany the manuscript: this is of use for publicity purposes.

The Blurb

'Blurb' is a slang term for the concise introductory information about a book which appears in the publisher's catalogue or on the jacket. It is valuable in giving an indication to the reader of what he can expect from the book. The blurb is prepared from information supplied by the author, who, being expert in his subject, can often stress important features which could not be appreciated by the publisher. The return of the proofs should therefore be accompanied by a short summary of the contents and a biographical note, which can be used in preparing advertising material, etc. The author can rely on the publisher's good taste in not making extravagant claims for the book, and blurbs for technical books are usually in keeping with the spirit of objective scientific writing.

The Preface

In the seventeenth century the preface to a book was called the author's Advertisement in the sense that it was his notification of the reason for writing the book and the intended scope of its contents.* A preface should still follow the principle of introducing a book to the reader, and, like advertisements in good taste, explain why he should read the book in preference to another. It is not the function of the preface to give the table of contents in different words: it should rather point out the 'high spots' and indicate who will derive benefit from reading the book.

It is always convenient in the preface to acknowledge any help

* See Newton's *Opticks* (London, W. & J. Innys, 1721 Edn.).

that the author has received from other authors or suppliers of information, although, if the list is long, it may be set down separately under the heading of 'Acknowledgements'.

The Foreword

Many authors and publishers feel that the value of a book is enhanced if an eminent person contributes a foreword in the nature of a recommendation for the book and its writer. It is certainly true that many readers will assume, and rightly, that a book which has been distinguished by such a foreword is worthy of attention. On the other hand, writers may be consoled by the words of an eminent professor to a young author: 'If your book is good, a foreword from me will be unnecessary; if it is bad, my foreword will not help to sell it.'

Indexing

A good index is essential to any piece of technical writing, whether it is in the form of a contents list for short reports or a full index for handbooks or full-length books. While it is possible to prepare an index of sorts by setting down a list of the words used in the text, a useful index requires time, skill, and trouble in its preparation.

Sir Henry Thring laid down the principles of good indexing in 1877:*

The basis of an index to a book of the ordinary kind is a series of titles or catchwords arranged in alphabetical order and indicative of the main topics treated of in the book.

The object of the index is to indicate the place in the book or collection of books in which information is to be found. Such an index is perfect in proportion as it is concise in expression, while exhaustive in its indication of every important topic of the subject to which it is an index.

It should be made clear at the outset that an author who looks on indexing his book as a chore to be hurried through as quickly as possible would be well advised to employ a professional indexer who will produce an adequate list for a fee which is commensurate with the complexity of the subject. On the other hand, the author is the person most familiar with his work, and he should look on the index as the final key to the information that he has taken such trouble to set down in the pages of his text.

* *Law Magazine*, August 1877.

There are certain recommended methods of constructing an index which will save the author time and avoid unnecessary repetition and cross-checking. Of these methods, the simplest is the following:

Do not start indexing until the galley- or page-proof stage. At the galley stage the main items to be indexed can be noted by underlining, but the page numbers cannot be added till the proofs are in page form.

Each item should be noted on a card (5 × 3 in., see p. 40) with cross-references, and at the same time the items should be marked in the proof to show that they have been entered.

For medium-sized indexes, slips of paper can be used instead of cards and these can be cut up subsequently and gummed in sequence on larger sheets.

When all the items have been assembled on cards or slips, the page numbers are added and the cards are classified; any less important items can be discarded at this stage.

Finally, the assembled cards are copied on to a single sheet with the attendant page numbers, and the alphabetical order is finally checked before sending to the printer.

A useful device for cataloguing numerous items, such as stocks or price lists is the special holder manufactured by Remington Rand Ltd. under the name " Flexoprint ". This contains a number of interlocking card strips which can be inserted in the typewriter and sorted after the items have been filled in. If necessary the holder and cards can be laid flat for photographing for offset printing. The system is used by the Post Office in preparing directories.

Catchwords

Where a word is of main importance and is likely to be required by the reader it is adopted as a ' catchword ', and subsidiary subjects can be arranged under this word as a main heading. For example, an index to *Electronic Engineering* shows the following catchwords:

Amplifiers	Editorials	Measurements
Book Reviews	Electronic Equipment	Microwaves
Cathode-ray Tubes	Letters	Radar

and under each catchword is a separate list of the articles relevant to it. This arrangement is of use to the reader who is interested in one aspect of the subject, or who has no definite information to help him locate a given article beyond the general content. The sub-divisions under the catchword follow an alphabetical arrangement as specified later in this paragraph.

Cross-references

An important decision which the author has to make in listing a title is ' How many times shall I put it down ? '. It must be remembered that a reader may not know the exact title of the article or reference he requires, he may know the author's name but not the title of the article, or he may know nothing except that a certain article on a certain subject appeared in the book dated 1950.

The rule of good indexing is that the article *must* appear once under its full title, with no alteration or abbreviation. Thereafter, it is permissible to give a cross reference to the title with slight (but only slight) modifications, and the number of cross references may correspond approximately with the number of nouns in the original title. For example, the main title of the work ' The Manufacture of Stainless Iron and Steel ' may be listed under :

> Manufacture of Stainless Iron and Steel
> Stainless Iron and Steel, Manufacture of
> Iron and Steel, Stainless, Manufacture of
> Stainless Steel, Manufacture of

the last title being included in case the reader did not know the full title of the work. How many cross-references are included in this way is left to the discretion and patience of the author, but another rule must be followed : When referring the reader to another part of the index, make sure that the cross-reference is given. Nothing is more annoying to the searcher to find the statement :

> Stainless Steel (see also Iron)

and then see no reference to iron under I.

Methods of Classifying

Although it seldom occurs in technical literature, the least useful index is that in which the author has listed words taken at random from the text regardless of their importance. Wheatley quotes

> Kind—A Kind of Dialogue designed for the Unthinking

as an example of this random selection. The reader expects that

T   289

the author will use some discrimination in presenting the items that may be useful to him, and the mere listing of a name or substance because it occurs in the text is wasting both paper and the reader's time.

The alphabetical arrangement, although liable to abuse, is the only satisfactory method of listing the items in due order. Two arrangements are possible : the strict letter order, as used in the Telephone Directory and in certain encyclopaedias, and the word order, which is preferred for ordinary indexing. An example of word order is

> Electronic amplifiers
> computers
> control
> Electronically coupled indicators
> Electronics in industry
> Electrostatic field

A writer in the *Publishers' Circular** warns against adopting the word order too literally when a variety of subjects is mentioned under a common head :

> Heart
> -burn
> —cabbage in salads
> , organic diseases of
> , with Sauce Blanquette

Another example of literal mis-classification is

> Lagging boilers
> current

Author's Names. The name is listed surname first. If the author is known under two names (e.g. having received a title) the original name is retained as an alternative :

> Thomson, Sir Wm. (Lord Kelvin)
> Kelvin, Lord (Sir Wm. Thomson)

Hyphenated names are entered under the first half of the double-barrelled name : Smith-Rose, R. L.

Prefixes are not usually listed in the alphabetical order, and some indexers prefer to put them after the name, e.g. Graaff, van der but it seems better to include them as part of the name, as done in *Who's Who.*

Compound Words. The compounds should be listed in the order

* July 5, 1952.

in which the words commonly occur, and no break should be made for the sake of conforming to the alphabet.* For example, High Tension should be listed under H and not under Tension, High.

An excellent guide to indexing for authors is *Indexing your Book* by S. Spiker (University of Wisconsin Press, 1955), and other books will be found listed on p. 330, Section 5.

Reprints and New Editions

After a book has sold satisfactorily over a period (which may be months or years) the publisher will usually notify the author that the stock of printed copies is running low. This does not mean that the book will shortly disappear from the market, for the publisher gives his warning well in advance, and there is also a time lag between the running out of the publisher's stock and the selling out of the copies held by the bookshops. The object of the ample warning is to enable the author to decide what is to be done to keep the book alive and up-to-date. This decision will be influenced by the subject matter and its treatment, the remarks of the book reviewers, and the trend of development. If the work is a standard textbook to cover a particular course it may only be necessary to correct a few inevitable misprints and errors in working. If the book is an account of a new subject, the development may have proceeded so rapidly that new references and comments may be necessary throughout the text. If the reviewers have criticized the presentation or the want of balance in the writing, the author has an opportunity of improving his work which he should welcome whole-heartedly.

To help the author in revising the text, the publishers usually present him with a copy of the book interleaved with blank paper, so that he may make notes and corrections as they occur to him.

If the author and publisher agree that very little correction or additional matter is needed to keep the book satisfactory, it will be reprinted, with the necessary corrections, from the type which is kept standing at the printers. The title page of the reprint will then bear the words: ' Reprinted with revisions ' or ' Reprinted ', with the date. Further reprints will then be listed on the back of the title page, with the dates on which they were run off.

If, however, the author decides and the publisher agrees that the

* Compare the reputed classification in an Army stock list: Webs, cob 2.

book can be improved by extensive re-writing and adding new material the work can then be justifiably called a new edition. The amount of alteration and addition which is required to warrant the words 'Second Edition' on the title page is within the publisher's discretion, for he runs the risk of offending book buyers if he sells them a second edition which differs only slightly from the first.

After the lapse of many years a book which has become established as a standard work may need a complete overhaul to maintain its place against competition and to maintain the author's reputation. It is then that an author has to be particularly on his guard against allowing obsolete matter to remain in the text, and it is not sufficient to add notes to each chapter. Some of the points that require special checking are:

(a) Illustrations of obsolete equipment*
(b) Retention of obsolete symbols and abbreviations
(c) Reference to twenty-year-old papers as " recent "
(d) Omission of new references in some chapters
(e) Reference to obsolete standards and data.†

In revising the text, the author should be particularly careful to alter the present tense to the past when describing inventions or apparatus made ten or twenty years ago.

Should an author die during the currency of his book his widow (or his executors) will, of course, continue to benefit by the royalties paid on the sale. When the need for revising the text arises it is usual for the publisher to arrange for a competent reviser to undertake to keep the book up-to-date, and a portion of the royalty is diverted to the reviser, with the agreement of the executors. The author of a well-established book may therefore be confident that his heirs will continue to reap the reward (or a substantial part of it) of his knowledge and experience.

Copyright

Copyright is the right of ownership of an author over his original work, whether manuscript, drawing, photograph, or similar material. It endures for his lifetime and for a period of fifty years after, and

---

* The manufacturer of the equipment will rightly resent the implication that his products have not advanced during the life of the book.

† The word " capacitor " has been accepted as standard for over twenty-five years, but new authors are still using the old-fashioned word " condenser ".

the conditions are governed by the Copyright Act of 1956 (which supersedes the Act of 1911).

Subject to the exceptions given below, the Copyright Act gives an author protection against infringement, that is, the unauthorized use of his material. It is not necessary to use the author's own words to infringe his copyright: an obvious paraphrase of the text matter or an imitation of a drawing would be an infringement. It has often been said that there is no copyright in an idea; the rights exist in the method of expressing the idea.

There are occasions when copyright material may be used without constituting an infringement; those of particular interest to the technical writer are:

Any fair dealing with a literary work for the purpose of research, private study, criticism, review, or newspaper summary, provided that there is sufficient acknowledgement.

Part I, Section 6 of the Act

The inclusion of short passages of copyright literary material in a collection intended for use in schools, provided that the collection is described as such and the copyright work is not already published for use in schools. Sufficient acknowledgement is also required.

Part I, Section 6(6)

There are also special exceptions relating to legal actions requiring copies of documents, single copies required by libraries, and periodicals subscribing to the ' Fair Copying Declaration ' (see p. 38).

Copyright of Commissioned Work

It often happens that the writer of a technical article is commissioned by the publisher of a periodical to produce it to a specification and for an agreed fee. The publisher usually claims the copyright in the article, and the fee is paid on this understanding. If the writer is employed by a publisher to produce articles the copyright is automatically owned by the publisher so far as it relates to his own or any other periodical, but the Act does not give the publisher exclusive copyright of his employee's articles.

An important condition, which affects many writers employed by commercial firms, is cited in Section 4(4) of the Act, and this is quoted below:

Where . . . a work is made in the course of the author's employment by another person under a contract of service or apprenticeship, that

293

other person shall be entitled to any copyright subsisting in the work by virtue of this part of the Act.

A scientific paper which is accepted for reading before a learned society is usually accepted on the condition that the copyright is transferred to the society. This is an obvious precaution to prevent the author of the paper from reading it to another society within a short time, or publishing it in another periodical other than the society's own proceedings.

Copyright in Technical Writing

The attitude of a technical author to his published work differs from that of the artist or novelist. His object in writing a paper or article is to disseminate knowledge and to gain recognition for his own ability, and he is therefore hardly likely to object to seeing his statements quoted as widely as possible, *provided that he is acknowledged as their author.* It is probably for this reason that few actions for infringement of copyright are threatened in the technical publishing field, unless the infringer is guilty of flagrant copying or of passing off another's work as his own.

It must be clearly understood that acknowledgement of the source of information is not a valid defence against an action for infringement of copyright, and where there is any doubt about the original author's attitude it is always best to obtain written permission to quote passages of any length from another's work.

This particularly applies to the reproduction of figures or photographs, which have often been obtained at considerable expense. Written permission should always be obtained for reproduction from another book or article, both from the author and the publisher of the work.

An interesting point for technical writers occurs in the re-drawing of circuit diagrams, which are covered by the term ' drawings ' in the Copyright Act. The original draughtsman of the push-pull valve stage shown in Fig. 4.50 could no doubt claim copyright in this particular method of setting out the connexions, but the work of a technical writer would be hampered if he had to obtain permission for reproducing each diagram or part of a diagram. So far as the present authors are aware, no action for infringement of copyright in a circuit diagram has been taken, but the possibility remains.

Copyright in other Countries

Under the International Copyright Union* the author of any country which is a member of the Union has the same copyright privileges in other countries of the Union (with certain minor modifications). British copyright now extends to all countries of the Commonwealth, America, and Europe with the exception of the U.S.S.R. and satellite countries, who are not signatories to the Universal Copyright Convention.

The Universal Copyright Convention came into force in the United States in September 1955; prior to that date certain restrictions were in force on the importation of books, but these have now been removed.

Each copy of a book must be marked ' Copyright ', with the name of the author(s) and date of publication. A special mark © is used to denote that the book (or an article) is copyright and the declaration is usually found on the verso of the title-page (see this book, for example).

A standard work on copyright is *The Law of Copyright* by J. P. Eddy (Butterworth & Co., London, 1957), which gives a reprint of the Copyright Act with annotations.

A Hypothetical Case

The following hypothetical case, which was discussed at a meeting of ASLIB,† illustrates some of the difficulties that may arise in copyright :

The Basic Facts. Handmade Pinions Ltd. had been making a vital part for chronometers for fifty years and were virtually the only suppliers of the part. At the instigation of a customer they engaged Dr. Verrey Keen as a research engineer in January.

In July of that year, Dr. Keen, while still in their employ, wrote a paper showing that the insistence of Handmade Pinions Ltd. that the vital part must be made by hand was wrong, and demonstrated that it could be made by suitable machinery, thus eliminating a bottle-neck in the manufacture of chronometers.

---

* Formed at the Berne Convention in 1886 ; the agreements at this convention were amended in 1908, 1928, and (in Brussels) 1948. The Universal Copyright Convention has been ratified by Gt. Britain 1957

† Reported in full in *ASLIB Proc.* **5**, 2, 87 (1953), and abstracted here by permission of the Director.

The Managing Director of Handmade Pinions Ltd. was presented with the paper. On studying it he wrote to Dr. Keen : ' This is all nonsense. Obviously your work has no value for us. You may take extended leave until your contract expires at the end of the year.'

In September Dr. Keen was asked by the local Philosophical Society to give them a lecture. Without reference to anyone and without taking steps to ensure that members only were present, he read the paper prepared for Handmade Pinions Ltd.

A member of the audience took down the paper in shorthand and sold the report to the Editor of the *Chronometer Saturn*, who published it in full in December.

On the 1st January in the following year Dr. Keen started employment with the Chronometer Research Association. At a symposium held by the Association in March, attended by representatives of members, the following happened :

(*a*) At the request of the members present, Dr. Keen read his paper again and there was a discussion on it.

(*b*) The Information Officer of the C.R.A. demonstrated a new photo-copying machine. At the request of each of the 35 members present, he helped each one to make a single copy of Dr. Keen's paper in the *Chronometer Saturn* during the demonstration.

The matter then received considerable publicity, and the daily press wrote up the story as showing lack of initiative in the clock industry. The matter was mentioned in the House of Commons and a demand arose for copies of Dr. Keen's paper. For the purpose of determining the copyright position, the following statement of claims was then prepared :

Claims by the Parties. Dr. Keen claims copyright as the original author, and that Handmade Pinions Ltd. had disclaimed any interest by the ' nonsense ' statement of the Managing Director.

He also claims that in repeating the paper at the C.R.A. meeting he was merely reading a published article in a private gathering.

He also claims that the 35 copies of the paper in the *Chronometer Saturn* were made individually for study and research and that the publishers of the journal had signed the Fair Copying declaration.

Handmade Pinions Ltd. claim the copyright on the grounds that Dr. Keen wrote the paper in the course of his employment and must be considered as having been commissioned to write it by the Company. At no time had they formally disclaimed their copyright interests, and Dr. Keen gave his lecture to the Philosophical Society without their permission.

The Editor of the *Chronometer Saturn* claims the copyright at least so far as the presentation of the paper in his journal was concerned. He also states that Dr. Keen had given no indication that the meeting of the Philosophical Society was private, or that he had reserved the copyright. In the circumstances he claims that it is immaterial whether the original copyright belongs to Dr. Keen or the Company.

The Editor also considers that the Information Officer of the C.R.A. had deliberately produced and circulated 35 copies of the paper as published in his journal in infringement of his copyright ; the actual mechanics of reproduction were a mere blind, there being no question of single copies being made for private study.

The Information Officer of the C.R.A. claims that he was fully entitled to make a single copy of the paper under the Fair Copying Declaration for any member of his Association for private study, and he has no reason to doubt that each copy was in fact wanted for such a purpose.

Legal Opinion (An opinion on the case was given by a member of the legal profession) :

The first question to be decided was whether Handmade Pinions Ltd. or Dr. Keen was the first owner of the copyright under Section 5 (1)(b) of the Copyright Act 1911.* This involved a consideration of whether there was a contract of service, and if so, whether the work was made in the course of Dr. Keen's employment. It is also necessary to consider whether the Company had disclaimed any rights which they had, as a result of the Managing Director's comment.

On the evidence it appeared clear that there was a contract of service and that Dr. Keen was not a consultant but a servant of the Company. It also appeared to be reasonably clear that the paper was not produced in the course of his employment, since he was not employed to do anything except improve existing methods of manufacture.

On this basis, Dr. Keen was the first owner of the copyright and the question of disclaimer by Handmade Pinions Ltd. did not arise, although if the Company had been the first owners it was unlikely that they had disclaimed any rights in the circumstances.

With regard to the meeting at which Dr. Keen read his paper, it was important to determine whether the meeting was a private or public one. On enquiry, it seemed that the meeting was private, so the sale of the shorthand note by a member of the audience was a breach of confidence and an infringement of Dr. Keen's rights. It is assumed that the report in the *Chronometer Saturn* possessed sufficient original material to entitle it to copyright, subject to Dr. Keen's rights against that journal.

It remained therefore to consider whether the reproduction of 35 copies of the newspaper account was ' fair copying ' within the meaning of Section 2(i) of the Act [*now Section* 6(1)—*authors*]. After consideration of the authorities, it appeared clear that neither the Act nor the Fair Copying Declaration afforded any defence. However, since everything done at the symposium was done with the consent of Dr. Keen who could have restrained any further publication of the *Chronometer Saturn's* report, it was improbable that any action would lie, other than on purely technical grounds, against the Information Officer or the members of the Association.

* This discussion took place before publication of the Copyright Act 1956 ; the relevant section in the new Act is 4 (4).

Defamation

As is well known, any statement which is damaging to the interests or reputation of another person may be held to be libellous and render both the writer and publisher liable for damages. It is not necessarily a good defence to prove the truth of the statement.

While it is seldom that a technical author would be guilty of uttering a direct libel or defamatory statement, it must be remembered that a disparaging statement about another's work or writing might be defamatory; care must be taken in commenting in such a way that the reputation of another author (or manufacturer of a product) might be damaged.

Critical statements in the nature of reviews of books or products are generally held privileged, but successful actions have been taken against critics,* and it is safer to be guarded in one's statements when reviewing another's work.

Translations

A reader of scientific literature in other languages may sometimes feel that a particular work would benefit a wider section of the community if it were translated into English. Before undertaking what may prove to be a tedious and unprofitable task, there are several points to be considered. It is possible that the book already has a market in the Commonwealth or America in its original language, and the market may therefore not be as good as expected. Secondly, a working knowledge of the language of the original is not sufficient for a good translation: the writer must be fluent and idiomatic, with a certain knowledge of the equivalents of technical terms in the subject. There is on record a translation in which a Russian phrase referring to a multi-stage amplifier using tetrodes was rendered as ' a cascade of shaded lamps '.

If the writer feels confident that he can do justice to the original text, the first step is to approach the author or the publisher of the original work for permission to translate. This granted, the next step is to find a British or American publisher willing to produce the work. A copy of the original with a short specimen translation will have to be submitted—sufficient to show the technical quality of the work.

* See J. Dean, *Hatred, Ridicule or Contempt*, London, Constable, 1953.

The economics of publishing translations are less satisfactory than ordinary publishing projects because there are more to share the profits. In addition to the British or American publisher and the translator, the original publisher and author expect their proportion of the proceeds—sometimes in the form of a lump sum in lieu of royalties. When it is remembered that the work of translating may take a year, depending on the translator's time and enthusiasm, the return is not great. With the added risk that a finished work may be two or three years out of date, the publisher may be excused from being enthusiastic about the prospects of a translation, however well done.

Authors should note that countries which do not subscribe to the International Copyright Convention may issue translations of their work without permission having been sought or granted. Payment may be available in blocked currency, but as the author is seldom aware of the copyright infringement he will find it difficult to obtain redress.

Planning a Book

This chapter can be usefully concluded by quoting the advice issued by a technical publisher to would-be authors :*

' Do consult an experienced publisher at an early stage. Write first : talking is nearly always a waste of time until he has studied the costs involved and the probable markets.

There is a widely held belief that if a publisher can be *personally* interested in a project, he can in some occult manner assure its success. In fact, like any other producer, he only stays in business so long as he gives the public (whether they are readers for pleasure, or lecturers in chemistry) what they want, at the right price and in the right form.'

* The Cleaver-Hume Press Ltd., reproduced by courtesy of Mr. P. J. Edmonds.

APPENDICES

APPENDIX 1

CASTING-OFF TABLES

ALL the faces shown in the following tables are suitable for technical publications. Their individual characteristics are outlined in Chapter 8, p. 255.

The point size refers to the body of the type. When the body is larger than the fount, e.g. ten point on eleven, the point size is used to calculate characters per line and the body size to calculate lines per page.

If $x =$ the number of characters per line (from the tables)

$y =$ the depth of page in picas

$z =$ body size in points

$n =$ number of characters per page of letterpress

$$n = \frac{x \times y \times 12}{z}$$

Example :

A page is set to 24 picas measure, 44 picas deep, in ten point on eleven point body, Baskerville. From the table,

Number of characters per line $= 67$

$$\text{Number of lines} = \frac{44 \times 12}{11} = 48$$

Number of characters per page $= 48 \times 67 = 3216$

TABLE 1   BASKERVILLE   SERIES 169

Point Size	\multicolumn{13}{c}{Number of Picas Per Line}
	12	14	16	18	20	22	24	26	28	30	32	34	36
8	37	43	50	56	63	71	77	83	89	95	103	109	115
9	34	40	46	52	59	65	71	77	83	89	95	101	107
10	32	38	43	49	55	61	67	73	79	83	89	95	101
11	28	33	38	43	49	55	59	65	69	75	79	85	89
12	26	30	35	40	45	49	55	59	63	69	73	77	83

TABLE 2 BODONI   SERIES 135

Point Size	12	14	16	18	20	22	24	26	28	30	32	34	36
					Number of Picas Per Line								
8	38	45	52	59	65	73	79	87	93	101	107	115	121
9	35	41	48	54	61	67	73	79	85	91	99	105	111
10	33	39	45	51	57	63	69	75	81	87	93	99	105
11	31	37	42	47	53	59	65	71	77	81	87	91	97
12	26	30	35	40	45	49	55	59	63	69	73	77	83

TABLE 3 CASLON OLD FACE   SERIES 128

Point Size	12	14	16	18	20	22	24	26	28	30	32	34	36
					Number of Picas Per Line								
8	46	54	62	70	79	87	95	103	111	119	127	135	143
9	37	43	50	56	63	71	77	83	89	95	103	109	115
10	35	41	48	54	61	67	73	79	85	91	99	105	111
11	33	39	45	51	57	63	69	75	81	87	93	99	105
12	28	33	38	43	49	55	59	65	69	75	79	85	88

TABLE 4 GARAMOND   SERIES 156

Point Size	12	14	16	18	20	22	24	26	28	30	32	34	36
					Number of Picas Per Line								
8	38	45	52	59	65	73	79	87	93	101	107	115	121
9	35	41	48	54	61	67	73	79	85	91	99	105	111
10	33	39	45	51	57	63	69	75	81	87	93	99	105
11	31	37	42	47	53	59	65	71	77	81	87	91	97
12	27	31	36	42	47	51	57	61	65	71	75	81	87

TABLE 5 GILL LIGHT   SERIES 362
         GILL MEDIUM   SERIES 262

Point Size	12	14	16	18	20	22	24	26	28	30	32	34	36
					Number of Picas Per Line								
8	37	43	50	56	63	71	77	83	89	95	103	109	115
10	33	39	45	51	57	63	69	75	81	87	93	99	105
11	31	37	42	47	53	59	65	71	77	81	87	91	97
12	27	31	36	42	47	51	57	61	65	71	75	81	87

TABLE 6 GILL BOLD SERIES 275

Point Size	Number of Picas Per Line											
	12	14	16	18	20	22	24	26	28	30	32	34	36
8	34	40	46	52	59	65	71	77	83	89	95	101	107
10	28	33	38	43	49	55	59	65	69	75	79	85	89
11	26	30	35	40	45	49	55	59	63	69	73	77	83
12	24	29	33	38	42	46	50	54	60	64	68	74	78

TABLE 7 IMPRINT OLD FACE SERIES 101

Point Size	Number of Picas Per Line											
	12	14	16	18	20	22	24	26	28	30	32	34	36
8	37	43	50	56	63	71	77	83	89	95	103	109	115
9	34	40	46	52	59	65	71	77	83	89	95	101	107
10	33	39	45	51	57	63	69	75	81	87	93	99	105
11	31	37	42	47	53	59	65	71	77	81	87	91	97
12	27	31	36	42	47	51	57	61	65	71	75	81	87

TABLE 8 PERPETUA SERIES 239

Point Size	Number of Picas Per Line											
	12	14	16	18	20	22	24	26	28	30	32	34	36
8	40	48	55	62	69	77	83	91	99	105	113	121	127
9	38	45	52	59	65	73	79	87	93	101	107	115	121
10	37	43	50	56	63	71	77	83	89	95	103	109	115
11	34	40	46	52	59	65	71	77	83	89	95	101	107
12	30	35	40	46	51	57	63	67	73	79	83	89	95

TABLE 9 PLANTIN OLD STYLE SERIES 110

Point Size	Number of Picas Per Line											
	12	14	16	18	20	22	24	26	28	30	32	34	36
8	37	43	50	56	63	71	77	83	89	95	99	103	115
9	34	40	46	52	59	65	71	77	83	89	92	95	107
10	33	39	45	51	57	63	69	75	81	87	90	93	105
11	31	37	42	47	53	59	65	71	77	81	84	87	97
12	27	31	36	42	47	51	57	61	65	71	73	75	87

U

TABLE 10   TIMES ROMAN   SERIES 327

Point Size	Number of Picas Per Line												
	12	14	16	18	20	22	24	26	28	30	32	34	36
8	37	44	50	56	62	70	77	84	91	96	100	105	114
9	35	41	48	54	60	66	72	77	86	92	98	104	108
10	32	37	42	47	53	59	64	68	75	82	88	94	99
11	28	32	38	43	50	56	58	64	69	73	78	83	89
12	24	28	33	36	41	44	49	53	58	62	67	71	76

Tables 1–9 are based on those given in *Printing Design and Layout* published by Virtue & Co., to whom acknowledgements are made.

APPENDIX II

PRINTERS' AND AUTHORS' PROOF-CORRECTION MARKS

Selected from British Standard 1219 : 1945 to which reference should be made for a full list.

Marginal Mark	Correction Wanted	Mark in Text
ꕤ	Delete	/ through character or ⊢—⊣ through word(s).
#	More space	∧ or #
◡	Close up	embracing, for example, last and first letters of two words separated by too much space. ⊃ embracing characters to be deleted.
ꕤ	Delete and close up	.... under matter to
stet	Leave as printed irrespective of other marks	remain unaltered.
caps. *Sm. caps.* *caps or s.c.*	Change to capitals Change to small caps Capital initials ; small caps for remainder	≡ under initial letters. = under remainder.
l.c. *Bo.*	Set in lower case Set in bold type	encircle letters to be altered. ‿‿ under words to be altered.
ital.	Set in italics	Underline letters or words to be altered.
rule *rom.*	Underline Change to Roman type	Underline words affected. Encircle words or characters to be altered.
w.f.	= wrong fount. Replace by character of correct fount	Encircle character to be changed.
𝄎	Character to be printed in superior	Encircle character to be altered.
𝄎 or ∧	Character to be printed in inferior	Encircle character concerned.
ꇗ	More space between lines or paragraphs	Amount of space, e.g. 3 points, may be inserted in margin.
eq. #	Make spacing equal	∧ between words concerned.

307

Marginal Mark	Correction Wanted		Mark in Text
trs.	Transpose	⌒⌣	around words in wrong order.
centre	Place in centre of line	⁝ ⁝	in position wanted.
□ ⌊	Indent one em	⊏	
⊐	Move to left	⊐	at right side of matter to be moved.
⊏	Move to right	⊏	at left side of matter to be moved.
move over	Move position	[ ]	Indicate new position limits.
take over	Move to next line	⊏	
take back	Move to previous line	⊐	
raise	Raise	‾ ⊤ ‾ ‾	*over* matter to be moved.
lower	Lower	_ ⊥ _ _	*under* matter to be moved.
‖	Correct vertical alignment		
═	Straighten lines		
n.p.	New paragraph	⊏	in front of first word.
run on	Do not paragraph	⌒⟶	between paragraphs.
⊙ ⊙	Insert punctuation mark	⋏	
(/)/	Insert parenthesis	⋏ ⋏	insert where the addition is required
⋏ /-/	Insert hyphen		
-em /—/	Insert one-em rule		

Notes on Proof Correcting

The compositor is not a diviner, and corrections should be made clearly in the code to which he is accustomed. When in doubt he will conform to the author's mark as closely as possible. Marginal comments or instructions should be ringed round to distinguish them from corrections, and lengthy instructions should be marked ' Printer : ' to prevent them being set in the text by accident (see also p. 244).

The end of each correction in a line of text should be signalled by drawing an oblique line after the mark. This line is shown in the table above after the parenthesis signs in the margin. Hyphens and dashes are identified by a stroke before and after : / - / ; punctuation marks are usually ringed round to avoid any possible confusion with ink spots.

Continental Practice

It is customary in Germany to make all proof correction marks on the right-hand margin of the proof, and in France and some other countries the marking is on the left-hand margin. Neither of these conventions can be so helpful to the compositor as making the correction in the margin closest to the part of the line concerned. In British and American practice the marks in the margin are made in the order in which they occur in the corrected line. Some continental countries, however, use a complete code of reference marks of which the following are specimens : *η Ц 9 ί Υ Ł 7J*. These marks are placed against the wrong letter and also against the correction in the margin, with the object of identifying them. There appears to be no definite order in which the code marks are used (unlike the printers' reference marks in the text), and to the British proof reader they seem unnecessarily complicated to make and to understand.

Variations of the British standard markings which may be found in continental proofs are :

Wavy underlining for italics	# to indicate a *raised* space
Single underlining for bold type	⌐ for New Paragraph

In general, the British standard proof marks are understood readily by continental and American compositors, but in case of doubt it is always advisable to write the desired correction clearly in the margin.

ABRIDGED GLOSSARY OF TERMS
USED IN PRINTING AND PUBLISHING

In these definitions the term 'book' includes other forms of publication—booklets, periodicals and brochures.

Author's Corrections. This term is applied by the printer to any work which has to be done by the compositor on the type matter after the corrected proof has been returned.

Bleed-off. The printing of illustrations so that one or more edges of the block overhang the edge of the printed page.

Blocks. Metal plates mounted on wood or metal backing, from which the figures or illustrations for a book are printed.

Blocks : Half-tone. Photographs are reproduced by means of 'half-tone' blocks in which the various shades of grey are simulated by breaking up the black into a regular series of dots of various areas. See p. 208 for details.

Body. A term referring to the dimensions of the metal on which the type character is cast. See p. 168.

Bold Face Type. A type face which is blacker or heavier than the text type, often used for side-headings or for certain symbols. A typical bold face type is **Clarendon.**

Box.

Type matter which is surrounded by a border, or rule, is said to be set in a box.

Braces. Printer's " braces " are : { }

Cancelled Matter. Type matter prepared for printing but not used. Such matter is said to be " killed ".

Caps. Capital letters (abbreviation).

Caption. Commonly used to describe the explanatory text under an illustration. An alternative term is " legend ".

Case. The cover of a book ready for binding.

Centre Head. A heading mounted in the centre of the page of type matter.

Clarendon. A heavy type face (see Bold Face Type).

Clean Proof. Proof submitted after the typographical errors have been corrected. Proofs from an uncorrected galley are often distinguished by a blue pencil line drawn down the text.

Coated Paper. Paper which has been treated with china clay or other material to give it a high finish.

Colophon. This term originally referred to the printer's or writer's device or emblem placed at the end of a book, but is now loosely applied to a decorative device on the title page or spine of the book.

Colour Plates. Illustrations printed from two or more colours (black is counted as a colour), which usually require special paper.

Compositor. The printer's craftsman who sets or composes the lines of type and prepares the pages for press. Abbreviated to " Comp."

Contents. A list of chapter headings, paragraph headings, or other sections of a book, inserted after the title page.

Copy. The general term applied by a printer to all material sent to him for typesetting, including the illustrations.

Cut. A term sometimes applied to illustrations, particularly in American practice.

Die. The stamp used for impressing a design or lettering on the cover of a book.

Dummy. A book made up from unprinted sheets to give an idea of the size and binding.

Em. Printer's unit of type measure (see Point). The length of a line of type matter is expressed in so many ' ems '.

Figure. This term is usually applied to the line drawings which illustrate a book, apart from its use in a mathematical sense.

Folio. One side of the page of a book. Odd-numbered folios are on the right-hand side of the book.

Format. The general style of a book—size of page, style.

Forme. A steel frame complete with type and blocks arranged in correct page order to print the finished pages.

Fount. Of type. Sometimes spelt and pronounced " font ". The complete collection of capital and small letters, figures, and other symbols which make up a complete case of type.

Galley. A shallow tray in which the compositor sets the lines of type as they are composed. Proofs taken from the type matter at this stage are called ' galley proofs ' or ' slip proofs '.

Gravure. A method of printing in which the design or lettering is engraved on a metal plate or cylinder, the grooves being filled with ink.

This method of printing is ' intaglio ', as opposed to relief printing from raised type or blocks.

Half-title. The title page of part of a book, bound in front of the part to which it refers. A " bastard title " before the title page.

Imposition. The arrangement of pages in the forme (*q.v.*) so that they will print in the proper order on the finished and folded sheet.

Indenting. Beginning a line of type at a short distance inwards from the left-hand edge.

Insert. Printed pages of illustrations separate from the main pages of the book and subsequently inserted by hand.

Italics. *Sloping type, such as this line is set in. The direction to* the printer to set in italic is a <u>single line ruled under</u> the word or letter.

Jacket. A loose cover for the bound book, sometimes ornamented with a picture, and designed to be attractive to the reader.

Justify. To space the words in a line of type to make it conform to a standard length. If this line were not justified it would look like this.

Kill, To. To destroy type matter which is not required. (See Cancelled Matter.)

Layout. The working instructions for making up a page or display of type matter. A rough sketch of the finished job with instructions for type size, etc.

Leading. Insertion of thin strips of metal (usually lead alloy) between lines of type to give additional white space.

Line Drawing. A general name for drawings in which the effect is solely achieved by the use of black lines on white paper.

Linotype. A machine for setting type mechanically, in which each line is cast as a solid bar—hence the name.

Lower Case. Printer's term for letters which are found in the lower case of types on the composing bench. This line is set in lower-case type, as distinct from capital letters. Abbreviation: l.c.

Margin. The blank area round the edge of type matter on a page. The attractive appearance of a book is greatly enhanced by the correct proportioning of the margins.

Monotype. Machine for casting type in single units, which are then automatically assembled to form the words and lines.

MS. Abbreviation for " manuscript ", usually also applied to typescript.

Old Style. Type face which is characterized by oblique serifs (*q.v.*).

Over-matter. Type set for making up, but not used in the final page.

Over-run. Matter left over after the type has been set to fill a given space ; or, to turn over words from one line to the next.

Pagination. Numbering of the pages in a book. (See *Folio*).

Plate. A printed page or illustration on different paper from that used for the body of the book, usually inserted separately in the binding.

Point. The printer's standard unit of type measure. A point is approximately $\frac{1}{72}$ in., so that 12-point type measures $\frac{1}{6}$ in. depth (see p. 168).

    The unit of measurement is the 12-pt. ' em ', which is sometimes called by its old name ' pica em ', and the length of a line is reckoned in pica or 12-pt. ems.

    This line of type is set to 21 ems in length (about $3\frac{1}{2}$ in.).

Proof. Any printed impression used for correcting or altering supplied by the printer or blockmaker. The proofs of a printed illustration are usually called " pulls " or " cuts ".

Recto. The right-hand (odd-numbered) folio of a page.

Revise. A second proof submitted after the corrections have been made.

Roman. Name for the upright type faces as used in this line. The sloping type is *Italic* (*q.v.*).

Rules. Printer's term for lengths of brass or lead strip which are used to print lines of various thicknesses. (See *Box*).

Run-round. To set type matter closely round an illustration where it does not occupy the full width of the type matter on the page.

Running Head or Headline. The title of the book or the title of the chapter set at the top of the page.

Script. A type face designed to imitate copper-plate hand-writing.

Serif. The small projection at the ends of the letters which rounds off their appearance. This type is ' serif' type. The block-letter type faces are known as " sans-serifs ".

Set. The width of a type character.

Side Head. A sub-heading placed at the side of a paragraph instead of in the centre òf the page.

Signature. A complete folded and printed sheet of 8, 16, 32, or 64 pages. The book is made up of several signatures collated in order and bound. A reference number or letter is placed at the foot of certain pages to denote the signature and to guide the collator in making up the book.

Small Caps. The complete fount of type contains CAPITALS, SMALL CAPITALS and lower case letters.

THIS LINE IS SET IN SMALL CAPS.

Solid Matter. Type set without extra spacing leads.

Sub-title. A second or explanatory title under the main title. It is usually preferable to make the main title short, leaving any qualifications or explanations to the sub-title.

Text. The name for the type matter which forms the bulk of the book.

Upper Case. Printer's term for Capital Letters, which are kept in the upper case of types on the composing bench.

Verso. The left-hand (even-numbered) folio of a page.

Wrong Fount. A letter or symbol which does not match the main body of the type and which has been accidentally inserted from a different fount. The letters " w.f." are used to draw attention to this.

Note the wrong fount used in the line above.

X-height. The height of lower-case letters without ascenders or descenders, such as that of the letter ' x '. A term used to compare the sizes of type character on the body.

ASSOCIATIONS FOR TECHNICAL WRITERS

1. The Society of Technical Writers

P.O. Box 22, Newton Centre 59, Mass., U.S.A.

The Society publishes *Technical Writing Review*, a quarterly journal at a subscription rate of $2.00 a year.

2. The Technical Publications Association

46 Brook Street, London, W.1.

Membership is open to those who are wholly or in major part employed in the production of the following publications:

Literature produced for the specific purpose of enabling the recipient to instal, operate, maintain or otherwise utilize the related equipment to the best advantage.

3. The P.T.I. Group (Presentation of Technical Information Group)

Electrical Engineering Dept., University College, Gower St., London, W.C.1. Secretary : B. C. Brookes, M.A.

Membership is open to those engaged in the presentation of technical information, and allied arts. Founded by Prof. R. O. Kapp.

4. The Association of British Science Writers

The New Scientist (Dr. T. A. Margerison, Secretary), Cromwell House, Fulwood Place, W.C.1.

A non-political professional body, the object of which is to raise the standards of science writing and the status of science writers. Ordinary Membership is open to bona fide science writers who earn the major part of their income from this source.

5. The Society of Indexers

4 Fitzroy Street, London, W.1. Secretary: G. Norman Knight.

6. The British Association of Industrial Editors

12 Thayer Street, London, W.1.

The editing of House Journals is a specialized form of journalism requiring high qualifications and a knowledge of literature. In order to raise the status of such publications, the Association was formed in 1949.

A CRITICAL BIBLIOGRAPHY ON THE PRESENTATION OF TECHNICAL INFORMATION

Note by one of the authors : This Bibliography was originally prepared in a more complete form at the invitation of UNESCO, but economic difficulties prevented its publication.

The condensed version given here is intended to be representative of British and American lists; the length of review of each book should not be taken as a measure of its importance. Some books which are now out of print are included, in the expectation that they are still available in reference libraries.

The author would like to acknowledge the help received from his colleagues in the publishing world who have placed information and copies of books at his disposal, and also the help of individual contributors of notes and reviews.

G. P.

CONTENTS

SECTION 1

General Works on Language and Composition

FOWLER, H. W. *Modern English Usage.* First published 1926, reprinted 1930 and after. (London, Oxford University Press, 742 pp.)

A standard work of reference on the correct use of English words, phrases and idioms, with examples and comments, forming an essential aid to good writing and clarity of expression.

GOWERS, SIR ERNEST. *The Complete Plain Words* (London, H.M. Stationery Office, 1957), 216 pp.

A book on the correct use of English, with examples, written by a senior Civil Servant for the use of Government officials, members of the armed services, and staffs of public bodies.   In an introductory chapter on Legal English, the author justifies some of the involved phrases used in drafting Parliamentary Statutes, but recommends the simple and direct form of writing in dealing with the public.   Four chapters dealing with the choice of words are followed by a list of " over-worked " words with many examples and a chapter on punctuation.

This book originally appeared in two parts, *Plain Words* and *The A.B.C. of Plain Words.*

GRAVES, ROBERT ; HODGE, ALAN. *The Reader over Your Shoulder*: A Handbook for Writers of English Prose (London, Jonathan Cape, 1943).   2nd abridged edn., 1947, reprinted thereafter.

In Part 1 of this book, a review of the characteristics of English prose—classical, romantic, and recent—with illustrations of style is followed by the enunciation and exemplification of 25 basic ' Principles of clear statement '.   In Part 2, the authors take selected passages from well-known authors, examine them very critically and show how they depart from the principles previously set down.

GUTHRIE, L. O. *Factual Communication* : A Handbook of American English (New York ; London, The Macmillan Co., 1948) (3rd impr.), 448 pp.

This book deals with the practical uses of English in articles, talks, letters, and reports, with a secondary accent on the finding of information. A discussion on the characteristics of a factual message is followed by instructions for preparing and delivering talks.   The problems of speaking and writing are thoroughly discussed with examples and model reports.

KIERZEK, J. M. *The Macmillan Handbook of English.* 3rd edn. (New York ; London, The Macmillan Co., 1954), 579 pp.

A new, completely revised and expanded edition of a well-known treatise on the writing of technical English.   The growth and structure of the English language is analysed with numerous examples as an introduction to the process of planning and writing reports, research papers and business letters.   The second part of the book deals with the " mechanics " of writing as regards both grammar and the technique of setting out the manuscript, use of titles, headings, italics, etc.

ONIONS, C. T. *An Advanced English Syntax.* 6th edn. (London, Kegan Paul, Trench and Trubner, 1932), 166 pp.

This presents the main facts of English syntax in a systematic form.

The author states that the word " advanced " in the title refers only to the place of the book in a series and does not describe the methods adopted in the discussion. The introduction gives a full scheme of sentence analysis; Part 1 gives a treatment of syntactical phenomena based on analysis of sentence, and Part 2 clarifies the use of forms, with a section on adverbial, adjectival, and noun clauses. One of the standard textbooks on English grammar and syntax. (Now out of print.)

PARTRIDGE, ERIC. *Usage and Abusage* : A Guide to Good English. (U.S. 5th edn), (London, Hamish Hamilton, 1957), 390 pp.

In his preface, the author states that this book is not designed to compete with Fowler's *Modern English Usage* (*q.v.*) but to supplement and complement it. Its style and arrangement closely follow this and Prof. W. Cabell Greet has annotated the work to fit it for American publication.

VALLINS, G. H. *Good English and how to Write it.* 6th edn. (London, Pan Books Ltd., 1957), 256 pp. paper cover.

This inexpensive book states clearly and simply the main principles of current English usage and good writing. The text contains many quotations of faulty passages, and examples (with answers) are given for practice. Some of the statements disagree with those of Sir Ernest Gowers in *The A.B.C. of Plain Words*. Useful notes on punctuation are given. Recommended for its wealth of concise information and readable style.

SECTION 2

The Technique of Technical Writing

AGG, THOMAS R. ; FOSTER, WALTER L. *The Preparation of Engineering Reports.* 1st edn. (New York ; London, McGraw-Hill Book Co., 1935) (11th impr.), 192 pp.

The authors' intention was to provide a guide to the actual writing of reports but they have also considered it desirable to include suggestions for obtaining and organizing the subject matter preparatory to writing. The nature, form, and types of engineering reports—both formal and informal—are first described and the component parts of the report are listed with illustrations. Examples are given of prefaces, tables of contents and abstracts. Under ' The Collection of Data for Reports ', hints are given on how to ask for information from other people, and the difficulty of framing questionnaires to elicit the desired facts is mentioned.

ALMACK, J. L. *Research and Thesis Writing* (Boston, Houghton Mifflin Co., 1930), 310 pp.

This book differs from the conventional guides to thesis writing in that it deals with the fundamentals of research and thesis-making with but minor attention to ways and means. Two introductory chapters explain the meaning of research and the thesis, the nature and criteria of the problems.

BAKER, C. *Technical Publications : their Purpose, Preparation and Production* (Chapman and Hall, London, 1955), 296 pp., 60 figs.

A guide to writing technical handbooks with particular emphasis on the illustrating of the text. The examples are mainly drawn from the aircraft industry, but the treatment is such that it can be read with profit by anyone concerned with technical presentation.

' It is not a textbook on English grammar or commercial art . . . it is nothing more than a guide for the technician to the techniques of presenting information and producing it in the best—and cheapest form.' —*Author's Preface.*

COLE, A. H. ; BIGELOW, E. W. *A Manual of Thesis Writing* : For Graduates and Undergraduates (New York, John Wiley and Sons ; London, Chapman and Hall) (5th impr.), 1949, 52 pp.

A concise guide to the preparation of material for theses, covering Problems prior to Composition ; Composition ; Final Tasks. The collection and arrangement of data are discussed together with preliminary plans for procedure. Under ' Composition ' the authors give brief notes on style, use of charts, footnotes and appendices, with recommendations on use of italics, punctuation, etc. An appendix gives examples of citation from various sources.

EMBERGER, M. R. ; HALL, M. R. (BRITTON, W. E.—editor). *Scientific Writing* (New York, Harcourt, 1955), 468 pp. + tables and diagrams.

The authors define scientific writing as all factual writing which aims at objectivity, accuracy, clarity and precision. The book describes in detail the preparation of technical papers and reports, with an appendix on the writing of business letters. Well illustrated.

HENDRICKSON, J. RAYMOND. *The Research Paper* (New York, Henry Holt and Co., 1957), approx. 96 pp.

Whenever possible, details of method have been pared down to essentials. The student is presented with one definite way of solving a particular problem, without being confused by unnecessary alternatives. The organization of the manual is methodical, proceeding step-by-step from an introduction to the library to final typing of the paper.

GAUM, C. G. ; GRAVES, H. F. ; HOFFMAN, L. S. S. *Report Writing*. 3rd edn. (New York, Prentice Hall Inc., 1950), 384 pp., 18 figs. in text.

A comprehensive guide to the writing of reports and business memoranda with 15 specimens of finished reports. After a general survey of the field of report writing, the authors deal with technical letter-writing (an unusual feature in books of this type) and the various forms of composition.

A well-prepared and useful guide to report writing.

JENKINSON, B. L. *Bureau of the Census Manual of Tabular Presentation* : An outline of the theory and practice in the presentation of statistical data in tables for publication (Washington, D.C., U.S. Government Printing Office, 1950), 266 pp.

A reference manual to the standards and practice of the U.S. Bureau of Census, giving a thorough reasoned treatment of the questions involved, useful also for other producers of statistics.

JONES, A. E. *Creative Exposition* (New York, Henry Holt and Co., 1957), approx. 576 pp.

This book combines a textbook of creative writing with a brief anthology of non-fiction and a handbook of usage. It is designed for the more advanced sections of composition, from the freshman level up.

KAPP, R. O. *The Presentation of Technical Information* (London, Constable and Co., 1948), 148 pp.

Although small, this book can be recommended for the excellent advice on clear expression, and the right use of words. Based on four public lectures given by the author in 1947, it stressed the characteristics and importance of 'functional English' and the demand for guidance in the art of exposition. In the chapter : ' Making it easy to understand ', the author lists a series of ' do's ' and ' don't's ' which are of particular value to technical lecturers and writers of papers.

Kemsley Manual of Journalism, The (London, Cassell and Co., 1954), 2nd edn. 424 pp., illustrated.

Although not mainly concerned with technical writing, this is an excellent guide to the entire range of newspaper work, and will be of interest to all who write for the daily press. Each chapter has been contributed by an expert in the particular subject.

LINTON, C. D. *How to write Reports* (New York, Harper Bros., 1954), 240 pp.

Gives the principles of expository writing, with refresher chapters on grammar and punctuation. A glossary of grammatical terms is included, and there are brief notes on visual presentation.

MILLER, W. J., SAIDLA, L. E. A. (editors). *Engineers as Writers ; growth of a literature* (New York, D. Van Nostrand Co., 1953), 340 pp.

This book is of quite a different character from any others here mentioned. It consists of selections from the works of fifteen outstanding engineering writers of different periods and fields, preceded in each case by a short biographical introduction and followed by comment on points of style and execution, finally by questions and suggestions for students.

MILLS, G. H. ; WALTER, J. A.   *Technical Writing* (New York, Rinehart & Co., 1954), 464 pp.

A comprehensive guide to the subject, including many examples of reports, business letters, forms and graphical presentation.   An appendix gives instructions for drafting a partial report.   Recommended.

NELSON, J. R.   *Writing the Technical Report.*   3rd edn. (New York, McGraw-Hill Co., 1952), 350 pp.

This book consists of four parts.   The first offers a review of those fundamental considerations which bear on the design and composition of the report.   The second gives specific directions for the set-up of the report, with several illustrative examples both of long and short form. The third part outlines a systematic procedure for the critical examination of a report (again with illustrations), and the last suggests a series of exercises for those who wish to use the book for class studies.   The large number of examples and practical illustrations makes this book of particular value to the student.

RALPH, R. G.   *Putting it Plainly* : For those who have to state facts in writing (London, Methuen, 1952), 150 pp.

The author is a tutor in English at the Royal Air Force College, Cranwell, England, and the book is intended to instruct the beginner in the art of writing clearly and accurately.   The treatment is in a humorous style, but the subject matter is well handled and the reader is helped by numerous examples.

REEDER, W. G.   *How to Write a Thesis* (Bloomington, Ill., U.S.A., The Public School Publishing Co., 1930), 216 pp.

An inexpensive and useful guide for graduates and writers of research theses.   ' Although the content of the thesis is not neglected in this book, the major emphasis is placed on the matter which common observation has shown to cause the student the greatest trouble : the literary style of the thesis '—from the Preface.

RHODES, F. H.   *Technical Report Writing* (New York, McGraw-Hill Co., 1941), 126 pp.

This book forms part of the publisher's Chemical Engineering series of textbooks, specifically intended for chemists who have to write technical memoranda and reports of investigations.   The last chapters of the book deal briefly with some of the simpler methods of analysing, correlating and depicting experimental data.

ROYAL SOCIETY, THE. *General Notes on the Preparation of Scientific Papers* (London, 1950), 26 pp.

A pamphlet produced in accordance with the recommendation of the Scientific Information Conference of 1948. An introduction giving advice on the writing and arrangement of papers is followed by chapters on Typescript, Title and Headings, Presentation of Numerical Results, Tables and Illustrations. A section entitled ' Nomenclature ' gives an annotated bibliography of reports and recommendations by the relevant societies for anatomy, astronomy, biochemistry, engineering, geology, mathematics, medicine, physics, physiology, statistics, and zoology.

SKILLIN, M. E. ; GAY, R. M., and others. *Words into Type* (New York, Appleton Century-Crofts Inc., 1948), 586 pp.

A comprehensive guide to the preparation of manuscripts for printing ; proof reading and correction ; style ; typography ; and rules for composition of type, with a section on grammatical construction and the use of words. The book is divided into six parts, the first of which gives details for the accepted forms of headings, footnotes, tables, etc. Although mainly intended for editorial reference, this book should be consulted by all seriously engaged in writing and publishing, and it is one of the most comprehensive of its type.

SOUTHER, J. W. *Technical Report Writing* (New York, John Wiley and Sons ; London, Chapman and Hall, 1957), 68 pp. paper bound.

A concise treatment of the fundamentals of the subject with examples and exercises. Reproduction processes are briefly mentioned.

TRELEASE, S. F. *The Scientific Paper* : How to prepare it, how to write it (Baltimore, The Williams and Wilkins Co., 1947).

A concise manual for students and research workers who are preparing scientific papers, but also useful for other technical writers. No attempt has been made to include the rules of grammar and rhetoric, although a few reminders are given. A useful check list of common errors in writing is given, with specific instructions for style, abbreviations, etc. This book can be recommended as a guide to writing technique.

TURABIAN, K. L. *A Manual for Writers of Dissertations* (Chicago, University Press, 1950 (reprinted)), 62 pp., paper cover.

This manual condenses the uniform standards of style for dissertations to be submitted to the University of Chicago, but does not include English grammar and composition. For the student who wishes to refresh his background on these subjects, the following are recommended : MANLY, J. M. and RICKERT, E. *The Writer's Index of Good Form and Good English* (New York, Henry Holt and Co.), and WOOLEY, E. C. and SCOTT, F. *New Handbook of Composition* (New York, D.C., Heath and Co.). Many of the rules are taken from the *Manual of Style* issued by the Chicago Press (*q.v.*) to which acknowledgement is made.

ULMAN, J. N., JR. *Technical Reporting* (New York, Henry Holt and Co., 1952), 184 pp.

Primarily for students and engineers just entering industry who ' have reporting jobs and something to say '. The author stresses the fault in technical writing of burying the fundamental theme in a mass of detail, a fault from which even many books on technical writing suffer. A number of principles that are not slighted by the technical writer are therefore omitted in favour of rules for the presentation of data in a clear form and common sense rules for composition and punctuation.

UNITED STATES DEPARTMENT OF THE INTERIOR. *Suggestions to Authors of Papers Submitted for Publication by the U.S. Geological Survey* (edited by G. M. Wood), 4th edn. (Washington, U.S. Govt. Printing Office, 1955), 120 pp., paper cover.

This revised edition has appeared after a lapse of twenty years and some sections have been entirely rewritten. The book constitutes a complete guide to technical writing of reports, although the bias is towards geology. There are numerous examples of good and bad construction, wrong use of words, and suggestions for improving style.

UNIVERSITY OF CHICAGO PRESS. *A Manual of Style*, 11th edn. (1949), 498 pp.

This manual was first published in 1906 and is accepted as an authority on style for printers, publishers, and all concerned with the preparation of manuscript for setting in type. Additions to this edition include (*a*) new entries in the Glossary of Technical Terms ; (*b*) Copyright law ; (*c*) New type faces and data on book type faces.

UNITED STATES GOVERNMENT PRINTING OFFICE. *Style Manual* (*Abridged*) (Washington, U.S. Govt. Printing Office, 1953), 292 pp., paper cover.

Issued to facilitate the setting out and printing of all U.S. Government publications, this is a useful guide to spelling (American), hyphenating, compounding, and special signs and abbreviations. There is a voluminous index and a list of plant names.

WALDO, W. H. *Better Report Writing* (New York, Reinhold Publishing Corporation ; London, Chapman and Hall, 1957), 223 pp.

' Designed for experienced writers to keep on their desks next to the dictionary, so that their composing and revising will be more satisfying and efficient '. Appendices of abbreviations, hyphened words, and titles of periodicals.

WEIL, B. H. *Technical Editing* (New York, Reinhold Publishing Corporation, 1958), 288 pp.

Part 1 : editing internal documents ; Part 2 : editing journals ; Part 3 : editing books and manuals ; Part 4 : editing graphic aids and other exhibits ; Part 5 : general, including translations.

Each chapter is contributed by an authority on the subject, and it is claimed that this is the first comprehensive book on the subject of editing.

WEIL, B. H. (editor). *The Technical Report* : Its preparation, processing and use in industry and government (New York, Reinhold Publishing Corporation, 1954).

This collective work sponsored by the American Chemical Society is planned to include 23 chapters by different experts grouped in five sections relating respectively to Functions ; Writing ; Processing and Distributing ; Filing ; Using the Technical Report.

WILEY, JOHN AND SONS. *Author's Guide for Preparing Manuscript and Handling Proof* (New York, John Wiley ; London, Chapman and Hall, 1950), 78 pp.

Originally issued under the title *The Manuscript : A Guide to its Preparation*, this book is primarily issued for the guidance of authors associated with the publishers. The information given, however, is of value to all potential authors in the details of finishing off their manuscripts and saving time and trouble in passing proofs for press.

WILLIAMS, G. E. *Technical Literature* (London, Allen and Unwin, 1948), 118 pp.

A handbook addressed chiefly to engineers and physicists to assist them in preparing papers for professional institutions. The author is in the Editorial Department of the Institution of Electrical Engineers and some of his recommendations are made from the viewpoint of that organization. The approach is practical, and much of the book is devoted to the preparation and editing of manuscripts, layout, and proof correction.

SECTION 3

Books on Printing, Binding and Publishing

CAMBRIDGE UNIVERSITY PRESS. *Preparation of Manuscripts and Correction of Proofs* (Cambridge, University Press, 1951), 19 pp.

' This pamphlet was originally prepared for the guidance of authors of works printed at the Cambridge University Press, but it is hoped that it may have a wider usefulness, since most of the methods described and principles laid down represent the common practice of to-day. Some of the matters discussed are given more detailed treatment in other

pamphlets of this series ', such as the following two already published :
MORISON, S. : *First Principles of Typography*, and CAREY, G. V. : *Making an Index*.

CHAUNDY, T. W. ; BARRETT, P. R. ; BATEY, C. *The Printing of Mathematics* : Aids for authors and editors and rules for compositors and readers at the University Press, Oxford (London, Geoffrey Cumberledge, 1954), 105 pp.

As implied in its sub-title and explained inside the dust-cover " this book does for mathematics what Hart did for general printing in his book *Rules for Compositors and Readers*. It is designed not only to help the printer, but also to assist authors to understand the technical problems which are peculiar to the composition of mathematics."

JOSEPH, MICHAEL. *The Adventure of Publishing* (London, Allan Wingate, 1949), 208 pp.

' This book offers a survey of post-war publishing problems, a few suggestions for their solution, some information for the newcomer to publishing which he may not find elsewhere and a great deal of probably unpalatable advice to all concerned with the welfare of the book trade ' *—from the author's Preface*. Although this book may seem from the foregoing extract to be mainly of interest to publishers and their staffs, there is much to be learned from it by the would-be author, particularly from the chapter ' Publisher and Author '. (Out of print.)

KNIGHTS, C. C. *Printing : Reproductive Means and Materials* (London, Butterworth Ltd., 1932), 370 pp., illustrated.

One of a series of books in the " Library of Modern Advertising " this gives a full account of modern printing processes, including letterpress, printing, offset litho, gravure, etc. A section covers colour reproduction by blocks and gravure, line and tone blocks, inks and machining.

OXFORD UNIVERSITY PRESS. *Rules for Compositors and Readers at the University Press*. 36th edn. (London, Oxford University Press, 1952), 144 pp.

A useful standard work of reference, first published in 1893. Although originally intended for the printing staff of the O.U.P., the recommendations on spelling, punctuation, and setting out manuscript have been widely adopted elsewhere.

PHILLIPS, ARTHUR. *Setting Mathematics, with a Glossary of Mathematical Terms and Nomenclature of Signs*, 32 pp. *The Monotype Recorder*, **40**, 4 (The Monotype Corporation, London, 1956).

Although issued as a part of a complete volume, this monograph can and should be obtained separately by all interested in the setting of mathematics. The typographical examples are drawn from the Monotype

Corporation's catalogue, but this does not limit the usefulness of the book as a complete guide to mathematical symbols and setting.

PERRY, K., BAAB, C. T.   *The Binding of Books* (Peoria, Ill., U.S.A., The Manual Arts Press, 1940), 160 pp.

A well-written and well-illustrated practical account of all the processes which are employed in bookbinding.   The authors cite the qualities of this particular book as an example of the desirable features in a well-bound production.

STEER, VINCENT. *Printing Design and Layout.*   4th edn. (London, Virtue and Co., 1951), 412 pp.

This is described as a manual for printers, typographers and all designers and users of the printing and advertising arts.   In addition to varied and detailed information on design and layout of printed pages it contains a catalogue of nearly 500 type-faces of all countries and a series of charts to facilitate calculations of type area.   Consideration is given to the basic laws of design, typography, type faces and rules for calculating type areas and spacing.

TARR, J. C. (editor).   *Printing Theory and Practice* (London, Pitman and Sons, 1946–52).

A series of 29 separate volumes covering all aspects of printing practice and economy.   Each volume is obtainable separately and is self contained, uniformly bound.

UNWIN, SIR STANLEY. *The Truth about Publishing.*   6th edn. (London, Allen and Unwin, 1950), 360 pp.

A classic work on the profession of book publishing, giving a detailed account of the economics, policy and procedure in a typical British publisher's office.   The author states that the comparative few modifications to the text of the book when translated into other languages shows that the problems of publishing are not peculiar to any one country or generation.   After describing the procedure on delivery of the manuscript at the publisher's office, the author deals with estimating, " casting-off ", and the cost of books.   The evils of over-production are pointed out.   Typical clauses in author's agreements are discussed, with notes on various extraneous rights.   The processes of book production, publicity and marketing are all dealt with in a candid series of statements, and the book concludes with an analysis of the costs of a modern non-technical book (the figures are now out-dated by rising costs).

WHETTON, H. (editor).   *Practical Printing and Binding* : A complete guide to the latest development in all branches of the printer's craft (London, Odham's Press, 1946), 456 pp., fully illustrated. Reprinted 1956.

A practical book, written by a panel of experts, on modern printing methods.   The sections cover :   Letterpress Printing ;   Stereotyping ;

Lithography ; Pictorial Reproduction ; Photo-gravure ; Music Printing ; Warehouse Practice ; Paper-making ; Inks ; Costing and Estimating ; Bookbinding ; Machinery. Although mainly intended for the apprentice in printing or those who wish to have a general survey of the technique, this book can be read with interest by technical authors as a useful guide to the craft with which they have only slight acquaintance.

GRANNIS, C. B. (editor) *What happens in Book Publishing?* (New York, Columbia University Press, 1957), 400 pp.

A comprehensive survey of the publishing field by various experts, including chapters on sales promotion, management, and various specialized forms of book. A good bibliography is supplied at the end of each chapter.

WILLIAMSON, H. *Methods of Book Design* (London, Oxford University Press, 1956), 448 pp.

A treatise on the technique of book production based on the author's wide experience. Much of the information is useful to all concerned with editing and printing. Recommended.

SECTION 4

Books on Collection of Material and References

Bibliographical References. British Standard No. 1629 : 1950 (London, The British Standards Institution), 18 pp., paper cover.

HOLMSTROM, J. E. *Facts, Files and Action* (3 vols.) (London, Chapman and Hall, 1951, Vol. 1, 450 pp. ; 1953, Vol. II, 280 pp. (Vol. III in preparation.)

The first volume deals with sources and background of facts, mainly British, needed in planning. The second is a treatise on systems of filing, indexing and circulation for the storage and processing of such facts. The third, not yet published, will deal with their practical application in ' the art of getting things done '.

HOOK, LUCYLE ; GAVER, MARY V. *The Research Paper* : Gathering Library Material, Organizing and Preparing the Manuscript. 2nd edn. (New York, Prentice Hall Inc., 1952), 86 pp., paper cover.

The greater part of this book describes in detail the procedure for consulting American library files with examples of classification, file cards (annotated by the authors), and catalogue data. Selections from various American digests and indices are reproduced in facsimile, with explanatory notes and comments of the meaning of code numbers and abbreviations.

WINCHELL, C. M. (editor). *Guide to Reference Books.* 7th edn. (Chicago, American Library Association, 1951), 645 pp.

A comprehensive list of over 5500 entries, first published in 1902 and now completely revised and amended by the present editor assisted by a sub-committee of experts. The general arrangement of the material follows the Dewey system of classification, but is based on subject matter rather than title : for example, the Index Medicus is listed under Medicine instead of under Periodical Indexes.

ZIMMERMAN, O. T. ; LAVINE, I. *Scientific and Technical Abbreviations, Signs and Symbols.* 2nd edn. (Dover, New Hampshire, U.S.A., Industrial Research Service, 1949), 541 pp.

Based on information supplied by the American Standards Association, the American Institute of Chemical Engineers, the U.S. Department of Commerce, and many other organizations, this is a compilation of abbreviations, letter and graphical symbols and code signs in common use in nearly every branch of American scientific practice.

SECTION 5

Indexing

BROWNE, G. E. *Indexing. A handbook of instruction* (London, Grafton, 1921), 137 pp.

This well-known book deals with the preparation of indices of the simpler kinds, such as are met in ordinary books and volumes of periodicals. It is not intended as a guide to the preparation of complex indices like those to encyclopaedias, or for catalogues of collections. This very practical work describes the way to prepare an index and how to divide the work, if necessary, between skilled and unskilled assistants. It should also be read by those who will be concerned with cataloguing.

CAREY, G. V. *Making an Index* (Cambridge, Cambridge University Press, 1951), 14 pp.

Discusses the use of separate slips, the advantage of preparing too many rather than too few entries in the first instance, and the subsequent sorting. The choice of name entries and points arising in alphabetization are discussed briefly. The information given may be sufficient for the compilation of a very simple index to a book, but no more.

CLARKE, ARCHIBALD L. *Manual of Practical Indexing.* 2nd edn. (London, Grafton, 1933), 276 pp.

Indexing, whether separate author and subject or a dictionary arrangement, involves essentially the same technique as regards choice and order of entries. What varies is the part corresponding to the collation, depending on whether the index is to a volume of a periodical, a collection of periodicals, a library, a book, a bibliography, or a biography. These differences the author indicates. He assumes a knowledge of author arrangement, but discusses subject entries at some length. Card indexing and filing and a coding scheme relating letters to numbers in a decimal classification for correspondence are discussed.

SPIKER, S. *Indexing your Book : A Practical Guide for Authors.* 2nd edn. (Madison, University of Wisconsin Press, 1955), 28 pp.

A well-written pamphlet giving practical examples of preparation of index items, arrangement, and analysis with a sample of the finished copy for printing.

WALSH, JOHN W. T. *The Indexing of Books and Periodicals* (London, E. Arnold (Publishers) Ltd., 1930), 118 pp.

The choice of entries and their arrangement under " catchwords ", display of entries and grouping are discussed. Rules for alphabetical arrangement and name arrangement are given, and hints on how to prepare an index during the correction of the slip proofs. The use of index cards or slips is recommended, with a key to the page references constructed by calculation from the slip proofs.

WHEATLEY, H. B. *What is an Index ?* (Published for the Index Society) 2nd edn. (London, Longmans, Green and Co., 1902).

Although now out of print this book is quoted as the first practical guide to indexing, and the recommendations laid down by the author have been adopted by other writers on the subject.

SECTION 6

Guides for Authors

AMERICAN CHEMICAL SOCIETY. *Directions for Assistant Editors and Abstractors of Chemical Abstracts* (Colombus, Ohio, U.S.A., 1939), 30 pp., paper.

In addition to general instructions for abstractors, this booklet includes recommendations for symbols, nomenclature and abbreviations of chemical terms which will be useful for authors writing on this subject.

CHAPMAN AND HALL LTD. *Suggestions to Authors on the Preparation of their Manuscripts* (London, 1951), 26 pp., paper.

These suggestions are the outcome of many years' experience in the publishing of scientific and technical books. The notes are recommendations rather than instructions, as it is realized that an author does not wish to write to a set of rules. The points mentioned are those which are the most frequent subject of query—*from the Preface.*

HYGIENE AND PARASITOLOGY, JOURNAL OF. *Notes on the Preparation of Papers for Publication in the Journal of Hygiene and Parasitology* (by G. H. F. NUTTALL) (London, Cambridge University Press, 1940).

One of the most useful handbooks of instruction issued by a scientific journal, containing much of value to all technical writers.

INSTITUTE OF PHYSICS, THE. *Notes for Authors: A Guide for Contributors to the Institute's Journals and other Publications* (London, 1959), 36 pp., paper.

A series of notes for technical authors on the correct method of presenting papers and figures for publication. A useful section on drawing circuit-diagrams is included. The recommendations are, in general, on the lines of those given by the Royal Society.

INSTITUTION OF ELECTRICAL ENGINEERS, THE. *Handbook for Authors* (London, 1950), 42 pp., paper.

A booklet dealing particularly with the presentation of electrical papers to the Institution, but containing much of general interest to technical authors. There is a Glossary of recommended abbreviations and specialist terms.

LANCET, THE. *On Writing for the Lancet*—Abridged Extracts from Supplement to *The Lancet*, January 2, 1937, London.

LONDON MATHEMATICAL SOCIETY, THE. *Notes on the Preparation of Mathematical Papers* (London, C. F. Hodgson and Son, 1932), 20 pp.

This pamphlet, which has been compiled by the Secretaries of the London Mathematical Society, embodies the suggestions which have been given for many years to the authors of papers to the Society. The difficulties of setting mathematical signs and expressions are explained, as is the best method of setting out formulae to save time and trouble for the printer.

REINHOLD PUBLISHING CORPORATION. ' *What the technical book editor expects of authors* ' (by G. G. HAWLEY). *J. Chem. Educ.*, **31**, 2 (February 1954), 77–80, New York.

(Notes and extracts from a paper presented as part of the symposium on ' What Editors Expect of Authors and Why ' at the 123rd Meeting of the American Chemical Society, Los Angeles, March 1953, whose writer is attached to the Reinhold Publishing Corporation.)

SCIENCE. Extracts from ' *Suggestions for Contributors to " Science "*.' *Science*, **119**, 3092 (2 April 1954), Washington, D.C.

These suggestions, if followed by authors, will serve to expedite the reviewing and processing of articles and to reduce appreciably the costs of processing and printing.

WISTAR INSTITUTE OF ANATOMY AND BIOLOGY. Philadelphia, Pa.

A pamphlet of eight pages entitled *A Guide for Authors ; the Wistar Institute Journals* gives sound and useful advice regarding the manuscript, footnotes, illustrations, legends for text figures and plates, literature citations, abbreviations and symbols, tabular matter.

INDEX